MARX
SLIPPERY ROCK
CRAWFORD

MAX SHULMAN'S
GUIDED TOUR OF CAMPUS HUMOR

BOOKS BY MAX SHULMAN

BAREFOOT BOY WITH CHEEK

THE FEATHER MERCHANTS

THE ZEBRA DERBY

SLEEP TILL NOON

THE MANY LOVES OF DOBIE GILLIS

Editor: MAX SHULMAN'S GUIDED TOUR OF CAMPUS HUMOR

MAX SHULMAN'S

guided tour of campus humor

THE BEST STORIES, ARTICLES, POEMS,
JOKES, AND NONSENSE FROM OVER
SIXTY-FIVE COLLEGE HUMOR MAGAZINES

HANOVER HOUSE
Garden City, New York

Endpaper drawings by Bill Crawford

LIBRARY OF CONGRESS CATALOG CARD NUMBER 55-10517

PRINTED IN THE UNITED STATES

FIRST EDITION

ACKNOWLEDGMENTS

The editor and publisher are grateful to the following copyright owners, publishers, authors, colleges, and editors for their splendid co-operation in granting permission to include in this book selections from the publications listed below:

Kitty Kat, University of Arizona.

Associated Students, University of California, from *Pelican.*

Associated Students, University of Washington, from *Columns.*

The Banter, Colgate University.

Brown University, Associated Dean of Students, from *Sir Brown.*

Mr. Thomas S. Brush, for Katharine Brush's *Football Girl,* copyright, 1931, by Katharine Brush.

Stanford Chaparral, Stanford University.

The Cornell Widow, Cornell University.

Crimson Bull, Sigma Delta Chi Publications, Indiana University.

Dartmouth College, Office of Administration, from *Jackolantern* and *Dart.*

Mr. Pierre Henri Delattre, for his *Da Toll* from University of Pennsylvania, *Penn Pix.*

Dodd, Mead & Company, for *Homer and Humbug* by Stephen Leacock, reprinted by permission of Dodd, Mead & Company, from *Laugh with Leacock,* copyright, 1930, by Dodd, Mead & Company, Inc.

Doubleday & Company, Inc. for *She Shall Have Music* from *The Many Loves of Dobie Gillis,* by Max Shulman, copyright, 1950, by Max Shulman, reprinted by permission of Doubleday & Company, Inc.; for Love is a Fallacy from *The Many Loves of Dobie Gillis,* copyright, 1951, by Max Shulman, reprinted by permission of Doubleday & Company, Inc.; for chapters three, five, six, nine, and twenty of *Barefoot Boy with Cheek,* copyright, 1943, by Max Shulman, reprinted by permission of Doubleday & Company, Inc.; from *The Compleat Practical Joker,* by H. Allen Smith, copyright, 1953, by H. Allen Smith, reprinted by permission of Doubleday & Company, Inc.

Fresno State College, from *Caravan.*

The Gargoyle, University of Michigan.

Harcourt, Brace & Company, *Apes and Elms,* from *Collected Edition of Heywood Broun,* copyright, 1941, by Heywood Hale Broun. Reprinted by permission of Harcourt, Brace & Company, Inc.

Harper & Brothers, for *What the College Incubator Did for One Modest Lambkin* from George Ade's *Breaking into Society,* copyright, 1902, 1903, by Robert Howard Russell, copyright, 1904, by Harper & Brothers.

The Harvard Lampoon, Inc., Harvard University.

Robert C. Herron, for his piece from University of Cincinnati's *Profile,* 1953.

The Hoot, De Pauw University.

Hullabaloo, Franklin and Marshall College.

Mrs. Paul R. Huot (nee Patricia J. Woods) for her *Everybody's off on Something"* from College of St. Elizabeth's *The Sector.*

Jester, of Columbia University.

Johns Hopkins University, from *Blue Jay.*

Kansas City University, from *Kangaroo.*

J. B. Lippincott Company, from Charles W. Morton's *How to Protect Yourself Against Women,* copyright 1948, by Charles W. Morton.

Little, Brown & Company,, from Evelyn Waugh's *Decline and Fall,* copyright, 1928, 1929, by Evelyn Waugh.

Mrs. Walter McIntyre (nee Joan Mathews) for her *Events Prior to Death* from College of St. Elizabeth's *The Sector.*

The Marquis, Lafayette College.

Voo Doo, Massachusetts Institute of Technology.

Old Line, University of Maryland.

The Pennsylvania State University, from *Froth.*

A. D. Peters, London, England, from Evelyn Waugh's *Decline and Fall.*

The Pointer, Corps of Cadets, West Point, New York.

The Princeton Tiger, Princeton University.

The Purple Cow, Williams College.

Rammer Jammer, University of Alabama.

The Rivet, Purdue University.
Alonzo Clark Robinson, from his *Things Used to be Different,* copyright, 1939, by Alonzo Clark Robinson.
Shaft, a Brown & Jordan, Inc. publication, University of Illinois.
Simon & Schuster, Inc., from *The Herman Hickman Reader,* copyright, 1953, by Herman Hickman.
The Spartan, Michigan State College.
Sundial, Ohio State University.
Syracusan, Syracuse University.
T.C.D. Publishing Company, Trinity College, Dublin, from *T.C.D. Anthology.*
Texas Christian University, from *The Skiff.*
The Sour Owl, The University of Kansas.
James Thurber, for his *University Days* from *My Life And Hard Times,* copyright, 1933, by James Thurber. Originally published in *The New Yorker.*
University of Maine, Student-Faculty Publications Committee, from *Pine Needle.*
University of Minnesota, from *Ski-U-Mah.*
University of Missouri, Director, Student Publications, from *Showme.*
University of Nebraska, Committe on Student Publications, from *Corn Shucks.*
University of Oklahoma, Publications Board, from *Covered Wagon.*
University of Pittsburgh, Office of Dean of Men, from *Panther.*
Octopus, University of Wisconsin.
Vassar College, from *Vassar Miscellany News.*
The Spectator, University of Virginia.
Mrs. Gordon N. Walker (nee Barbara Jones), for her *For Women Mostly,* from University of Pennsylvania, *Penn Pix,* September 1950.
Mrs. Harry West (nee Lois Judge), for her *Ennui of an English Major,* from College of St. Elizabeth's *The Sector.*
The Yale Record, Yale University.
Yellow Jacket, Georgia Institute of Technology.

Detailed acknowledgment has been made in the back of this volume to a great number of people who generously supplied me with material and sources.

M.S.

CONTENTS

PART TWO: HISTORY REWRITTEN

The human pageant, as it never happened

PART THREE: VERSE

Songs nobody's mother ever taught him

PART FOUR: SATIRE AND BURLESQUE

Parodies of science, literature, and the arts

PART FIVE: SPORTS

Football and lesser mayhem

PART SIX: LACERATED LANGUAGES

Fractured French, Splintered Spanish, Lacerated Latin, etc.

PART SEVEN: JOKES

Little dandies, old and new, sweet and blue

PART EIGHT: THE OLD GRADS

What old grads write about undergrads

INTRODUCTION

BY MAX SHULMAN

One day not so long ago, while lying underneath my Chrysler trying to find the petcock, I got to thinking about the good old days when I was on the staff of Ski-U-Mah.

Ski-U-Mah, *rest its antic soul, was the humor magazine of the University of Minnesota. It perished soon after the last war, a victim of the faculty pique and student apathy that had beset it from its very beginning. It is a tribute to the ingenuity, perseverance, and larceny of* Ski-U-Mah's *succession of editors that the magazine lasted as long as it did.*

Well, sir, lying thus under the Chrysler and thinking green thoughts of Ski-U-Mah, *I remembered one year when the magazine was particularly shaky. I recalled the scheme—bold, imaginative, lunatic—that was devised to save it. It occurred to me that all of this might make a short story. So I wrote it and* Good Housekeeping *ran it and here it is:*

SHE SHALL HAVE MUSIC*

Ski-U-Mah was in a bad way.

"Something has to be done right away," said Dewey Davenport, the editor. "There's no time to waste. School starts in two weeks."

"Let's hear from the circulation manager," said Boyd Phelps, the associate editor.

They looked at me.

"Oh, Pansy, Pansy!" I cried.

Dewey put a sympathetic arm around my shoulder. "Get hold of yourself, Dobie," he said kindly. "Pansy is gone."

"Gone," I sighed. "Gone."

"And *Ski-U-Mah,*" he continued, "is in trouble."

"You must forget Pansy," said Boyd. "Try to think about *Ski-U-Mah.*"

"I'll try," I whispered bravely.

"That's my boy," said Dewey, giving me a manly squeeze. "Now, Dobie, you're the circulation manager. Have you got any ideas to build circulation?"

But I wasn't listening. Pansy's face was before me. The fragrance of her hair was in my nostrils, and I thought my heart would be rent asunder. Pansy, Pansy, lost and taken from me! "Pansy," I moaned.

"Dobie, she's not dead," said Dewey with a touch of annoyance. "Don't be so emotional."

"I'm an emotional type," I cried, and indeed I was. That was the seat of my trouble with Pansy; I was unable to contain my emotions in her presence. The very sight of her would make me spastic with

* From *The Many Loves of Dobie Gillis,* copyright, 1950, by Max Shulman. Reprinted by permission of Doubleday & Company, Inc.

delight. I would twitch, quiver, shake, jump, and whirl my arms in concentric circles. Pansy had looked kindly upon my seizures, but her father, a large, hostile man named Mr. Hammer, had taken an opposite view. He had regarded me with a mixture of loathing and panic, and finally, fearing for his daughter's safety, he had sent her away from me.

I had met Pansy the year before at the University of Minnesota where we had both been freshmen. I was immediately smitten. And who would not have been? What healthy male would not have succumbed to her wise but frolicsome eyes, her firm but succulent lips, her sturdy but graceful throat, her youthful but mature form? What man could have resisted her manifold graces, her myriad charms? Certainly not I.

I plunged headlong into the pursuit of Pansy, and I am pleased to report that my suit met with success. After she overcame her initial alarm at my exuberance, her affection for me burgeoned until it matched mine for her. Then I made a mistake: I asked to meet her folks.

"Gee, I don't know, Dobie," she said doubtfully. "Maybe we'd better wait awhile. I'm not sure how you and Daddy will get along."

"If he's your father, I'll love him," I replied, nibbling her fingers ecstatically.

"Maybe so," she said, "but what I'm worried about is what he'll think of you. He's a gruff, sober type, and—no offense, Dobie—you're kind of nuts."

"Nonsense," I cried, leaping goatlike around her. "Take me to him."

"All right," she said with a conspicuous lack of enthusiasm. "But, Dobie, listen. Try to make your outbursts as minor as possible, will you? Nothing massive if you can help it."

"Don't worry about a thing," I assured her, and we went forthwith to her costly home in South Minneapolis.

I must say that I have never behaved quite so calmly as on my first meeting with Mr. Hammer. I did not leap or spin; I did not cavort, dance, kick, whistle, or roll. Perhaps I twitched a few times, and I blinked a bit, and once I threw my hands over my head, but otherwise I was the very model of sedateness.

I cannot say, however, that the Hammers were impressed with my composure. Mrs. Hammer showed only slight evidence of nervousness —just an occasional shudder—but Mr. Hammer was openly agitated. He kept casting me looks of wild surmise; several times he inquired pointedly about my health. When I finally made my good-byes, he was flagrantly relieved.

"Well, what did they think of me?" I asked Pansy when I saw her on campus the next day.

"Mother seemed disinclined to discuss you," Pansy replied, "but Daddy was quite frank. He said you ought to be locked up."

"Hm," I said glumly, but my spirits instantly revived. "Don't worry, Pansy," I said confidently. "I will win him."

Overriding Pansy's earnest protests, I continued to call on her at home. The results were not what I had hoped. Her mother contrived to be absent whenever I came. Her father's attitude toward me progressed from dismay to consternation; his color evolved from a brackish white to a mottled purple. It seemed that there was nothing I could do to please him. My friendly grimaces only served to infuriate him. Whenever I gave him a jovial slap on the back, he recoiled in horror. It got so that the mere sight of me would set him whimpering. "No good will come of all this," I told myself darkly.

I was right. Mr. Hammer sent Pansy away from me. Instead of letting her return to the University of Minnesota for her second year, he shipped her off to New York City. There she was to live with her Aunt Naomi, a flinty old spinster, and attend Barnard College. Aunt Naomi had been charged by Mr. Hammer to reject all phone calls and destroy all letters coming from me.

And now here I was in the *Ski-U-Mah* office, separated from my truelove by half a continent and wishing myself dead.

"Dobie," said Dewey Davenport sharply. "Will you pay attention? *Ski-U-Mah* is hanging on the ropes. We've only got two weeks before school starts. We need circulation. That's your job, remember?"

"Pansy," I said, biting my lip. "Pansy."

"Ah, what's the use?" said Boyd Phelps dejectedly. "Even if Dobie had any ideas, it wouldn't help. Let's face it, Dewey. *Ski–U-Mah* is a dead duck. The day of the college humor magazine is over—not only at Minnesota, but everywhere. College kids have outgrown all that rah-rah stuff. The war, the A-bomb, the H-bomb—who's thinking about fun and jokes these days?"

"Nuts," replied Dewey. "College kids are still college kids. They're still smooching and driving convertibles and cutting classes and looking for laughs."

"No," said Boyd, shaking his head.

"Yes," Dewey insisted. "Here, I'll give you an example. Remember last year when Benny Goodman played a dance at the gym? They had the biggest turnout in the history of the university. Does that sound like everyone is sitting around moping?"

Yes, I thought, a soft smile playing on my lips, yes, I remembered that dance. Pansy and I had gone together. Oh, how we danced, how we stomped, how we whirled, how we hopped, how we—CLANG! A bell sounded in my head with the noise of a thousand alarms. An idea had come to me, an overpoweringly perfect idea! Everything was solved. *Everything!*

"I've got it!" I cried, jumping up and down. "I've got it!"

Dewey and Boyd looked at me askance.

"That's our answer," I said eagerly. "That's how we'll get subscriptions for *Ski-U-Mah*. We'll hold a dance."

"I don't get it," confessed Dewey.

"Look," I said. "We'll hire a big name band—Benny Goodman or Tommy Dorsey or somebody like that. Then instead of charging a dollar for a ticket to the dance as they usually do, we'll charge two dollars. The extra dollar will be for a year's subscription to *Ski-U-Mah*. It's a package deal, don't you see?"

Dewey and Boyd considered the idea. "Not bad, not bad," said Boyd.

"No, it isn't," Dewey agreed. "It's a fine idea. There's only one hitch. Have we got enough money in our treasury to hire a big name band?"

"We've got exactly one thousand dollars," said Boyd.

Dewey shook his head. "Not enough."

"We could try, " said Boyd. "Why don't we write a letter to the booking office in New York and see what they say?"

"No, no," I cried quickly. That wasn't what I had in mind at all. A trip to New York was the most important part of my plan—to see Pansy again, to live again, to be a whole man again. But, of course, I did not intend to mention *that* to Dewey and Boyd.

"Don't send a letter," I said. "They'll only turn you down. You can't expect them to send Goodman or Dorsey all the way to Minneapolis for a thousand dollars—unless, of course, some young clean-cut fellow appeared in person and persuaded them."

"You, for instance?" said Dewey.

"Not to brag," I said, lowering my eyes modestly, "but you will go far to find another as young and clean-cut as I."

"And you think they'd listen to you at the booking agency?" asked Dewey.

"I'm sure of it," I declared. "I'll come up there all neat and tweedy with my cowlick standing up and a lump in my throat and I'll tell them all about our great *Ski-U-Mah* tradition and how the magazine is in trouble and how everything depends on them and then I'll look up at them, trusting-like, with my eyes shining and a crooked little smile on my face. How are they going to resist anything like that?"

I took a stance and showed Dewey and Boyd what I meant.

"He *does* look kind of appealing," Boyd admitted.

"Yes, he does," said Dewey, examining me minutely.

I nodded energetically.

Dewey waved a forefinger under my nose. "Now listen, Dobie, your expenses have to come out of this thousand dollars so don't waste a cent. You'll travel by bus and you'll sleep at the Y.M.C.A. Eat as little as possible. Do your business as soon as you get to New York and then come right back. Understand?"

"Yes, yes, yes," I said, clapping my hands rapidly. I was going to Pansy, to Pansy to Pansy! Oh, happy day! Oh, kind fate!

The next morning Dewey and Boyd took me down to the Minneapolis bus depot and put me on a bus for New York. I got off the bus in St. Paul and transferred to an airplane. A tedious bus journey was not to be borne; I had to get to Pansy quickly. I felt a little guilty about spending the extra fare, but after all, twenty or thirty dollars would hardly make any difference when I came to hire a band.

As soon as I landed at La Guardia field, I rushed to the telephones. I looked up Aunt Naomi's number and dialed it with trembling fingers. An unfriendly feminine voice answered. "Hello?"

"Hello," I said. "Is Miss Pansy Hammer there?"

"Who is calling?" asked the voice suspiciously.

"This is Mr. Johnson. I am the dean of Barnard College."

"You sound awfully young to be a dean," said doubting old Aunt Naomi.

"Yes, don't I?" I replied with a hollow laugh. "In many quarters I am known as 'The Boy Dean' . . . But enough of this chitchat. I'm a very busy dean. Please put Miss Hammer on."

There was a short pause and then I heard Pansy's voice. "Pansy!" I cried, vibrating joyously in the phone booth. "Pansy, it's Dobie Gillis. I've come to you, my darling. I'm here in New York."

I heard a sharp intake of breath and then she said in a carefully controlled tone, "Why, yes, Dean. When do you want to see me?"

"Smart girl," I said approvingly. "Can you meet me in an hour at the airlines terminal building in New York?"

"I'll be there," she said. "Good-by, Dean."

Rubbing my hands gleefully, I got into the airlines limousine and rode to New York. I was at the terminal building in thirty minutes. That left another thirty minutes to wait before Pansy would arrive. I was much too agitated to sit still so I decided to go out for a short walk. I skipped down Forty-second Street and turned up Fifth Avenue. The gaily decorated shopwindows matched my festive mood, and soon I was singing lustily. As I passed a florist's shop, my attention was seized by a display of orchids in the window. No ordinary orchids these, but blooms as white and soft and lovely as Pansy herself. I went into the store.

A clerk slithered toward me. "M'sieu?" he lisped.

"I would like a dozen of those orchids," I cried, "for the loveliest girl in the world."

"*Quel sentiment!*" he exclaimed, embracing me.

"Quickly," I said, disengaging myself. "She comes."

He swished into action and in a trice he had fashioned a corsage that made me limp with rapture. "That will be one hundred dollars," he said.

I turned ashen.

"A glass of water?" asked the clerk. "A light wine, perhaps?"

I shook my head, for already I was recovering. After all, what difference would a hundred dollars make when it came to hiring the band? The whole deal was to be based on my personal appeal anyhow. In fact, the less money I had, the more pathetic I would be. And besides it would be worth a hundred dollars to see Pansy's face when I gave her the corsage—even if the hundred dollars was not mine. Smiling, I handed the clerk the money and raced back to the terminal building.

She was waiting for me. Fifty feet separated us when I first spied her. I covered the distance in three great bounds. "My darling, my angel, my dove!" I cried, kissing her with random accuracy.

"Dobie," she said simply.

We clung.

"A corsage," I said, handing her the orchids.

"Oh, they're lovely . . . But it's kind of big for a corsage, isn't it?"

"I'll fix that," I said, and draped the orchids around her neck like a Derby winner.

We laughed. Then, suddenly serious, I clutched her again. "I've missed you so much, Pansy."

She nuzzled my jowl. "And I you," she confessed.

"Is there no chance that your father will let you come back to Minnesota?"

She shook her head. "No. I start classes at Barnard next week."

"Shall I survive this year?" I croaked hoarsely, smiting my forehead.

"I know," she said softly. "It's going to be awful." She wept, nor were my eyes dry.

"But away with this gloom!" I cried. "At least we will have a little time together. Let us be gay. Let us taste all the joys that this great city has to offer."

"Heigh-ho," she replied airily, and linked her pretty round arm in mine.

Some may censure me for my activities on that evening, and I cannot really defend myself. Admittedly the expenditure of two hundred dollars of *Ski-U-Mah* funds was not an honorable act. I can only say this: I did not know when I would see Pansy again; there was money in my pocket; the town was full of pleasures; and even under the best of circumstances, I cannot think clearly in Pansy's presence. Call me wayward if you will; that was the way things were.

We had cocktails at the Plaza. We had dinner at 21. We saw *South Pacific*. We had supper at the Stork. We danced at El Morocco. We drove four times around Central Park in a hansom. After I took Pansy home, I checked into the Waldorf. No lesser hostelry would suit my exalted mood.

In the morning, of course, things were different. I lay between the Waldorf's excellent sheets jackknifed with panic. It took a long time before I was able to get up and count my money. Then, having discovered that my funds totaled slightly over six hundred dollars, I oozed to the floor in a moaning mound. An hour was spent in this position. At length I rallied myself. There was nothing to do but go down to the booking agency and try to get a band for six hundred dollars.

I prepared myself carefully. I yanked my cowlick until it stood like a mast on my scalp. I buffed my face until it shone like an innocent apple. I practiced digging my toe into the rug. I stood before the mirror and ran through my repertory of winsome expressions. Then I went down to the booking agency.

The booking agency occupied one large, shabby office. Part of the office was a waiting room; the other part, separated by a waist-high railing, was the business office. Seated on a bench in the waiting room were six huge, villainous-looking women. At a desk behind the railing sat a cadaverous, blue-jowled man with eyes like two bits of anthracite. The six women were staring dully at the floor as I entered. They looked at me with momentary interest, then sighed and looked back at the floor. I approached the man behind the railing.

"How do you do?" I said with a fetching smile. "I'm Dobie Gillis from the University of Minnesota *Ski-U-Mah.*"

He gave me a quick appraisal with his anthracite eyes and said nothing.

"I'd like to book a band for a dance at the university on September 14. I had in mind someone like Benny Goodman or Tommy Dorsey."

"How much loot you got?" asked the man.

"I beg your pardon?"

"Money. How much?"

"First," I said, smiling warmly, "I'd like to tell you a little about *Ski-U-Mah.* It's one of the finest traditions at the University of Minnesota. Yes, indeed. We all have a soft spot in our hearts for *Ski-U-Mah* out there. We certainly do."

"How much loot?"

"*Ski-U-Mah,* you'll be distressed to hear, has fallen on evil days. But now, with your co-operation, we believe we can save it. I know, of course, that sentiment and business are not supposed to mix, but I always say, scratch a businessman and you'll find a heart of pure gold."

"Kid, come on already. How much loot?"

"Six hundred dollars," I said, turning a look upon him that would melt a stone.

"Good-by, kid," he said.

"Vaughan Monroe would do," I said, tugging my cowlick.

"Kid," he said, "you got rocks in your head?"

"Perhaps," I said in a cracking treble, "you could suggest somebody?"

"Nobody," he said flatly, "will go to Minneapolis for six hundred dollars."

"Ahem, ahem." The sound came from behind me. I turned and saw the largest of the six women on the bench rise and approach me with a gigantic grin.

"Kid," said the man at the desk, "you're in luck. This is Happy Stella Kowalski and her Schottische Five. They just happen to be between bookings right now."

"Pleased to make your acquaintance, hey," said Happy Stella, crushing my hand in hers. The Schottische Five stood up and grinned fatly.

"You are a band?" I asked nervously.

"The best," roared Happy Stella. "Ask Al."

"The best," confirmed the man at the desk. "They play more Lithuanian weddings than any band on the entire Atlantic seaboard."

"We're a riot, hey," confessed Stella, prodding me with her outsized forefinger. "We wear funny hats. We black our teeth. We play washboards, gaspipes, pots and pans, all kinds of funny stuff. We fracture the people."

"You mustn't take this unkindly, Happy Stella," I said, "but I've never heard of you."

"Kid, where you been?" asked Al. "This is the hottest combination in New York. You don't know how lucky you are to catch 'em between bookings."

I scratched my head uncertainly. "And they'll come for six hundred dollars?"

"Ordinarily, no," said Al. "For *Ski-U-Mah,* yes."

He whipped out a contract, handed me a pen, and guided my hand over the dotted line. Then I shook hands with Al and Happy Stella and the Schottische Five—Rutka, Sletka, Dombra, Simka, and Majeska—and left the office with a breast full of misgivings.

I had not done well; there was no gainsaying it. For a moment I toyed with the idea of not going back to Minneapolis but finally dismissed the thought as cowardly. Besides, I didn't have enough money left to stay in New York. I went to the bus station, bought a ticket home with my remaining resources, and invested my last dime in a good-by phone call to Pansy.

Aunt Naomi answered. "Hello," I said, "this is Mr. Johnson, The Boy Dean. I want to talk to Miss Hammer."

"I have called Barnard College," said Aunt Naomi icily. "There is no Mr. Johnson on the faculty. You are Dobie Gillis, and if you try to communicate with Pansy again I will call the police."

"Please, Aunt Naomi," I could hear Pansy saying, "just let me say good-by to him."

"Very well," said Aunt Naomi. "But this is the last time, you understand?"

Pansy came on the phone. "How are you, Dobie dear?"

"Fine," I lied. There was no use to afflict her with my misery.

"Did you get Benny Goodman for your dance?"

"No," I said with a grisly smile, "I got somebody better. Happy

Stella Kowalski and her Schottische Five."

"Who?"

"It's a sensational new band. They fracture the people."

"That's nice, dear. When are you leaving?"

"In a few minutes."

"Oh, how I wish I were going back with you! I'll miss you so much, Dobie, so very much."

"Me, too."

She sobbed briefly.

"Don't cry, dear," I soothed. "Maybe we'll be together soon."

"It can't be soon enough, Dobie. When do you think you'll get back to New York?"

"Not," I said, "in the foreseeable future."

"Oh, Dobie!" she wailed.

"Good-by, Pansy, dear heart. I love you."

Gently I hung up the telephone and walked into the bus for Minneapolis.

Dewey and Boyd were waiting for me at the Minneapolis station. At first I tried to bluff it out. "Great news, fellows!" I shouted. "I booked Happy Stella Kowalski and her Schottische Five. What a coup for *Ski-U-Mah!*"

"Who?" said Dewey and Boyd with double horror.

I could not go on with it. Suddenly the truth came pouring from lips, the whole horrible story. "But I'll pay back the money I spent," I said in conclusion. "I'll pay it back somehow."

"I know you will, Dobie," said Dewey wearily, without anger. "That's not the point. What happens to *Ski-U-Mah* now? How do we get anybody to buy tickets for Happy Stella Kowalski?"

"They'll close the magazine this year if we don't make a profit," said Boyd.

"I know," I replied miserably. "I'm just a no-good rat."

Dewey put his arm around my slumping shoulders. "All right, Dobie. What's done is done. Now the only thing left is to try to sell some dance tickets."

And try we did. We collared everybody on campus; we applied all possible pressures. Our efforts were greeted with curt refusals, sometimes with astonishment. "Happy Stella who?" people would ask. When the night of the dance came around, we had sold exactly 150 tickets to an enrollment of 20,000 students.

At seven-thirty on the night of the dance I was in the gymnasium disconsolately hanging bunting. Dewey was sitting on the bandstand with his chin in his hand. Boyd had gone down to the railroad station to pick up Happy Stella Kowalski and her Schottische Five, who were due to arrive at eight o'clock. Suddenly a large, purple-faced man came running wildly into the gymnasium—Mr. Hammer, Pansy's father.

He spied me on top of the ladder. "You!" he roared, and shook me down like a ripe plum. "What have you done with her?"

"Hello, Mr. Hammer. Done with whom?"

"You know very well who. Where's Pansy? Her aunt told me you saw her in New York. Now where is she?"

"Isn't she in New York?"

"Gillis, I'll strangle you," he yelled, lunging at me.

Dewey thrust himself hastily between us. "What's wrong, Mr. Hammer?" he asked.

"Pansy disappeared from her aunt's apartment in New York two days ago. Gillis engineered the whole thing. He's got her hidden someplace. I'm calling the police. I'm charging him with abduction." All this delivered in a deafening bellow.

Dewey turned to me. "Dobie, tell the truth. Do you know anything about this?"

"So help me, Dewey," I cried earnestly, "not a thing."

"You're lying, you kidnaper," screamed Mr. Hammer. "I'm calling the police. Where is she?"

"Mr. Hammer, be reasonable," said Dewey. "Dobie's been here for more than a week. How could he have kidnaped Pansy?"

"He's got accomplices. He's a fiend. I knew he should have been locked up the minute I laid eyes on him. I'm calling the police."

At this point Boyd came walking in with Stella Kowalski and her Schottische Five. They were dressed in motley dirndls about the size of pyramidal tents. On their heads they wore hideous hats with ratty plumes. Under their arms they carried washboards, pipes, pots, plungers, and assorted hardware. Their front teeth were blacked out.

We stood and stared at them, even Mr. Hammer. Then suddenly I saw that the Schottische Five were six, and the sixth one was not a huge, gross cow-moose of a woman. She was slender and fair and beautiful even with blacked-out teeth. She was Pansy!

"Pansy!" The cry escaped my lips.

"Aha!" roared Mr. Hammer. "Caught you red-handed." There was a telephone on the wall nearby. He seized it. "Police!" he shouted into the mouthpiece. "Send the patrol wagon. Send the riot squad. Send everything you've got!"

Happy Stella strode over and grabbed Mr. Hammer by the lapels. "What's with you?" she said dangerously.

"You'll find out when you're behind bars," replied Mr. Hammer, trying vainly to free himself.

"Oh, you must be the old man," said Happy Stella. "Shame on you." She shook him until his eyes rolled freely in their sockets.

"Assault and battery," mumbled Mr. Hammer. "Kidnaping plus assault and battery. That's what I'm charging you with."

Pansy stepped forward. "There was no kidnaping," she said firmly. "I went to Happy Stella and asked her to take me with her. I thought Aunt Naomi might catch me if I tried running away alone."

"Don't say anything, Pansy," warned Mr. Hammer. "They've probably got you drugged."

"I am not drugged," said Pansy, stamping her foot. "I have never thought so clearly in my life."

She walked over and took my arm. "Daddy," she said with as much dignity as a girl can muster who has blacked-out teeth, "I love Dobie and I'm going to stay with him. If you send me to New York again, I'll run away again. I don't care where you send me, I'm not going to be kept apart from Dobie."

"Whatsa matter with you, hey?" demanded Happy Stella, giving Mr. Hammer another shake. "Can't you see these kids wanna be together? So what if Dobie is a little screwy? Who ain't?"

Mr. Hammer opened and closed his mouth several times, carp-fashion. "All right," he said at last. "All right. But, Pansy, you keep that maniac out of my house, do you hear? And if, God forbid, you should ever marry him, I don't want to hear about it."

Suddenly the street outside the gym was filled with the scream of sirens. The police Mr. Hammer had called were arriving. Car after car pulled up in front of the gym with a screech of tires. Dozens of cops with drawn guns came pouring into the gym. And behind the police came a mob of students, pressing in to see what the excitement was.

Dewey leaped up as though he had been stung. "Dobie, Boyd!" he yelled with wild excitement. "Get to the door. Don't let any students in unless they buy tickets. Here's how we save *Ski-U-Mah*."

We rushed forward and threw ourselves across the door. "Two dollars!" shouted Dewey to the mob. "Two dollars to come inside. Hurry, hurry, hurry!"

The students in the front ranks started to dig in their pockets for money, but the mob behind them surged forward. It looked for a moment as though Dewey, Boyd, and I would be swept aside. But Happy Stella came running to our aid with her Schottische Five. Buttressed by the musical amazons, we were able to hold fast until the crowd got their money out. Then we stood aside and let them rush through, throwing currency at us as they passed. The money showered over us, piled up on the floor around us.

It is difficult to describe what was happening inside the gym. I was not on the sinking *Titanic* or at the Battle of Gettysburg, but these, I think, are fair comparisons. All I can remember is humanity flooding in, filling the gym to the walls, and cops yelling and brandishing guns and Mr. Hammer trying vainly to make explanations over the din and Dewey cackling hysterically as he counted money.

It took about an hour before the cops left, casting foul looks at Mr. Hammer as they went. Then Dewey got up and made an announcement to the assemblage, telling them that they were at a dance. There was a little sullen muttering, but most of them took the news calmly. Then Happy Stella and her Schottische Five started to mount the bandstand.

"Miss Hammer," I said with a courtly bow to my truelove, "may I have the honor of the first dance?"

"Sorry," she said. "I'm playing a washboard solo for the first dance."

She gave me a loving, black-toothed smile and joined the musicians.

Well, enough of reminiscing about the good old days on Ski-U-Mah. *Now to the business at hand.*

There follows an anthology of college humor, gleaned from fifty years of campus publications in every section of the land.

I found, as you would expect, that the humor of the pre-World War I period and the humor of the 1920s is mostly hopelessly dated, and I have included very little of it.

I also found that dated or fresh, old or new, there continue to be characteristics common to all college humor. These are:

a) an irreverence toward authority;
b) a love for the outlandish;
c) a preoccupation with sex.

I list these items not in the spirit of criticism. It is perfectly natural to resent authority when authority stands squarely in the way of the simple, normal desires of any simple, normal undergraduate—to wit:

money, automobiles, romance, and the leisure to enjoy these few uncomplicated things.

It is also natural to love the outlandish when you are growing into a strange, murky world whose drives, aims, and standards are none of your own.

Finally, it is especially natural to be preoccupied with sex when the juices of post-puberty are new and strong and heady.

All this, I say, is natural, and the time, I say, to start worrying is when the American undergraduate stops *being motivated by sex and irreverence and love for the* non sequitur.

PART ONE

MISCELLANY

Stories, articles, essays, and sundry other works not readily classifiable

In most humor anthologies you will find a section at the end labeled "Miscellany." This is a grab-bag category, including all material not readily classifiable—stories that are not quite stories, essays that are not quite essays, articles that are not quite articles, belles-lettres that are not quite belle.

I can think of no better definitions than those above for the great bulk of college humor—so in this anthology "Miscellany" is the proud leader, not the embarrassed laggard, of all the categories.

FOR WOMEN MOSTLY

BY BARBARA JONES

With all the controversy about the relative uselessness of Penn men and Penn women, there seems to be a need for a certain amount of field work in the subject. Apparently each side is judged by the most objectionable of its kind, so—girls—here is submitted a carefully compiled report on Penn Men You Need to Avoid. If referred to before you accept dates, it may save you a lot of bitterness and gnashing of teeth.

Type 1. The party-boy. This one simply isn't himself until he gets outside of a little alcohol. Then he manages to be so much himself that you are bored to death. His conversation is either quiet or loud; when quiet, it consists of long accounts of drinking bouts, in which he took part; and when loud, it is usually carried on with his buddy across the room who wants everybody to sing the "Whiffenpoof Song," while our joyboy favors, "Roll Me Over in the Clover." For these occasions he is conveniently equipped with a foghorn voice that makes everybody turn around and look. If you happen to be sitting next to him you cringe and wilt and feel about two inches high. You gaze up at him with a sick smile that you hope will make everybody think you're having as much fun as he is.

There may be occasions in the course of the evening when he feels like dancing. Dancing, to him, consists of zooming around ricocheting off walls, other couples, moose heads, etc. They ought to jail him for flying low.

Then the fire-eater creeps up on him and he commences to be morose. In the life of every party-boy there is an unrequited love; and furthermore given even less than half a chance, he will tell you all about it.

It sounds vaguely like *True Confessions*. But because you have nothing better to do at the moment, you listen, and sympathize—outwardly, with him; inwardly, with the girl.

Finally he quietly passes out, wrapped comfortably around a chandelier or something, and one of his less enthusiastic brothers takes you home. All this is very interesting, provided you can hold him up long enough to get through the party. And he really isn't useless; he always makes a good bar rag.

Type 2. The lover. He is a ball of fire with the women—the sultry, slow-burning kind, of course. He overwhelms you with attentions. He leans so close to you when you talk that you get the impression he is concerned about the condition of your wisdom teeth. He has a special hungry, sick-dog look which he uses for gazing deeply into eyes. When you go away and talk to somebody else, he sulks. He may even follow you and turn you around to face him, and look silently at you. He is hurt. You have crushed him. You are ashamed. You monster.

An evening with him is like a nice quiet session with a boa constrictor. No amount of hinting around that, as far as he's concerned, you are of the let's-just-be-friends school of thought, will do; you have to pick up a bottle or something and slug him before he gets the idea. Then, kid, you're washed up. Your name is mud. Not only are you nasty, ungrateful, and a terrible date—but to top it all off, you're an icebox—and this is the sin unforgivable.

Type 3. The Great Mind. You have to prepare ahead of time for a date with one of these. If you're not read up on your Nietzsche and Schopenhauer, you've got two strikes against you before you start. You and Junior will sit down together, cozy-like, in a corner and solve world problems. Then for the sake of variety you might go on to metaphysics. You toss Absolutes and Causes and Effects back and forth for a whole evening. I won't say any more on this subject. There's nothing more to say.

Type 4. The Bohemian. This one's theme song is "I don't Care." He dreams of a garret for two on the Left Bank and a Jug of Wine, a Loaf of Bread—and Thou; and if Thou isn't crazy about the idea, Thou is inhibited, repressed, suppressed, a slave to convention, a conformist, and a louse. The boy knows he's a genius, but just because he dyes his hair pale green and wears a purple satin shoestring for a necktie, people don't appreciate him.

He has moods. Blue moods, black moods, red moods—all kinds. If he's having mood number 157E, keep away from him. Keep away from him anyway. Unless you've reserved a bunk at Byberry, that is.

Type 5. The dud. He gives you a fleeting impression of a horrible, sticky, gray nothingness. He doesn't smoke, drink, dance, drive, stay out late, or raise his voice. He isn't funny—he isn't interesting—he isn't clever. You talk into a vacuum. He is probably very good to his mother, but every time he comes out with that slightly hysterical giggle you feel like slapping him. He sits there like a rock in mid-stream and the party eddies around him. He has a wonderful time. You go home and get a nice big ax and go hunting for the person who got you the date.

Watch the aftereffects of this. He'll call you up, sure as next week. He'll call you again. He'll call you nine or ten times more. If you happen to be wandering around on campus with somebody whom you'd like to impress, he'll pop up out of his hole in the lawn and greet you like a long-lost sister. He's the world's best argument for mercy killing.

Type 6. The Missing Link. Not that we object to muscles, but there is a type that has too much of a good thing. He has an amazing supply of every kind of matter but gray. He looks like something out of the Old Stone Age—and talks surprisingly like it, too. His knuckles drag on the ground. He grunts occasionally to show he's alive. You expect him to stand up and hammer on his chest at any minute. He majors in-duh-phys ed, and takes Advanced Pencil Sharpening on the side.

He's a charming date if you're taking anthropology. Or if you have to write a criticism of *The Man with the Hoe* or *Of Mice and Men.* You couldn't find a better case study.

Of course you have to watch these creatures. If he gets playful you're liable to end up mashed into dog food. It's best to take along a whip and a light metal chair and be able to say "Back, Sultan," in an authoritative voice. Once your nerve fails, you're done.

Well, there they are. Now the object of the game is to go out and find one that doesn't fall into one of these categories. Then, if it's got blood and skin and if it moves around, you're set. Hang onto it. It must be a man. *Penn Pix (University of Pennsylvania)*

LATEST CRIBBING TECHNIQUE

Cribbing on examinations is apparently a world-wide practice. When Lord Frederic Hamilton was a foreign attache in India he realized how difficult it is to guess the age of natives for "wrinkles and lines do not show on a dark skin." Lord Hamilton also learned that dark skins have other advantages: "One of the European Examiners of Calcutta University told me that there had been great trouble about the examination-papers. By some means the native students always managed to obtain what we may term 'advance' copies of these papers. My informant devised a scheme to stop this leakage. Instead of having the papers printed in the usual fashion, he called in the services of a single white printer on whom he could absolutely rely. The white printer had the papers handed to him early on the morning of the examination day, and he duly set them up on a hand-press in the building itself. The printer had one assistant, a coolie lad clad only in loin-cloth and turban, and every time the coolie left the room he was made to remove both his loin-cloth and turban, so that by no possibility could he have any papers concealed about him. In spite of these precautions, it was clear from internal evidence that some of the students had had a previous knowledge of the questions. How had it been managed? It eventually appeared that the coolie, taking advantage of the momentary absence of the white printer, had whipped off his loin cloth, *sat down on the 'form,'* and then replaced his solitary garment. When made to strip on going out, the printing ink did not show on his dark skin: he had only to sit down elsewhere on a large sheet of white paper for the questions to be printed off on it, and they could then easily be read in a mirror." Lord Hamilton's conclusion: "The Oriental mind is very subtle." *Columns (University of Washington)*

A VERY SHORT, SHORT STORY

She was madly in love with him.
He was madly in love with her.
She was single, but wanted to marry him.
He was single, but wanted to marry her.
He stood on the right-hand side of the room.
She stood on the left-hand side of the room.
He removed his coat and vest and tossed them in a heap in the nearby chair.
She took off her tightly fitted red dress and hung it neatly in the closet.
He removed his shirt and necktie and threw them on the same chair.

She took off her slip and laid it carefully on the back of a chair.
He removed his pants and hung them on a hook in the back of the door.
She sat on the left-hand side of the bed and removed her shoes and stockings.
He sat on the right-hand side of the bed and took off his shoes and stockings. He stood up and took off his shorts and undershirt.
She stood up and removed very daintily her pants and brassière.
There he stood, a large muscular piece of manly flesh.
There she stood, the last word in feminine loveliness.
He put on some green-striped pajamas.
She put on a tightly fitting nightgown.
He climbed into bed on the right side.
She climbed into bed on the left side.
He reached up and pressed the button that put out the top light.
She reached up and pulled the cord that put out the reading lamp at the head of the bed.
He faced toward the left.
She faced toward the right.
He was in the M.I.T. Dorms.
She was in the Waldorf in New York.
So they both turned over and went to sleep.

Blue Jay (Johns Hopkins University)

UDDER DRIPPINGS

BY S. G. B.

From the files of *The Purple Cow* we feel we should publish the following for their future value as American documents.

7 November, 1948
Middlebury, Conn.

Dear Editor of *The Purple Cow:*

I think I ought to let you know as to how I have no intention of paying your bill ($1.00) sent to me November first. I am sure I did not subscribe to that magazine, and I am also sure that I don't want to.

If someone has taken it into his head to order me a subscription, he can just abandon the idea unless willing to pay for it.

Yours sincerely,

Marcia Wilkham

P.S. For your information, my name is Wilkham (W-I-L-K-H-A-M), not Wonkhaus, as someone on your staff seems to prefer to spell it.

November 11, 1948
Williamstown, Mass.

Dear Miss Wonkhaus,

We of *The Purple Cow* apologize sincerely for the error that has been made in your account. Would you prefer that we send you our check for the amount ($1.00), or would you prefer to have us just extend your subscription for two years, which we can easily do, and send you a bill for the additional amount ($1.00) required? Awaiting your reply, we are

THE EDITORS

November 16, 1948
Middlebury, Conn.

Dear Editors:

As far as I can see, there has been no mistake made in my account, except that I have been incorrectly billed to the amount of one dollar for a subscription to your magazine, which I do not want. All you have to do is cancel my subscription, and then withdraw the bill which I received. If you know who ordered this subscription for me, I wish you would tell him that I have no prejudice against *The Purple Cow*, but that I am not allowed to receive college publications by the rules of the Westover School, which I go to.

Yours,

Marcia Wilkham

P.S. There is a girl named Betsy Wonkhaus here, but she is not Marcia. I am Marcia. My name is therefore Wilkham, not Wonkhaus.

Williamstown, Mass.
November 23, 1948

Dear Miss Wonkhaus:

Your letter of November 16 has been referred to me. From your communication, however, we are unable to determine whether you wish also to subscribe for your friend, Marcia Wilkham. We notice that Miss Wilkham already has a subscription to the *Cow,* payment pending, but we will gladly add your name to our lists and bill you accordingly.

With thanks for your interest in our magazine, we are,

Very truly yours,

S. G. Birmingham

November 28, 1948
Middlebury, Conn.

Dear Steve:

You are the only person I know on that magazine and I want you to help me out in my plight. Betsy Wonkhaus came up to me in the corridor and said she had received a letter from you, mentioning my name. Well, I'm Marcia Wilkham. You remember. From Cleveland. From the way you talk in that letter, however, I think you must have forgotten me. All I want to say is that I don't want a subscription to the *Cow.*

I don't want a subscription to the *Cow.* I don't want a subscription to the *Cow.* I don't want a subscription to the *Cow.* Betsy Wonkhaus doesn't want one either. How she got dragged into this I don't know. Please just forget us both. We aren't allowed to receive college magazines at Westover.

Your old pal,

Marcia

P.S. Someone from Cleveland must have done this to me in the way of a not very funny joke.

Williamstown, Mass.
December 6, 1948

Dear Miss Tilkhaus,

Your letter to Steve Birmingham has been referred to me. How wonderful you are from Cleveland. I once went to Shaker Heights myself, or is that outside Cincinnati? I always get the two places mixed up, myself. We must get together some time.

I am delighted to hear of your interest in *The Purple Cow*—We are always anxious to start *Purple Cow* "Fan Clubs" at the different schools, so if any more of your friends, besides Betsy Wilkham, are interested in subscribing, please let us know. Would you ask Miss Wilkham to send us her remittance for one dollar as soon as convenient? We are always at your service, Marcia.

In the Cleveland spirit,

A. S. Peabody, Jr.

P.S. I know a Jenny Tilkhaus on Robin Road in Cleveland. I think she must be your cousin, which would probably make you one of the Warren Tilkhauses. Marvelous family. I once swam in their pool.

Andover, Conn.
December 14th

Dear Stephen,

Your father is in New York this week, so I have been alone with only the Ford, and I have P.T.A. on Tuesday, and a dinner to arrange for the Ladies' Society. I am quite busy, and so when I got Marcia Wilkham's letter, I was really upset. What in the world have you done to her? Now, Stephen, you know that borrowing money from girls is never *never* done! In my day, a young man was just simply ostracized from polite groups if he did that sort of thing, and I think it's just a *shame!* I have taken care of it, however, by sending Mrs. Wilkham my check for one dollar. I think she would rather have the explanation from me. I know I would, if I were in her position. I just know your father will be terribly upset when he learns of this, but I will try to keep it from him as long as I can. You must know he sees Mr. Wilkham nearly every day in his business. Please do not do anything like that again.

I think Mrs. Wilkham would appreciate a *nice* note from *you*. There's a good boy. Be nice to the Dean.

Yrs in haste

Mother

Williamstown, Mass.
January 2, 1949

Dear Miss Wilkhaus:

Your account with *The Purple Cow* is long overdue. We are sure that it must have been overlooked. Will you kindly send us your remittance for one dollar as soon as it is convenient?

THE EDITORS

Middlebury, Conn.
January 8, 1949

Dear Editors:

Go Away! Don't bother me! I hate *The Purple Cow,* and I hate everybody on your staff. I never want to hear from any of you again! And you can tell that skunk Steve Birmingham that if his mother insists on sending my mother checks, I will use the money to buy nylons, which I need more than your magazine. I'm not going to pay your bill, and Betsy Wonkhaus isn't going to pay hers either. I am going to move away from Cleveland.

Good-by,

Marcia Wilkham

P.S. I don't know Jenny Tilkhaus, and I hope I never meet her.

January 14, 1949
Williamstown, Mass.

Dear Marcia,

Good God, what have I done? You don't sound yourself, like all those times we saw each other in and around New York. And how did my mother get involved? From the tone of your letter, I can't help thinking that you must have fallen into one of those well-known "funks" caused by homesickness. I'm sure you must like Westover, and the girls there—they've always seemed very nice to me. When you get to college, I know you'll look back on these school days fondly, and you'll realize that they were the best years of your life. Try to join lots of extra-curricular groups. Get *into* things. You make your best friends that way. I know right now you must feel that you haven't got a friend in the place—well, you know, I felt that same way many years ago. Why not join the choir? You have a swell voice.

Best,

Steve

January 20, 1949
Scranton, Pa.

Dear *Purple Cow:*

Marcia has been forced to leave Westover as a result of a severe nervous breakdown—caused, as far as I can see, by the gross mismanagement of your accounts. Marcia arrived home last week with six copies of *The Purple Cow* and proceeded to rip the pages out one by one and paste them to her bedroom door, which had been only recently painted. We have sent her to Florida for a long vacation of sea and sunshine. If there were such a thing as justice, you should send some painters down from Williamstown to redecorate Marcia's bedroom. It's just a sight!

I am enclosing, after much thought, Mrs. Birmingham's check for one dollar, which I have endorsed. I hope this will take care of everything, except for the remaining copies of *The Purple Cow,* which I can assure you I will burn upon receipt.

Yours truly,

Mrs. A. E. Wilkham

P.S. I have a son at Taft who was thinking of going to Williams. You notice I say *was.*

Middlebury, Conn.
February 3, 1949

Dear Editor of *The Purple Cow:*

I am Betsy Wonkhaus, of the Westover School, Middlebury, Conn. I received today your bill for two dollars, which I assure you I have absolutely no intention . . . *The Purple Cow (Williams College)*

CARRY ME BACK TO COLD VIRGINNY

BY G. C. HUTCHINSON

(Scene: A typical Yale room, Sunday afternoon following the Junior Prom. From the victrola come the soothing chords of George Feyer. On the table rest a container and two half-filled glasses. On the sofa, Johnny and Ginny sit conversing. She has a beauty Aphrodite would envy, a radiance which outshines Phoebus, and a purity which shames the Vestal maidens. He challenges Adonis for appearance, Solon for wisdom, and Ulysses for determination.)

GINNY: Oh Johnny, I'm just *absolutely dead!*

JOHNNY: Helluva good dance, wasn't it, Ginny?

GINNY: And you know, after you left, Sallyboo and I talked until six. Oooh, she's such a sweetie, and we had *so much* to talk about. I haven't seen her since *Christ*mas.

JOHNNY: I thought maybe you'd be tired. A nice quiet afternoon, a little music, away from the crowds and all . . .

GINNY: You're such a sweetie. (Stretching) I haven't relaxed in *weeks.* (Becoming alert) You know who's *here?*

JOHNNY: Who?

GINNY: Jeannieboo Entwhistle! I didn't see her, but Sallyboo saw the back of her head when we were going into that restaurant after the dance. She was wearing that *hor*rible purple dress with that *ghast*ly silver stuff all down the front. You know the one . . .

JOHNNY: Umm, terrible dress.

GINNY: Well, she wore it *twice* last Christmas. I mean, you'd think she was a *pau*per or something. And you know . . . (Sip of drink) . . . I saw that *cute* Billyboo Sanders last night—and with what's-her-name Willis! I mean, what will happen next?

JOHNNY: I'm sure you'll know about it when it does, Gin.

GINNY: Now, sweetie. You know there's nothing so interesting as people. I mean, what would we talk about if there weren't people?

JOHNNY: You are right there, Gin, life is people. In order to know what life is all about, you have to get to know people.

GINNY: *So* right. I just wish I knew *ev*erybody!

JOHNNY: But if you knew everybody, you couldn't know anybody well. I think it's better to know a few people really well than lots a people only superficially.

GINNY: You're *so* right, sweetie. Like I've known Sallyboo all through Foxover, and I know *exactly* what she's going to do all the time. I mean, this business about loving Sam. Why, it's *silly*. But I knew . . .

JOHNNY: You and I ought to get to know each other better, Gin.

GINNY: Why, sweetie, we're the oldest of old friends. I mean, we're *open books* to each other.

JOHNNY: There may be some things you don't know. (He touches up their drinks.)

GINNY: Well, sometimes you *do* surprise me, sweetie. Like I told Sallyboo . . .

JOHNNY: It's like we were saying, the best thing is to know people really well. You and I, for instance. All we know about each other is through dance chatter. (More modulated) This is the first time we've really been alone.

GINNY: Isn't it *funny!* Like Christmas. You turned up just *every*where. Even at that awful party in Baltimore. I just don't think I'll *ever* go there again.

JOHNNY: You can't tell a person all that you want to at a party. You can't get off alone for long, and being alone is the only time you can really get through all you want to say. (He moves closer.)

GINNY: I *know*. You remember when Wah-Wah went off with that *dream* from Lake Forest at my party last June? Well, the talk that started!

JOHNNY: You know, you and I are very much alike. We're always running into each other, but just this afternoon have I really begun to . . .

GINNY: You know, that's *true*. No matter where you go, you always see the same people. You'd think we were on a merry-go-round or something.

JOHNNY: But seriously, Ginny, we were saying about getting to know each other . . .

GINNY: Johnny, you're so *cute* to put your arm around me. It *is* chilly in here. You're so thoughtful, just like a brother.

JOHNNY: I'd be more than a brother, Ginny.

GINNY: I've never had a brother. You know, Lottieboo—she's my roommate—has the most adorable little brother. He's the *fun*niest thing I've ever heard.

JOHNNY: You know, Gin, this is the greatest time of our lives. We can do anything we want, and just chalk it up to experience.

GINNY: Oh, I *know!* I did the silliest thing last week. They were having this sale, and I bought the *big*gest . . .

JOHNNY: Let's put this afternoon up to real experience.

GINNY: I really couldn't afford it, but it was *so* cute, and . . . Johnny-sweetie, can I have a cigarette? Mother says there are some times when you should always ask for a cigarette. (They light cigarettes.) Mother is the *cu*test thing. She always knows *just* . . .

JOHNNY (suddenly): Let's go over to the Row, Ginny. Maybe we'll find a good party going.

GINNY: Sweetie, you always know *just* what I want to do. I mean, *every*body will be there. *Ent*whistle and Wah-Wah and that absolute *dream* from . . .

(Her voice trails down the hall and fades out.)

CURTAIN

Yale Record

HENPECKED CHARLIE

"Charlie!"

"Yes, Mother."

"Charlie, come here this minute!"

"Yes, Mother."

"What is this I see here from college? An eighty-nine in physics?"

"Yes, Mother."

"You ought to be ashamed of yourself."

"Yes, Mother."

"An eighty-nine in physics! Why, your cousin, Otto, got a ninety-one, and he's six months younger than you are."

"Yes, Mother."

"Why, I wouldn't show my face in the house. How can I look your Aunt Minerva in the eye when her son Otto, who is six months younger than you, got a ninety-one in physics and you only got an eighty-nine? How can I look her in the eye?"

"I don't know, Mother."

"You don't know. That's fine, you stupid ox. First you get an eighty-nine in physics, and then you don't know. I wonder whether your cousin, Otto, would answer his mother like that."

"I wonder, too."

"You wonder! If you spent more time studying instead of wondering you wouldn't get an eighty-nine in physics. You wonder! That's a fine answer! I know your cousin, Otto, would never answer his mother like that."

"Cousin Otto doesn't have to. He got a ninety-one."

"Oh, so you admit that he is better than you are. You admit that you can't hold a stick next to him."

"No."

"So you have the nerve to argue with me? I suppose you think you are better than your cousin, Otto. I suppose you don't know that when Otto was sixteen he was earning money."

"So was I."

"Oh, you were? Otto was out selling magazines, and you spent all your time shooting immies. Do you call that making money?"

"Well, we shot for stakes. I won thirty-five cents one week."

"Indeed. You won thirty-five cents one week. Your cousin, Otto, was earning two and three dollars a week and he was six months younger than you."

"Yes, Mother."

"Yes, Mother; yes, Mother. Is that all you know how to say? I wonder if Otto answers his mother back the way you do. Oh, why are some people blessed with all the good things of life? Why can't I have a child like other mothers have—like Otto?"

"Like who?"

"Otto. Otto, your cousin. Otto, your *smart* cousin. Otto, your *industrious* cousin. You should remember that name—that is, if it isn't too difficult for you; or am I expecting too much. It wouldn't hurt you if you spent some time with your smart cousin, Otto."

"I hate Otto!"

"You what!"

"I hate Otto! I hate Aunt Minerva! I hate the whole darn family!"

"Charlie!"

"Otto is a little guy with a big nose, and I hate all little guys with big noses. He's two feet shorter than I am and only weighs a hundred and four pounds. He wears glasses, and he's got a bad body odor. He's an insignificant, unconsequential little twerp, and I hate him. He's a greasy grind; he doesn't know how to dress; he doesn't know how to dance; he doesn't know how to play ball. He doesn't know how to do anything except study. I'm worth twenty Ottos any day, and I don't want to hear his name mentioned any more. I hate him!"

"All right then, we won't talk about Otto. We'll talk about your cousin Emil!" *Sir Brown (Brown University)*

RUSTY'S WRECK

BY WARREN T. MUSGROVE

Rusty is my blood cousin. Of course, I've got a lot of cousins that always come and spend the summer with me when school is out, so many that we have to make pallets down on the front porch and through the hall so that they can all have a place to sleep. But I like Rusty best because he is always getting me out of trouble. Like the time the Bandage Aid Society caught me and he helped me get away.

When it happened we were having to leave home and go way down below Birmingham to Uncle Ben's house on account of we'd mixed the babies up in the wagons and trucks on the last night of a protracted meeting.

Mixing the babies up wasn't so bad I guess but there in the dark it was hard to tell what we were doing and we got one of the Saluers girl's babies what didn't have no daddy and put it in Deacon Donohue's truck with the rest of his youngens.

That wasn't so bad either only the people down at the store got onto Deacon Donohue right sharply the next evening, talking about how glad they was that the rightful father of the baby had done gone and claimed it. Well, Deacon Donohue blowed up right there on the store porch, threw his flour and lard right down there on the bench, and took off for home to get his gun.

Goober Green saw him coming around up the road with his shotgun and Goober cut across the pasture and told us about it. Pa said right away that the best thing for us to do was to take off through the woods and hit the pike road and see if we couldn't catch a ride and go down to Uncle Ben's and stay a spell.

We coulda rode a big bus and not had to try to catch a ride if we'd had time to get our money. But it was way down in the holler where Rusty had fastened it in a snuff can and wrapped it up in a brown sock and tied it in the top of a big hickory tree.

Well, there we were on the pike road trying to catch a ride. We waved at cars and thumbed at cars and yelled at cars but they all kept whizzing on toward Birmingham without so much as slowing down.

Then we sat down in the damp weeds there by the side of the road and smoked us a cigarette and watched dusky dark come up out of the pines while two hoot owls down in the swag argued about what color chickens they ought to catch that night. And Rusty turned his back to the pike road and said he wouldn't ride with the shiftless people if they wuz to try to hire 'em to ride.

Purty soon we heard a crash-bang up around the curve and then some people a-hollering and yelling like something terrible had happened.

I told Rusty to less go and rescue them cause it sounded like a wreck, but he just rolled another cigarette and said it was the wrath of the Lord done fell down on their heads for being so selfish and not letting us ride; that he had done hardened his heart and could sit there like a pillow of salt and watch their blood run clean to Birmingham.

But then he got up and we ran up there as fast as we could. Two cars had run together there on the curve and knocked each other off the road and smashed up pretty good. But there didn't seem to be nobody much hurt excusin' a man that had a leg bleeding fairly well. And we didn't get to see much of him because the highway patrolman shoved him in his car and went screaming off towards Birmingham. And pretty soon another car stopped and picked up the other man and two that was in the wreck and hauled them way.

Rusty told the man that we would guard the wrecks until the patrolman got back and the man thanked him and gave us a quarter apiece.

Some people pulled up in a car and asked who got hurt in the wreck and Rusty told them that one woman had both legs cut off just above her knees, a man broke his arm, and a crawling baby got smashed up so bad that it had to be picked up in a shovel and that we'd be much obliged for a ride to Birmingham.

The man asked us why we didn't go home to our mamas and Rusty told him that he could go you know where. Then the man drove off and left us standing there by the wreck.

I asked why he wanted to tell so many big lies when it wasn't gonna do us no good about getting a ride. But Rusty didn't say nothing. Just ran the toe of his shoe over the smudge pot the patrolman had left and didn't say a word.

A carload of boys and girls drove up and Rusty told them the same tale only a lot bigger and they drove off and left us standing there in the darkness except for the flickers from the smudge pots, and it was looking like we were going to have to spend the night there.

Rusty ran his hand over the smashed side of the car and kicked the broken glass there on the road with his foot. "It ain't right to have this here wreck with people stopping to see hurt people and then having to drive off disappointed. And furthermore, I don't aim to stand here and watch no such."

Then Rusty started hopping around on one foot and holding his head to one side and slinging his arms around something terrible like. "Good people," he said. And there wasn't nobody there but me. "I have been wrecked something awful—busted every blasted organ in me, drove the steering wheel down my throat and lodged the gas tank in my left kidney."

He grabbed me by both shoulders and looked me in the eyes. "Can't you see I'm hurt?"

"No," I said.

"I've been in a wreck, and you are going to tell people about it while I lay down here on the side of the road."

I didn't have no hankering to do a heap of long-winded talking to them people in them cars so we decided to let me be the one that got busted up in the wreck and for Rusty to be the one to tell about it. We got a white blanket out of the back seat of the green car and rubbed it on the ground some and sopped up a little blood there where the hurt man had been sittin' and then I lay down on the side of the road and Rusty covered me up with that blanket.

Pretty soon a car stopped and a man yelled, "Anybody hurt?"

"Nope," Rusty said. But I heard the car door open and slam shut and then I could hear a man breathing real hard right over me. I peeped under the edge of the blanket and I could see his white face and his lips a-trembling there under his hat.

"Is he dead?" the man asked.

"Might as well be. The doctor said it'd be just wasting gasoline to haul him to the hospital 'cause he is going to die anyway. He's past all remedies. Every bone in his body is broke in three places and he's lost five gallons of blood already."

"That's awful," the man said just barely loud enough for me to hear him.

"Awful the devil! He had it coming to him." Then Rusty kicked me in the hip and I heard the man jump and holler like it'd been him that got kicked. And it hurt me bad enough that I'd hollered if I hadn't been grittin' my teeth to keep from laughing.

"You know how come him to have that wreck?" Rusty said.

The man didn't say nothing.

"Well I do and I'll tell you. He was driving intoxicated with a gallon of whiskey in both hands and two girls sittin' in his lap and now the Lord is punishing him for it."

I guess they ain't no telling what Rusty would have told if a carload of women hadn't drove up about that time and caused him to have to start the whole thing right over again; about how many bones I had broke and all the blood and how the doctor'd given me up for gone and about how wicked I'd been.

I heard one of the women tell Rusty that we were powerful lucky 'cause she was president of the brand-new Bandage Aid Society what they'd just got through forming up that night, and that she had five of her members and part of her equipment there with her.

Through the crack in the blanket I could see a medium-size woman acting sorta nervous like, running back toward where the other women stood and then running back to look down at me and saying, "Girls get the kits out of the car."

They pulled off my overalls in spite of what Rusty said about how wicked I was and deserved to die. And they kept talking about how first aid could save a body's life sometimes when the doctor failed.

I said they pulled my overalls off but I'll take that back. They first talked about pulling them off, but one of the women said that the book stated in many cases it was better to cut them off and that she believed that this was one of them cases. So they cut them off in little strips. And one of them pulled off her corset and wrapped it around my leg where she said I had all the symptoms of a compound fracture. Somebody pulled my right shoe off and tied up my big toe where I'd stumped it three days ago a-running down on the bluff.

Then they opened my shirt. They had already cut the sleeves out of it. But when they opened it down the middle and saw some blood Rusty had put on my chest, one of the women said "Sucking Wound," and then kneeled down and feinted right across me.

They picked her up and drug her to the car and some one of them mentioned something about giving her first aid but the president said, "No," that you always took care of the worst cases first. That they would get around to her after a while.

Then they all got in a powerful fight about how to treat a sucking wound and finally one of the women went to the car and got the book. But when she came back with the book open she was talking about shock and said I stood a good chance of catching shock it looked like to her, with all them sucking wounds and broken bones.

Then they all grabbed a hold to me, talking something about a fireman's carry. I believe one woman said she wanted to try out the fireman's carry on me but I'm sure glad she didn't 'cause that sounded even worse than some of the other things they did do. Anyway though, they all got hold to me and drug me down the hill and propped my feet up on the side of the bank. But on the way down they cut my head a little on a sharp rock and mentioned about me having a head wound.

They turned to the section on head wounds and one of the women said, "Lord have mercy, it says here that you can't put a turniquet on for bleeding of head wounds." Another one asked if it wouldn't be all right just to put one around my neck, if that wouldn't stop bleeding of the head. And another one said that she might have something there, but be sure and not forget to loosen it about every twenty minutes, but the woman with the book said, "Look here," that she'd found something about pressure points and then in a minute they had their hands all over my neck and face and one finally said she'd found the pressure point as she soused her thumb in my neck there somewhere close to my Adam's apple. She said she knew she'd found it 'cause the wound had stopped bleeding.

I was gettin' good and ready to prop my elbow under me and look around and see if I couldn't light a shuck for the woods and get out of all that conglamorated mess. But right then I heard Rusty a-whispering to me there just like he'd been able to read my tormented mind right through the blanket.

"Don't go crazy," he said. "Lay still and we'll get us a ride to Birmingham. Don't go sissy and quit right when everything is going good."

I didn't know exactly how he figgered things was going good but I gritted my teeth harder and allowed that I wouldn't be no sissy.

Then I heard somebody say, "Young man, how did you come out of this wreck without getting wounded?"

I looked out to see who the young man was that they was talking about and saw them all gathering around Rusty there by the smudge pot.

"I ain't hurt," Rusty said. "Never had a broke bone in my life. And besides that I wasn't exactly in this here wreck. I mostly just happened along after it was committed."

"Oh yes, you were in the wreck too," the president said, pointing her finger at Rusty as he sorta backed up there against the smashed-up car. "You told us about that when we first got here. You must be suffering from shock something terrible to be talking out of your head that bad."

"He's getting sick," another of them said. "Look how white his face is. The excitement has been holding him up and now he is about to feint."

Then they all grabbed Rusty and laid him down there by the smudge pot and in a minute I saw one of them going at him with the scissors all ready to cut his britches off just like they did my overalls. And then I heard him yell, "Get away from here woman. Don't touch me on account of my back is broke half in two."

A woman said that it wouldn't do at all to move him with a broke back lessin' they had a good straight board under his back. And I guess they must have gone off down the pike road looking for a board 'cause their voices kept getting farther and farther away. And the first thing I knew somebody jerked the blanket ofna me and there stood Rusty right over me.

"Let's take off," he said. "Before them women get back up here. They ain't no telling what they are gonna do to us if we don't."

"About our ride," I said.

"Ain't no matter," he said. "We can catch a ride tomorrow."

So I hopped up and crawled in what was left of my overalls, mostly just gallouses and frazzles. But when I looked down I knew I couldn't take off looking like that and I grabbed the blanket and crawled back under it.

Time I got good covered up, Rusty snatched the blanket off again and asked what was the matter. And I told him that I didn't aim to show my nakedness to the world. He looked pretty mad for a minute and then he said he'd see what he could do.

First thing I knew he was back from one of the wrecks pulling the brown paper ofna as pretty a pair of white ducks as you ever laid eyes on.

I crawled in them and we headed out through the woods toward a light what looked like it might be a place where we could spend the night.

I had to hold the white ducks up but they fitted mighty good and I figured they'd be the stuff to wear down to the church house on Sunday nights. And Rusty had made them come in powerful handy to help me get away.

Of course, I've got a lot of cousins that always come and spend summer with me, but I like Rusty best because he is always getting me out of trouble. *Rammer Jammer (University of Alabama)*

CONFESSIONS OF A PEANUT BUTTER ADDICT

BY JACK LYNCH

We don't usually care to have anything to do with this sordid type of story, but George "X" is a former University student, and he asked us to publish this with the hope of saving others from such a ghastly ordeal as his own.

It is a typical story of neglected parents, furtive meetings in darkened parks, thrill seeking—but this is George's story. Let him tell it.

Call me George "X," and heed me. I too was a University student—trodding the paths of the Quad, winking at loose-looking girls, keeping a wary eye out for birds, sticking pins in dolls of professors . . . but wait. My story starts way before this.

I guess it began that cold winter afternoon when I was still in high school. We got out at three, and a bunch of us were sitting on a curbstone in the old neighborhood, waiting to snipe cigarette butts flicked out of passing cars.

Our folks all worked at Boeing. The cops kept breaking up our football games in the park—said it tore up the grass.

Tommy Can suggested we go over to Shirley Ruddlehumps and ask her to wrestle with us, but that was old stuff. Besides, Shirley always won.

Then, I guess it was Jimmy Spit who got us all started.

"Hey guys," Jimmy said. "Ya wanna try somethin different? Really different?"

We said sure. We'd try anything for a little excitement. (Oh Fate!) Jimmy took all of us over to his place. We went down in the basement. It was dark there, but Jimmy said it was better that way. He went upstairs, and when he came back he had it—a giant jar of peanut butter!

"Gee," said Tommy Can. "What is it?"

"Just try it, just try it," Jimmy answered. We mixed in the oil at the top of the jar, and it got real soft and smooth. We spread it on pieces of bread. I shut my eyes and ate.

That first bite was dynamite! The insides of our mouths tingled funny-like, and I felt just a little sick. The second piece of bread was better. I didn't get sick. It began to stick to the roof of my mouth. Man, that was great! I should have stopped then, but I couldn't.

"Where'd ya get this stuff?" I asked Jimmy.

"Old Man Dingle at the grocery store took me in the back room and showed it to me last week. He gives it to me regular now for working around the store on Saturdays."

The rest of the guys turned chicken, and wouldn't eat anymore. But the next week I went up to see Old Man Dingle. He gave me a whole jar of the stuff. I began to spread it on my bread a little thicker.

When I finished the jar, Old Man Dingle told me I'd have to start paying for it. I wasn't going to do it at first, but then he showed me some stuff a little different. He called it Homogenized. It already had the oil mixed in it and packed a helluva wallop.

I began filching dimes and quarters out of my Mom's purse so I could buy the stuff. After a while, even the "Homo" began to lose its bounce. I started eating it on my toast at breakfast, covering it with strawberry jam so the folks couldn't tell I had it. I'd make my lunch sandwiches with it, and have it at dinner too.

By now I had started at the University. Between classes, I'd sneak off campus and have a quick sandwich.

I told Dingle the stuff wasn't good any longer. I was getting shaky whenever I quit eating it. Then Dingle let me in on the Big Stuff. He took me into the back room, and brought out a jar like I'd never seen before. It was called "Crunchy," and had real chopped peanuts in it.

Man! Now I was living. I'd eat a sandwich of it and be off. It was like getting up on a big brown horse, and it'd take me anywhere I wanted to go. I was big then—the biggest man on the campus. I'd go right past the U. cops and give them the dirtiest look I could. No one was bigger than I was.

Before long, I couldn't take it on the bread anymore. I couldn't get enough that way. I used to reach in the jar with a big spoon and eat it straight. Oh Crazy! Now I had it—the Mainliner!

But Dingle wouldn't give it to me unless I did things for him. I had to go around to all the other grocery stores at night and hide dead cats near them, making the places smell lousy. I had to lie in wait for delivery trucks from the other stores and let air out of their tires.

Finally, Dingle told me I had to follow the paper boys around the neighborhood, and sneak up to clip the Safeway ads out before folks took them in their houses. That's how I was caught. . . .

I went up to one house and tore out the ad, but on the back side of it was a five-line story about a meeting of the Hyacinth Garden club. The president of the club lived at the house where I clipped the paper.

She caught me. I was sent away. They wouldn't give me the Crunchy anymore—just the Homo, and they kept cutting the doses of that. Soon I was back to the stuff with oil on top. It took a long time, but they finally let me go. Dingle lost his peanut butter license.

That's about it. I'm no good to anyone now—just a hulk of my former self. Got a job collecting garbage, so I can clean out any old peanut butter jars thrown out.

There's just one thing you might remember—a little peanut butter once or twice a week won't hurt you, but when you starting putting it on your morning toast—look out! *Columns*

MY LIFE WITH SARAH

BY RUSSELL ROTH

I am a bitter, friendless fellow with only two attributes: one, owing to my extreme height and slender girth I can stand in postholes for long periods of time without fatigue, and two, I have no salivary glands and therefore can stare at pretty girls without drooling.

Mine is, however, a solitary life. I was talking it over with my girl Sarah the other night, over a goblet of bay rum. I was telling her how dull my existence seems, and how I wish I could be sharp like the rest of the kids.

"How, Sarah," I screamed, anguish in my voice, the goblet stuck halfway down my throat, "can I be smooth like Ronald Colman, a great lover like Robert Taylor, and virile like Clark Gable!"

Sarah thought it over for a while. A fly settled on the table in front of her. Her long tongue flicked out snaring the unsuspecting insect. She smiled modestly, and her teeth fell into her bay rum, immediately dissolving.

Finally she looked up. She smiled toothlessly. "I like bay rum," she said.

I lost my temper. And then, leaving her to extricate her head from her rib cage as best she could, I strode out the door just in time to be commandeered by the fire department as a ladder.

This was not the end of my misfortunes, however. Ah, no. I went to the Homecoming dance after obtaining a note from the keeper of the anatomy building. And, fool that I am, I took Sarah, with whom I had effected a reconciliation. Not that she wasn't beautiful the night of the dance, for she was: a cheery fire burned in her tiara, her finely chiseled face was free of wood shavings, and her lovely gown, hand-woven by Margaret Culkin Banning, was cut so low she had to keep walking back into it. She was fairly bursting with youth—in fact, three hundred pounds of it got away from her through a ripped seam.

But despite her gaudy trappings and the new cotter pin in her knee, she was still the Sarah of old; Sarah of the Sells-Floto circus days when she carried the elephants from the train to the big top; Sarah of the old Gaiety days when she was a strip-teaser until she slipped off the stage and killed the orchestra and all the customers in the first three rows; Sarah of the days when she was a coal barge, plying the waters of the Mississippi.

We had no tickets to the dance. Sarah doesn't believe in tickets. She held my arm out toward the man at the door. He tore it in half and handed the stub to her. She grinned toothlessly. "You carry it," she shrieked indulgently at me. Annoyed, I placed the arm in my pocket and followed her into the ballroom.

We came in one door, and eighty-five couples went out the other. This was a physical necessity. Sarah immediately started trucking, and her clutch slipped. She sank to the floor. Twenty-five more couples went out the other door. After the railroad crane came, we got the others out from under her—some of them, that is. A few people were pressed into the floor, creating a vivid mosaic effect.

By this time I was very angry. "What's the matter with you?" I shouted.

She grinned toothlessly. "I used to be a cider press!" she shrilled.

I hit her in the mouth. That made her shut up like a clam, but after repeated kicks in the patella, she finally consented to open her jaws and let me get my shoulder loose. I then went home immediately, deserting Sarah, the Sarah I had once ardently loved, and I went back to my posthole, where I am to this day. *Ski-U-Mah (University of Minnesota)*

THE HOURS

BY DEX NILSSON

It was a warm October night, and they had just gotten in from a date at the show.

A slow breeze drifted through the half-open window into the dimly lit room; the small lamp on the dresser furnished the only light. It was after hours.

She lay stretched out on the lower bed. A white bathrobe, in contrast to the gold and black spread, was the only thing she wore, and it hung closely to the trim smooth lines of her figure. Her blond brushed hair glistened in the warm light, her soft brown eyes flashed over toward the window, and her warm moist lips spread into a devilish smile.

He wiped the perspiration from his sun-browned face and forehead, then thrust the handkerchief back into the pocket of his blue trousers. He looked nervously at his watch and then shrugged his shoulders as he noticed it was nearing midnight. He pulled his tie down and loosened the white shirt collar. He ran his hand through his brown hair, and the smoke of his cigarette spun dizzily upwards.

"I had a wonderful time tonight, Bob. I really did," she said rather coyly. "But I think we should stop now, I'm getting awfully tired."

"Well, you know how it is. And you *are* pinned to me, aren't you?" he replied. "By the way, where are your roommates?"

"Oh, don't worry about them. None of them care. This sort of thing happens often, anyway."

The smile flashed on her face again. She leaned forward a little too far for the robe she wore.

He was feeling the heat more than ever. He puffed on his cigarette.

Marcia lay with a dreamy look in her eyes. "Look out the window, Bob. See that moon?" Her voice was barely a whisper. "Just like that night down on the lake this summer."

"Remember that?" Bob said softly. "We had a lot of fun didn't we? If they didn't have these damn hours here, things could be like that now instead of like this."

Bob began thinking of the things he shouldn't—of that night when he pinned her down on the lake and now about her lying there in the dim light of her room talking softly to him. Marcia was also thinking of that night, of many times, and then suddenly of tonight.

"Really, Bob, I did have a swell time tonight, but I am getting awfully tired. It's so late."

"Well, maybe you're right. How about tomorrow night? Maybe if we get started earlier, it won't be like this. Tomorrow, OK?"

"Well, OK."

"I guess I'd better go. See you tomorrow, same time. 'Bye, Marcia."

" 'Night, Bob."

Bob slowly pulled up his tie and mashed his cigarette onto the floor. He hung up the phone, and stepped out of the booth into the hall.

The Rivet (Purdue University)

MY AUNT AND THE COUNTERFEIT HALF DOLLAR

When I left for Cleveland and field experience, my mother asked my Great Aunt Agatha to keep an eye on me. Mother is optimistic—Aunt Agatha hasn't been able to keep track of her key case, her check book, the latest copy of the *Atlantic* or the laundry list for the past sixty years. Two weeks later, I moved into the big house in Shaker Heights to keep an eye on *her*.

My Uncle Alec usually makes sure that she remembers her most important appointments and doesn't forget to clip her United States Steel coupons, but the bank of which he is vice-president was opening a branch that summer and he was pretty busy. Great-uncle Alec is a fine man, but he's a banker, with a banker's mind, and doesn't understand things that are illogical, like Aunt Agatha. Thirty-five years he's been married to her, and still gets confused. Like the night Aunt Agatha came to dinner with a counterfeit half dollar.

"It clunks," she says, "and all the others ring. There's no date on it, but it's obviously an inferior product of the last administration."

My uncle Alec took the coin and dropped it to the table. It clunked. "It's a counterfeit," he said. "It's lead."

"Just as I thought," said my Aunt Agatha. "Well, you can pick me up a new one in the morning."

"What!" shouted my uncle.

"Get me a new one. It shouldn't take long—you're right there with all that money."

"Agatha," said my uncle, "you don't get good money for bad. Somebody slipped you a bad half dollar—"

"The May Company," said my Aunt Agatha.

"The May Company," agreed my uncle, who has learned not to get excited over trifles. "You are out fifty cents. The government will not redeem it, the state of Ohio will not redeem it, and by heaven the Second National Bank will not redeem it!" He then explained why—a short lecture ending with a laudatory address on the virtues of the Federal Reserve system.

"I don't know what the Federal Reserve system has to do with it," said my Aunt Agatha, pulling back her half dollar. "I think I shall write a letter to the *Plain Dealer*."

The next Saturday was my day off, so Aunt Agatha and I went shopping. I was surprised when she turned into the May Company—she doesn't like the May Company. Of course, she also doesn't like Higbees, Halle's or Sterling Linder Davis—the only store she really approves of is a tiny shop on Euclid where the owner agrees with her on the superiority of Sheraton over Hepplewhite.

I didn't say anything, though, and half way down the aisle I saw a blue cashmere sweater I couldn't afford. By the time I had bought it,

I had lost Aunt Agatha. I saw a crowd over by linens, and dashed. In the middle was Aunt Agatha, surrounded by three clerks, the floorwalker and the department manager. Lying on the table was the half dollar.

"I suppose," said my Aunt Agatha, "that I deliberately tried to pass bad money."

"No, no," said the department manager, but my Aunt Agatha flung him her charge-a-plate. "I'm closing my account," she shouted, and stalked out, picking up the half dollar on the way. But just as she left, she turned around. "I suppose," she said, "you think I make them in my basement!"

"It's a question of principle," said my Aunt Agatha on the way home. "The innocent should not suffer for the sins of the guilty."

"What about the innocent May Company?" I asked.

"*Innocent!* They gave it to me."

"Maybe they didn't notice," I said soothingly.

"They noticed it quickly enough when I tried to give it back," said my Aunt Agatha, and I had to admit she was right.

I decided the incident was closed when Aunt Agatha re-opened her charge account a week later, but the next day Uncle Alec asked for the half dollar. "I don't have it," said Aunt Agatha.

"Where is it?" asked the suspicious Uncle Alec.

"I spent it," said Aunt Agatha. "At Perkin's supermarket. They sold me two quarts of sour milk three years ago, so now we're all even."

"Agatha!" shouted my uncle.

"Now Alec, don't start telling me about the Federal Reserve system again. We must be logical. Perkin's hasn't been the same since they stopped selling sorghum molasses."

My Great Uncle Alec is a banker, but my Great Aunt Agatha is a financier. *Sundial (Ohio State University)*

NEW YEAR RESOLUTION

December 18, 1951

Dear sir,

For many years, I have been sorely troubled by the overly complicated ways in which many of our everyday words are spelled. Accordingly, I would like to outline below a ten year program which I believe would eliminate easily and painlessly the complexities of our modern methods of spelling. Any efforts on your part to promote the adoption of this system will be appreciated.

The year 1952 would be devoted to the successful elimination of the soft "c", which is obviously replaseable by "s." Likewise, in 1953, all other "c's" would become "k's." Thus, we sertainly would have no further konsern with this konsonant. However, sinse it would still be found on all typewriter keyboards, we would use it as a replasement for ce bocersome "th." Cis would okkur in 1954.

Next, ce suffix "ing" would be attakked. Cis problem would be solved by removig ce exsess "n." 1955 will be sufficiently long for akkomplishig cis khange.

Sertainly you are beginnig to see ce progress we are makig. 1956 would see ce end of al double konsonants, long nocig but exses bagage. Now, cese cigs are realy shapig up! 1957 would be haled as ce yer to remove unesesary dubled vowels. Onse agan, words bekome simpler. In 1958, cose anoyig final "e's" wuld disaper. Anocer step to esy, efortles spelig.

C last cre yers wuld ad c finishig tukhes. In 1959, al "y's" wuld giv wai to "i's" and in 1960 cis sam "y" wuld tak c plas of "sh." Finali, in 1961, all "ph's" and "gh's" wuld bekom "f's."

Cer iu hav it. Ten yort iers and evericig is rift. Spelig is somecig to b lafed at. A khild kan now use an alfabet unklutered wic exses leters. Welkom to c brift ag of komplet konkord on c mater of korekt spelig!

Sinsereli iurs,

Matcew Smic
Wayigton D.C.

Old Line (University of Maryland)

LETTER HOME

BY HARRIS CARNABY

Dear Sam,

Well, rush week's over and I've had my first blind date. The guy that fixed me up said that my date traveled strictly with the upper set. (I found out later she kept the lowers in her dresser in a glass of Lysol.) I called her up and asked her if she would be free Friday evening. She said no, but that she'd be reasonable.

When I went over to the sorority house to meet her, she came down in one of those new creations. A gownless evening strap. If it was cut any lower, she would have been barefooted. It wasn't so bad though, because if it hadn't been for her Adam's apple she wouldn't have had any figure at all. She had a huge lower lip, but it wasn't very noticeable because her upper lip covered it. However, she did have beautiful eyes, especially the pink one. I was a little worried, but when we got to the dance she proved to be the life of the party. The gang went simply wild when she yawned and her ears disappeared. That night she wore open-toed shoes and she persisted in embarrassing me by constantly picking up cigar butts with her toes. About that time I thought it might be wise to dance, so we entered a jitterbug contest. Fifteen minutes later we were disqualified. One of my feet touched the ground.

She consumed so much alcohol that, near the end of the evening, I was afraid to let her smoke. When we got up to leave, she fell flat on her face. I would have picked her up, but I remembered what you told me about having nothing to do with fallen women.

Corn Shucks (University of Nebraska)

13 THINGS WE LIKE TO HEAR GIRLS SAY

1. Sure I do.
2. No, Bob, it doesn't make any difference when we get home tonight.
3. Let's go Dutch.
4. My, but I'm cold, Jim.
5. Why bother? There's no one home here.
6. No, Ed, I've never seen the Tower in moonlight.
7. I get high as hell on one beer.
8. Bob, you don't think this bathing suit is too tight, do you?
9. Aunt Jenny just left me two million dollars.
10. But, Bob, I know mother wouldn't mind your staying another week or so.
11. Chaperone, what chaperone?
12. We can move in with the family, Bob.
13. Yes.

Corn Shucks

BUT, DARLING, DON'T YOU SEE

BY ROBERT C. HERRON

She was forever handing me articles to read from the *New Yorker* and always sympathizing with me about how frightfully unfortunate it was that I hadn't gone to one of the eastern schools because, really, after all, dear, it's just too excruciatingly unfortunate.

Fleur Cowles was her idol and wasn't it a pity that the New York sales of "Flair" weren't enough to keep it going, because one just couldn't expect the sales in the hinterlands (she loved the word) to support it. But the "Flair Annual" is so divinely unique that I suppose we should be thankful for small favors.

At Chambord's, where we dined once a week, she insisted on ordering in French although there was no necessity of doing so, and to demonstrate her complete sophistication she always ordered something plain, but *good,* like lamb chops, but SHE ordered the wine because, dear, I have spent two years in the *provinces* where it's made and I KNOW.

One evening she was explaining to me why Bernstein's "Age of Anxiety," based on the Auden thing, you know, was so absolutely vital. I excused myself for a moment and went to the kitchen to get the meat cleaver. I came back into the living room and chopped her into little pieces and then flushed her down the commode. She always loved the bathroom—it had been done by Robsjohn-Gibbings before he became so completely commercial. *Profile (University of Cincinnati)*

COLLEGE BRED

Daddies send their children to college either because they went to college or because they didn't. Maybe Daddy can't estimate the value of an education, but he can certainly tell you the cost of one. Some students, however, work their way through school (reform school) and in some rare cases, school works its way through them.

The college is the fountain of knowledge where youth goes to drink—and the coeds there answer more questions over the phone than they do in class. A coed with brains may go to the head of the professor's class, but a coed with class goes to the head of the professor. Some coeds pursue learning; others learn pursuing. Coeducation was once a race for supremacy between the sexes, but now it's neck and neck.

Then there's the college man, an appetite with skin over it. If all college men who sleep in class were placed end to end they'd be more comfortable. College men like suits with stripes, ties with dots, and letters with checks.

Maybe someday we'll get that B.A. (which means the holder has mastered the first two letters of the alphabet) and a sheepskin to cover our intellectual nakedness. Then we'll wake up to the fact that we've finished college and Daddy about the same time.

Sour Owl (University of Kansas)

THE REAL FIRE LAWS OF MT. HOLYOKE FEMALE SEMINARY OF ABOUT 1857, AND THE BURLESQUE OF THEM BY STUDENTS OF MT. HOLYOKE COLLEGE IN THE 1870'S

SOME OF THE ORIGINAL FIRE LAWS

Leave no matches out of the safe.
Carry no lamps to the wood room.
Place the fender before the (wood) stove on leaving the room.
Leave no wood or kindling on the stove hearth or zinc.
Carry no fire from one room to another.
Do not leave the upper door (coal stove) closed.
Do not leave a lamp burning.
Avoid lighting matches on the walls.

BURLESQUE FIRE LAWS

If a fire breaks out in the seminary, the young lady who first discovers it may have permission to pour a pail of water on the fire, even if it is in silent study hours. If it is not then extinguished, she may go at once to Miss Ward, who will give her permission to go to the North Wing Parlor and inform Miss Edwards. Miss Edwards will give her permission to go to the room for her section teacher, who will send her to the bell-girl and cause a long bell to be rung. The young ladies will then assemble in the seminary hall, and Miss Ward will rise and say, "Good morning" or "Good afternoon, young ladies," as the case may be. "We have ascertained that a fire has broken out in our building, and it will be necessary for you to do some benevolent work. All who are willing to assist will arise." Their names will then be taken in alphabetical order. Then Miss Ward will say, "You may all arise. Those who have leaky pails may remain standing, while the rest may be seated." Their names will be taken, and then they may go to their rooms, take their pails, and carry them to the long drying room, and exchange them for whole ones. The bell will then ring again and all will meet in the seminary hall. Each section, with its section teacher at its head, will then march to the Connecticut River, fill their pails and return.

To avoid confusion, no two young ladies must empty their pails on the fire at the same time. No one must leave her place until the one immediately preceding her has returned.

If it becomes evident that the building will burn down, a long bell will ring again, and the young ladies will meet in the seminary hall. They will then be told to go to their rooms at the close of the exercise, put their rooms in order, being especially careful to dust the upper shelf in the closet and the top of the mirror. Each will then pack her trunk very neatly, remembering we put dresses on the top. Money must not be put in the trunks. Each will lock her trunk and place it in the hall. No one need call upon Cornelius for assistance, as he will be otherwise engaged, but when he has time he will take them downstairs.

The seniors and the senior middles will then march promenade step out of the south door, the juniors and junior middles step out of the north door. Then, as the young ladies will be scattered through the town, a long bell will be rung through the streets, and they will all march to the graveyard, where a teacher will be found seated on a monument, ready to excuse all excusable exceptions made during the fire.

N.B. First-class exceptions will not be excused.

A. M. R.

(*From photostat supplied by the library of Mt. Holyoke College*)

THE FORMAL DANCE

BY PETE WHELAN

"Harry?"

"Yes?"

"The orchid is lovely. I thank you, I think it's a new moment here, leading to something new, something better. Harry, listen to the music coming in from the ballroom. Isn't it strange out here, just us on the balcony?"

"I've noticed something too."

"What did you notice, Harry? Listen now. Do you hear the waterfall in the back. Listen. Do you hear it now? Now listen to the music . . . It's coming from the ballroom. It's a waltz. It's "The Blue Danube." Oh, Harry. It blends with the waterfall. They mix in together almost like a cocktail. Why, it's the grandest cocktail in the whole world."

"You're standing in front of the men's room."

Froth (Pennsylvania State U.)

RAISIN COOKIE

BY DAVE FELDMAN

Like I say, I've been in better brigs, and I've been in worse ones. Take the one down in Quantico. Nice brick building, inside heat, plenty of chow, even if it was rotgut. And Mare Island had one that must've been a hundred years old, and it smelled it.

It's funny that I'm in here at all. Not funny, I mean, but odd. Queer. One minute I was standing my post. The next minute I was locked up.

I could blame it all on Johnny, the Navy baker, but I don't work that way . . . he was out of it. Or I could blame it on my damned stupidity. And I should.

I was out there guarding the east gate at San Pablo Naval Air Station. The gunny sergeant had put me on the midwatch again, that hellish twelve to four. It seems that the gunny and I didn't get along. Well, anyway, when we got up at eleven-thirty in the dark, I was bitching along with the rest of the watch because the lieutenant had fouled up our order for box lunches. The only good thing about that midwatch was the chow you got before you went out on post. If the lieutenant didn't goof off.

We went out on post without any chow, and with just enough of that acid they call Navy coffee to leave a foul taste. My post at the east gate should have been secured, there was so little traffic, but gunny wanted me out there, awake. God knows why. About two cars an hour come through.

The first hour went pretty fast. The second hour dragged on and on, and I beat the billy-club against the shack time after time. Then I stripped the .45 down, knowing that if the O.D. came out I'd lose my stripes. I'd finished assembling it when Johnny Carrillo drove up from inside.

"Hi, Johnny," I yelled, "how's the bakeshop?" Johnny was a second-class baker at the Navy galley. Nice guy. "And how's the new baby?"

"Don't know. The old lady was supposed to call, but she didn't."

"Jeez, that's a pity." Carrillo was one of the few bakers that wouldn't cut a Marine's throat.

"I brought you a sack of raisin cookies, Carl. We just took 'em out of the oven a few minutes ago."

He handed me the brown paper sack out of the back seat of his '33 Dodge.

"Hell, Johnny, you know that I never eat on duty," I laughed. I took a bite of one and stowed the rest inside the shack in the desk.

"Say, Carl." He didn't look at me. "I've never asked this before, 'cause I know you're on the spot, but I was worried about——"

"O.K., Johnny. I know you don't have a liberty card. But go on home to your wife."

"Hell, Carl, thanks. I'm due back on duty in three hours."

"I know," I said. "But if you get caught, you went over the fence and got in your car. Your car was outside, see?"

"Sure, Carl, I'll protect you." He put the Dodge in gear and eased away.

The war was two years over. Johnny had brought me food before, so it wasn't bribery. He really looked worried. What else could I do?

I spent the next half hour in the shack. I had just taken a big bite of cookie when I heard an awful screech of brakes. I jumped out of the shack and started to draw my .45. I stopped drawing when I saw the black Navy car with the brass in the back seat. The damned seaman deuce who was driving had left the lights off all the way to the shack. No wonder I hadn't seen 'em come. And we had orders to report all brass aboard and off the station.

"What is the captain's name, sir?" I muttered. I tried to stow the chow in my mouth to one side.

"Sentry, what are you eating?" He ramrodded it out. Any captain who stayed awake till two-thirty would.

I managed to say, "Nothing, sir."

"Dammit, Corporal, I know you are. And what were you doing in that shack?"

"Keeping warm, sir."

"Driver, pull over the side, and ahead, so you don't block the gate. I'm going in the shack with the guard."

I opened the door for him, and he bristled in, just a little man. In seconds he had eyed the whole shack, and he went over to the desk. We both knew there was chow there.

"All right. What chow is it?"

He should have been a Marine . . . saw his duty and did it, all else be damned. No reprieve. "This ought to be good for two stripes, and when I talk to the colonel, we'll see about brig time." He stated it as facts, no emotion. He didn't know it took three years to make two stripes. "Eating on post is as bad as drinking or sleeping on post, to me." I knew the colonel was of the same mind. "Any man who can't obey orders deserves brig time." He meant it, and station orders would get me a summary court-martial. A summary court would mean an automatic bust, and then we could argue about the brig time. "Corporal, I want to know what you were eating."

"I was eating a raisin cookie, sir." He'd caught me, so I knew enough to make a martyr of myself. "I didn't have any supper."

I never expected to see him turn a hair. But he did. I knew it wasn't the supper part, either."

"Raisin cookies?"

"Yes, sir." I cowed a little, and bent my head. My voice was quivery.

Damned if he didn't relax his taut frame just a little.

"Corporal." This was followed by a long pause. "I don't waste words." He looked out to see if his driver could hear us. He closed the door to the shack.

"You know that I can make you a private." I nodded. "You know that I can have you on bread and water starting tomorrow."

"Yes, sir." I said it very haltingly.

"Then why in God's name did you disobey post orders!" He bellowed that one.

"No excuse, sir."

He eyed me a moment then said, "I may report this to the colonel tonight. I ought to wake him up and tell him." He cleared his throat and waited. I waited for him to talk.

"I should call the colonel, but I'm going to give you a break." He watched me closely.

"Yes, sir?"

"I don't waste words." He was still feeling me out. "I haven't brought anything home for my two young boys tonight. For some damned reason, they'd be very happy if they had some raisin cookies."

"I see, sir."

"Do I make myself clear?"

"Yes, sir."

Like I said, I've been in better brigs, and I've been in worse ones. But this time I think I got a raw deal. When the captain came into the shack, I'd just eaten the last raisin cookie.

Kitty Kat (University of Arizona)

STORY FOR WEE ONES

BY BOB SYMONS

Once upon a time in a land far, far away, there lived a little lad who wanted only one thing for Christmas. That thing was a sexy.

He had heard his brothers talking about sexies, and he had been led to believe a sexy was a very desirable thing. And so on the night before Christmas he sent a letter to Santa Claus saying: "Dear Mr. Claus, please, Mr. Claus, I have been a very good boy all year and there is nothing I would rather have for Christmas than a sexy. If you love me at all, Old Nick, oh boy, send me a sexy for Christmas—for God's sake."

Now when Mr. Claus received this letter he was deeply touched, and so he set all his little gnomes to work making the finest sexy in the world for this little boy. They painted the sexy in all sorts of bright colors with lipstick and pancake and leg make-up and eye-shadow and eyebrow pencil. Then Mr. Claus put the sexy in his bag and hopped in his sled and went tearing off over the roof tops like dammit.

When he got to the little boy's house he popped down the chimney, and what should he find but two stockings hung up over the fireplace. Santa placed his finger aside of his nose and remarked, "Not such a dumb kid." So he put the sexy into the two stockings and popped up the chimney quick as a flash.

The next day the dawn broke a steely gray, but this did not bother the small boy at all. He went tearing downstairs. When he saw his sexy he let out a joyous squeal, and started to tear his sexy apart to find out how it was put together. After he had it all apart he could not find out how to put it back together; so he threw it away. All of which goes to prove that a sexy does one no good unless one knows how it is made. *Stanford Chaparral*

APPENDIX A: HOW TO TAKE NOTES

"BREVITY AND CONCISENESS IS THE SOUL OF NOTE-TAKING" LEANDER GORMLEY, '02

THE PROFESSOR SAYS:	YOU WRITE DOWN:
"Probably the greatest quality of the poetry of John Milton, who was born in 1608, is the combination of beauty and power. Few have excelled him in the use of English language, or for that matter, in lucidity of verse form, *Paradise Lost* being said to be the greatest single poem ever written."	"Milton—born 1608."
"When Lafayette first came to this country, he discovered America, and Americans, needed his help if its cause were to survive, and this he promptly supplied them."	"Lafayette discovered America."
"Current historians have come to doubt the complete advantageousness of some of Roosevelt's policies."	"Most of the troubles and problems that now face the United States are directly traceable to the bunglings and greed of President Roosevelt."
". . . it is possible that we do not completely understand the Russian viewpoint."	"Professor Mitchell is a Communist."
"Pages 7 through 15 are not required but will prove of unestimable worth to the student in preparation for the term examination."	"Omit pages 7 through 15."

"Socrates was a Stoic, but it should be pointed out that Stoicism is very different than cynicism. A cynic is contemptuous of all things, especially human nature, whereas a Stoic is one who accepts all things as they are without complaining."

"Socrates was a cynic."

"The examination will test the student's over-all comprehension of the subject, and a thorough knowledge of theories behind the facts and their relevance to fields other than Political Science will be absolutely necessary."

"Bull exam."

". . . the papers will be marked on a scale . . ."

"Bull exam."

"The class Friday will probably be the most important of the year since we will throw it open to a general discussion of the main problems which have come to our attention throughout the course. Attendance will not be taken."

"No class Friday."

"George Washington, incidentally, loved apple pie and there is an unimportant but amusing story in this connection. One day he was walking down the street with a book in his hand and happened to meet a young lady who was carrying a bunch of apples, and . . ."

"George Washington loved unimportant but amusing stories. One day he was walking down the street looking for a piece of apple pie when he met a girl with a bunch of books in her hand and . . ."

"We come now to the well-known theory of relativity. The student must remember that time, motion, and many such connected concepts are not absolute but actually relative, or referred to another concept. Thus when we walk past a tree, we are not *really* walking past a tree, but actually the tree is partially walking past us, since . . ."

"Write Jane Monday night."

Yale Record

GREEK PRIMER

ALPHA—used to mean half of.
Ex: Alpha pint of bourbon.
BETA—synonym for "ought to."
Ex: You Beta beat it before the cops come.
GAMMA—baby talk for Grandma.
Ex: What big teeth you have, Gamma.
DELTA—used in cards.
Ex: He Delta hand of pinochle.
EPSILON—a laxative.
Ex: Go get a nickel's worth of Epsilon salts.
ZETA—to repeat a phrase.
Ex: Zeta again, Virginia Dare.
ETA—to devour.
Ex: I Eta slab of horse meat.
THETA—to devour (plural).
Ex: Theta whole cow.
IOTA—a duty.
Ex: Iota slap your face.
KAPPA—a pair.
Ex: Dem girls was just a Kappa broads.
LAMBDA—a pugilist phrase.
Ex: So I Lambda guy on da snoot.
MU—love song of a cow.
Ex: Mu, Moo.
NU—recent.
Ex: What's Nu?
XI—dialect.
Ex: Xi in love? I is.
OMICRON—expression of pain when dancing.
Ex: Ouch! Omicron!
PI—the great American dessert.
Ex: Gimme a piece of cherry Pi.
SIGMA—part of warning.
Ex: Watch out or I'll Sigma dog on you.
UPSILON—an explanation.
Ex: See the acrobat. Upsilonded on his head.
PHI—expressed condition.
Ex: I'd go away Phi had the dough.

CHI—slang for a man.

Ex: He's a helluva Chi.

PSI—cockney for an American expression.

Ex: Psi it again, Virginia Dare.

OMEGA—part of a prayer.

Ex: Omega good girl out of me.

Rammer Jammer

DA TOLL

BY PIERRE HENRI DELATTRE

"You said it before and you'll say it again, but you don't mean it," said Saul's wife.

"Dum boozle I don't," he boasted, tugging at the extremities of his zoot suit with resolution. "I'm gonna make a clean-up, so help me. We ain't gonna be no ribs expisition no more, no more."

"Ho, ho," said his wife, tossing a bone into the soup pot, "hee, haw, ho."

"You may laugh, you may jeer, never fear."

"Shakespeare," she added.

"But I got big plans. I'm gonna build me a portable toll. It's a stunt what can only be done in New York."

"This one I got to see," she said, walking out the kitchen door and onto the fire escape and leaning over the rail. "Hey girls, hubby's gonna strike it rich, so bye-bye now, I'm moving to the suburbs."

The glad guffaws of many, many women echoed around the tenement well.

"Okay for you, turkey-head, when I make my pile I leave you behind."

Mrs. Saul leaped to her knees on a chair. "Aw, honey, I didn't mean it. Please don't leave me behind."

"You old fatty," he said, wiggling his bow tie with his Adam's apple and exiting through the kitchen door.

"Sammy," said Saul to the part-time janitor in the laundry room of the basement, "can you dig me up some old lumber?"

"Where da hell from?"

"You know you got some old hunks of wood stuck somewhere."

"So what for?"

"I'm gonna build me a portable toll, something can only be done in New York."

"Well, in dat case," said Sammy, peering carefully into Saul's eyes, "in dat case it's yours for free. Got some I been concealin' away in da coal bin."

Thus it was that Saul got busy on his latest project, and in the alley he could be heard hammering steadily for a week. He abandoned his zoot suit for dungarees, he even quit his job making change at the Penny Arcade. He took this affair seriously and the tenement people were impressed.

"What da hell's he doin'?"

"He's building an outhouse."

"He's gonna keep a great dane."

"Foo! It's beans in da noggin."

The night the job was completed, Saul tugged at his wife's shoulder as they lay in bed. "Listen," he whispered, "we gotta be awful careful. This can't come out no fluke. We can't have no whispering campaigns spreading themselves around."

"You mean . . ."

"I mean we gotta silence everybody on dis deal. Mum's de woid."

"Geeze!" said his wife. Even she was impressed.

In the morning, Saul painted his little house brown. It was nothing more than a stall, a three-walled affair with a flat roof and one side completely open.

He sent his wife around to each family in the tenement and this is what she said:

"I think Saully has it this time, so keep it mum, because if it leaks out, we're through—just plain old through."

When she was asked what the shack was, she answered, "It's a toll," and they said, "Oh yeah?"

Saul went back to the Penny Arcade for about a week, but as he explained it when he came home with news he had quit, this time for good, "I just did it so's to get money enough for dem tires."

"What tires?"

"For da toll."

"Oh yeah?"

And it took him only a day to get the shack on wheels—two very small wheels. Saul made wooden blocks which he set underneath the front and back so as to keep the shack level and steady on the ground. He attached two long poles to the sides and thus gave it a trial run up and down the alley. He would pull it along much as a horse pulls a milk wagon, stop, then see how fast he could set the blocks in place so that it stood stationary. He could be seen timing himself on this action with a borrowed stop watch. The neighbors were awed. They huddled around and speculated, but, remembering Saul's plea for secrecy, they asked no questions.

Everyone in the tenement had a feeling that this time it would work. As Saul set out in the morning with his shack, and a knapsack on his back, they exchanged the opinion that maybe a "dinger" was in the offing.

When Saul got back in the evening, he was trotting briskly with his shack rumbling merrily behind.

The waiting crowd was enormous but quiet and awed. They had patience as he set the blocks under his construction, dashed to the basement, and came back with a tarpaulin which he fondly threw over the thing.

He climbed to the fifth step of the fire escape, then stopped, and, looking meditatively at the crowd, pulled his knapsack from his shoulder and took out a cigar box. He opened the lid and beamed at its contents for a while, then reached in and filled his fist with bills and change.

"My friends," he began carefully, "It behooves me now to say a few well-chosen words to youse because youse have kept da tight lip I asked for. Well, I made it, dat's all, and I'll make it again and again till death do me part, so help me God." So saying, he threw the money into the air, and the cheering crowd scrambled for it.

"Shut-up, good people," said Saul. "Let's not go jugglin' da ball. Mum's still da woid."

At this the neighbors became quiet again and, smiling, returned to their apartments.

From that day on, it was a common sight to see Saul return on the trot from a clean-up, with his little shack behind.

Mrs. Saul sat on her fire escape in a new canvas deck chair and sported her fur coat. She was proud, but her fine sense of balance kept her from redecorating the apartment or anything extreme like that.

Said she, "We're saving our money for the suburbs." Everyone seemed to approve her prudence.

Things had been going incredibly well. Every day Saul came home with a cigar box full of dollars and change. He and his wife would count it and toss it into a cardboard box which soon had to be stored away in the closet and replaced by a larger one.

The Sauls bought a television set and held open house three nights a week for the benefit of those who kept mum. Nobody was unhappy in that tenement house, for Saul lent freely of his fortune. He became a kind of king and counselor; whenever someone had a scheme he consulted Saul. Whereupon Saul folded his arms and listened sagaciously, now and then blinking his eyes or nodding his head, before advising that the scheme be tried, and adding: "God bless youse."

Everyone loved him, respected him, and enjoyed his television set.

Then, one day, bright and early, Sammy, the part-time janitor, knocked on Saul's door.

"I wanted to catch you," he said to the tenement king, "before you was off wid da shack."

"Da toll."

"Oh yeah, da toll."

"And what is it you want?"

Sammy scratched his neck and shuffled his feet. "I know it ain't da code, Mr. Saul, but . . ." He looked at Saul for encouragement.

"Go ahead, Sammy. Out wid it."

"Well, I know da code around here is such that each person's supposed to mind dere own business, but I was wondering if youse could let me come along just once. It ain't I wanna horn in, I'm too old for dat, it's just, well, I gave you da wood for da damn thing and now I'm curious as hell about what you did wid it. I'm just itching wid da bug of curiosity, I am."

Saul paced the floor, he cocked his head this way and that, he put a hand to his chin; then finally he gripped Sammy's shoulder solidly and grunted: "All right, Sammy, I'll let you do it. But"—and here he put a finger on his lip—"mum's da woid."

"Mum," said Sammy with determination, as he crossed himself and hoped to die.

"Then get ready and follow me!"

Saul and Sammy trotted down the streets of New York, each pulling at one bar of the shack on wheels.

"See," said Saul, slackening his pace and finally signaling Sammy to stop. "This couldn't happen anywheres but in New York. Other places they ask you what de hell you're doing. Here nobody even notices."

It was true. The unusual little house with the two men pulling it did not even attract a second look from passers-by.

"They just don't give a damn," said Saul.

"Where we going?" asked Sammy.

"Nowheres in particular."

"What say?"

"We're just cruising around, looking for a good place to stop."

"Oh yeah?"

"And I guess over dere's as good as anywheres." He pointed to where three streets from different angles converged into a single wide street which ran slightly uphill.

"Are you gonna explain it to me?" asked Sammy curiously.

"Sure I am, Sammy. Don't worry none. You'll get your curiosity quenched and you'll learn something at da same time. Ready? Here we go."

They trotted the shack over to a place where three streets converged into a wider one. With great speed Saul placd the wooden blocks underneath the shack to steady it. He then stepped inside the open wall which faced the street, pulled a curtain, and within a minute emerged dressed in a blue uniform Sammy recognized as the one Saul had worn behind his change-making counter at the Penny Arcade.

"Now, you see, you gotta figure all the angles, mull da predicament over in your mind," said Saul. "That's how you make a thing like this sure-fire stuff. Like fer instance, you gotta figure the psychological angle. If this wuz done outside of New York, pfft!" He snapped his fingers. "It just sure as hell wouldn't woik. You gotta figure as dese people are fresh from da habit. They've been through da Holland Tunnel or over the Washington Bridge or God knows whatwithal, and they're climatized, as you might put it."

"Climatized?"

"You got me. Now just stand over dere, inconspicuous like, on da other side of da street, and watch me operate. Notice dat when dere's a big bunch of cars, I let 'em go. I only pick on individuals with foreign license plates."

So saying, Saul stepped just inside his shack and stayed there until a pack of cars had passed. Then he stepped onto the vacant street and hung a sign on the wall which read:

CARS FIFTY CENTS

TRUCKS ONE DOLLAR

KEEP MOVING

DO NOT HONK HORN

TRUCKS KEEP RIGHT

No sooner had he hung up the sign than a car drove toward him from a side street. Saul put up his hand and frowned. The car stopped. Saul smiled and said "Good morning folks" as he took a dollar bill from the driver, stepped inside his shack, and returned with the man's change. "Keep moving, now," he shouted as he waved them on. When the car had disappeared over the rise, he looked up the three streets, and, noticing several cars approaching, the last of them a police car, he quickly flipped his toll sign over and disappeared into the shack.

The police car slowed down and a cop stuck his head out of the window, but he seemed only conventionally surprised and drove on.

"Nothing excites them any more," shouted Saul to Sammy across the street, as he flipped the sign back over just in time to catch another customer to whom he gave some advice on how to find a cheap hotel.

And thus, for several minutes, business became a flourishing, though spasmodic affair. Then Saul signaled Sammy to come back across and told him they better move to another spot.

"Da hardest part to remember," Saul pointed out as they trotted briskly away, "is you must never get a New York license. One home fish on your hook and you're in the caboose."

"Why didn't you stay dere?" asked the janitor.

"Better keep moving to firdle grounds. Some look all day for a tunnel but some come back after a while."

"You'll get caught," said Sammy. "Sooner or later someone'll start asking questions."

"In New York," said Saul, nodding at the passive masses, "who asks questions?" *Penn Pix*

RUST IN PEACE

BY J. H. DOLE

"The riddle of Harry Houdini is as much a mystery today as it was at the turn of the century when he baffled the experts the world over," said Edgar, pacing thoughtfully into our room.

I flipped another page of *Esquire,* and pretended to read. Sometimes when you pretended to read Edgar would go away.

"One time in Germany," continued Edgar in the strong voice we had come to know so well, "the Krupp Munitions Works constructed a magnificent pair of handcuffs in the hope of embarrassing the master. They presented the manacles to Houdini, and asked if he would care to try his hand at escaping from them." Edgar paused, and fixed us with his beady eyes. "Gentlemen, do you know what happened?"

Sam looked up from his crossword puzzle. "He escaped from them," he said.

"Ah," said Edgar with a smile, "then you have heard the tale. Yes, in a matter of minutes Harry Houdini was a free man. Before their very eyes he was a free man."

"Amazing," said Sam. I turned over another page. I was very careful not to say anything. Sometimes if you kept absolutely quiet Edgar would go away.

"Now then," said Edgar, putting his hands behind his back and striding to and fro, "many men have attempted to explain this knack that Houdini had for removing his person from theoretically inescapable situations Locked in dungeons, chained and thrown into ice-bound rivers, padlocked and buried in coffins—many were the situations and many have been the explanations; yet none have been satisfactory. My friends—" Edgar pivoted and looked at us, his face shining with triumph—"my friends, I have at last solved the tantalizing riddle of Harry Houdini."

There was silence for a few moments. Then Sam looked up, a new interest lighting his eyes. "You mean," he asked, "that if we close all the windows, and lock the door, that in a matter of minutes you will escape, leaving us alone to brood over your skill?"

Edgar chuckled indulgently. "Oh come, Sam," he said, "that would be child's play. I had in mind something bigger—something that would be a true test."

Sam sighed. "Oh," he said. He went back to his crossword puzzle.

Don't encourage him, I thought. But my curiosity got the better of me. "Something bigger, eh?" I asked tentatively.

"Precisely," said Edgar happily. "If I could escape from just such an impossible predicament as Houdini himself once did, why, then I'd have proved that I have his secret. Locked, of course, in my brain." He smiled to himself. "Tomorrow," he continued in a businesslike tone, "I shall leap off one of the New Haven docks, bound and locked in heavy chains. I would like you to be my assistants."

Sam was on his feet. "I'd be delighted," he said. "The whole idea has tremendous appeal for me."

"I'll be there too," I promised.

"Wonderful," said Edgar, clapping his hands. "You two are real friends."

The next day was damp and foggy. We three stood on the dock and looked downward into the cold muddy water. Edgar stood pensively, weighted down by his heavy chains. It had taken us a good half hour to get them on him. "I am ready," he said simply.

Sam stepped forward eagerly, but Edgar held up his hand. "First," he said, "I must ask you not to breathe a word of this to anyone. It would be especially embarrassing to me should I fail, after all my boasting. It is our secret."

"All right," I said. "But just how do you propose to escape, anyway?" We had put the chains on pretty tight.

"Ah," said Edgar, "that would be telling, wouldn't it?" He paused, and then said gently, "Come gentlemen, history is waiting."

Sam and I picked him up, and with some difficulty swung him off over the end of the dock. He made a fine splash.

Pretty soon some bubbles came to the surface, then everything was calm. Then there were some more bubbles, and after that nothing happened.

After a while Sam spoke up. "Look," he said, "I've got a ten o'clock I don't want to cut. What do you say we come down here after lunch and see how old Edgar is doing?"

Well, there didn't seem to be much happening there at the dock, so I agreed.

As a matter of fact we haven't heard from Edgar for some time now. Sam and I go down to the dock every morning just to check up on his progress, but I don't think he's doing very well. Naturally we haven't told anyone what happened. Edgar would want it that way. After all, it's our secret, isn't it? *Yale Record*

THE BLUE GNU

Once upon a time there was a gnu named Hugh. And Hugh was a blue gnu. And he was married to a gnu named Sue. And every time Sue would call Hugh, she would coo—"Yoo Hoo, Hugh—you blue gnu you. Yoo hoo, Hugh, yoo hoo." And Hugh would answer, "Yoo hoo, Sue you cute gnu you, Yoo hoo, Sue, yoo hoo." And they called each other often, did these two gnus—for they were happily married. Every day Hugh would dash off to his daily work of getting his name into crossword puzzles under the title "a three-lettered animal," and when his day's work was done, he would dash home to Sue, and Sue and Hugh would spend their evenings doing whatever blue gnus do.

There was only one thing that kept their marriage from being perfect. They both longed for the patter of tiny feet—the happy laughter of a little one. But year after year went by and still the only thing they had running around their house was a fence.

They even considered adopting a little baby gnu, but neither of them knew a gnu who wanted to be adopted; do you?

Gradually they began to quarrel—just a little bit, did Hugh and Sue. Hugh would say, "Foo to you, Sue, you blue gnu you—foo to you, Sue." And she would coo, "And poo to you, Hugh, you blue gnu you. In fact, poo pa doo."

This sad state of affairs, I'm sorry to say, went on for some time, and still there was no patter of tiny feet about the home; still no little ones to brighten their later years.

But one day—ah, beautiful day—Hugh came sadly home from work. He was in a nasty humor and was just spoiling for a fight. He opened the door and stalked in, all ready to begin the quarrel.

But wait—there was something different about Sue today. The frown was gone from her face. There was a happy, bashful look in her eye, as she stood there in the doorway.

"Why, Sue," said Hugh—"Why, Sue. Is there something on your mind?"

And Sue smiled a lovely smile and said, "Yes, Hugh, I have gnus for you—" *Ski-U-Mah*

LIMERICKEY

BY J. S. STEVENSON

Howie was a good man, it was just that he didn't like to pass up opportunities to get something for nothing. He went out of his way to find sneak previews, had in his library the A-Ames volume of every encyclopedia ever offered through the mail, and had developed an absolute mania for little piles of assorted miscellany entitled "take one." Otherwise, as I say, Howie was a good man.

Then he discovered the limerick contest.

It happened one evening on his way back from the Waldorf Cafeteria. He had picked up a copy of the New York *Daily Mirror,* because of its "Lucky Buck" listings, and was glancing through it by the dim light of the streetlamps on Chapel Street. Howie suddenly stopped. There before him was a full page ad describing how easy it was to win an oil well. *AN OIL WELL!* All he had to do was finish, in rhyme, the sentence, "I'm glad I use Dial . . ." Well, Howie was a pretty good man, but he wasn't absolutely celebrated as the cleanest guy around. He had never even heard of Dial soap. Nevertheless, he was determined, and walked back to his room counting barrels.

After a few pencil-chewing minutes, Howie came up with

"I'm glad I use Dial whenever I wash;
I've used it to clean me since I was a frosh."

Howie's roommate Earl looked up from his prone position studying on the floor, raised an eyebrow, slowly shook his head from side to side, and went back to reading. Howie thought for a while, scribbling a bit and read

"I'm glad I use Dial, its lather's so creamy;
When I use it the girls think I'm really quite dreamy."

Earl sat up straight. "Just wait a second," he said. "I suppose you're trying to win something, but you'll never do it with *that*. You need something different—even bizarre." That was Earl all over, always looking for the *macabre,* like the skull he used for an ashtray in his bedroom. "How about

I'm glad I use Dial, made from glycerine and lye—
The last time I used it I burned out my eye.

—or even better—" by this time there was a decided gleam in Earl's eye. "How's this:

I'm glad I use Dial, said Queen Cleopatra
As she carved off her leg with a blade from Sumatra."

The door to one of the bedrooms was slowly opened, and Paul stepped out and lit a cigarette.

"I'm glad I use Dial, because then I won't smell
And then my friends will think I'm swell,"

he offered.

"Not quite," Earl said. But Paul was not one to be discouraged by so slight a rejection, and suggested

"I'm glad I use Dial soap, it makes me feel so homey,
Because when I put it in water it gets all lathery and foamy."

"Good God, man!" shouted Walt from the bedroom. He bounded into the room nearly ready to throttle his roommate Paul, who was, after all, trying.

"You have no sense of poetry WHATSOEVER, man!" Walt was an English major and took things like this pretty seriously. "You need something like a literary tradition. You could satire, well, Kipling, for example.

I'm glad I use Dial, it cleanses my skin.
A much better soap than I'm Gunga Din!

or show your knowledge of early prose form something like

I'm glad I ufe Dial foap, faid Tyndale to Wyclif;
Becaufe if I do fo I'm not quite fo tycklif."

By this time it was obvious that no one was listening to anyone else—each of them was writing furiously.

"I'm glad I use Dial, it's so wonderfully sweet;
It cleanses my arms and my legs and my feet,"

said Howie, who was beginning to catch on.

"I'm glad I use Dial, but too much don't scrub;
A friend rubbed too hard and dissolved in the tub!"

shouted Earl.

Paul blew a smoke ring into the air and suggested

"I'm glad I use Dial, it's really swell
So please go to Hell."

This pleased him so much that he was about to repeat it when Walt started jumping up and down. "Listen, T. S. Eliot! Listen!

I'm glad I use Dial, I'm so glad you see—
Datta Damyatim Dayadvam—Shan—Ti!"

Sandy from across the hall, a serious sort of boy with a calculated cleverness, had strolled into the room about five minutes before to see what the commotion was all about. At last he could stand it no longer.

"I'm glad I use Dial. From senile sterility
It's borne me to heights of exceptional virility."

The entire room was now in high gear, everyone enthusiastically interposing his latest in a louder voice than the last.

"I'm glad I use Dial—give birth my long locks.
It burns at the stake shrieked the opera box!"

said Walt. Howie shouted—

"I'm glad I use Dial, said the bird to the bee.
It saves much explaining to children, you see."

Earl intoned

"I'm glad I use Dial, it not only kills germs,
But rids my whole body of maggots and worms."

For a brief moment Sandy's voice could be heard above the rest.

"I'm glad I use Dial, it's so Machiavellian.
It cleanses my arms and my legs and my bellian."

The room reached fever pitch. Faction faced faction. Instead of words, books and ashtrays soon became missiles. From an open window across the courtyard came two more gems:

"I'm glad I use Dial, the octopus said.
Or else, with eight arm pits, I'd be better off dead."

and

"I'm glad I use Dial; the rats in the wall
Inhale of it, pale of it, and die away all."

The sound apparently had reached all the way to the office of Fred, the college guard, who strode triumphantly into the room, held up his arms, and dramatically recited:

"I'm glad I use Dial, for filth is a sin;
But if you don't hit the sack, I'll turn you all in."

Slowly, grudgingly, the noise abated. Apologies were made, lights were turned off, and everyone found his way to bed, mumbling in rhythmic fashion.

Unfortunately, the next morning Howie could remember none of the limericks composed the night before. It didn't make much difference, though. Two weeks later Howie's Texas uncle died and left him seventeen oil wells in Dallas. Howie was rather pleased—especially since he never had to use Dial soap. *Yale Record*

PUMPERNICKEL

Without a change in expression, Sol Masky scratched his head twice, then turned the page. His eyes wandered listlessly over a number of words, before settling on the first that pleased them. There he continued. Since his feet were propped up, stark naked, against the end of the bed, his shoulders and neck carried most of his weight, which was very little anyway. Groping around with his left hand, he found a piece of bread near the end of his back and stuck it in his mouth. It tasted slightly sat on, but this bothered Sol proportionately little. He turned another page and began at its center.

"Sol, what time is it?" The voice coming from sleep, was soft, feminine, with a velvet huskiness; it would have thrilled any other man but Sol Masky.

"Two o'clock, dearie. Now go to sleep like a good girl."

"How can I sleep with the light glaring in my eyes? How many pages are you going to read yet, Sol?"

"Only twenty-five, dearie."

"My God, but you're a slow reader. An hour ago you said forty."

"I know, dearie. I guess I concentrate too much."

The blond hair of Mrs. Sol Masky (five million married men knew her as Vera Delight, the name to which Super-Super Productions, Inc., owned the copyright) was spread on the silk pillows like a loose bundle of hand-polished sunlight. Below the glistening hair was a pale face whose features showed economy, but delicacy, of structure. There was a very pretty mouth, but it was twisted now in preparation for a series of nasty remarks. Suddenly her eyes narrowed and threw sparks.

"Sol, are you eating in bed again?"

"Only a little piece of pumpernickel, dearie. I thought you wouldn't mind." Sol fingered his lean nose apprehensively. "Anyhow," he added weakly, "you ought to be asleep by now."

"Sure I ought to be asleep, but how can I?" Mrs. Masky had a small voice but it shrieked admirably. "All day long I make pictures which drive half the men in the world to distraction, and all night long you shine lights in my eyes. I don't care that you like to read detective stories, but couldn't you pay at least some attention to me. Make believe we still aren't married."

"I know, dearie, but this is a good story," Sol smiled conciliatorily, as he pointed to the cover, which showed approaching Death in four different poses. "See, it's *The Corpse Strikes Back,* by Thaddeus Thug. It already had seven murders. Right now the corpse is after the detective. I couldn't quit now, could I?"

"All right, act as if I'm not even here. But don't get crumbs all over my new spread." The slim body, known from Hollywood to Bangkok and back again the other way, turned over on its side and wriggled slightly. The thin body in the other bed tensed at the vision of imminent murder. Only the gentle workings of Sol's lower jaw spoiled the perfection of a spectacular silence. As it oscillated periodically, the point of his chin cut neat ellipses in the air. There's nothing like pumpernickel for endurance and dependability.

Eventually, the jaws sagged apart, out of horror or fatigue. For half an hour only Sol's nose moved, silently twitching.

Twin arms, built especially for Vera Delight or Venus de Milo, began to stir and fret like frightened animals. The most famous figure in the world squirmed on a mattress of down. Languorous eyes opened and blinked like those of an owl tortured by daylight. Marble shoulders rose and turned toward the night lamp. A voice of passion whispered, "Sol honey, what day is tomorrow?"

"The twenty-sixth of March, dearie. Why?"

"And when is our divorce? I always forget."

"Our what? Oh yes. Just three weeks from last Thursday. It'll be around in no time," he consoled. "I've got the two best divorce lawyers in the state working on it. You won't even have to go to court if you don't want to." Sol's mind scurried away from law courts and back to scenes of blood and swift vengeance, murder on foul murder, and nameless guilt. He waded again into a sea of gore and grew exultant.

Four feet away a goddess grew petulant. "Did you always read so much, Sol? In bed, I mean."

"I don't know, dearie; I guess so. You know how it is—you sell real estate all day and at night you want a little adventure, and—you know—romance. But I guess maybe this eating in bed isn't too good for me."

"No, it will spoil your digestion, Sol. How many pages do you have to read yet?"

"Only about twenty." *Lehigh Review*

LOUSY DAY

BY BOB LEMON

It wasn't a very nice day. In fact it was a stinking, lousy day. It was only six in the morning and already it was lousy. I pulled my coat collar up tighter around my neck, jammed my hands in my pockets, swore at a bird that was sitting on a stone wall, and trudged on toward the *Record* office.

"Good morning," said the Calhoun guard. "Getting up early to study?"

"No," I growled, "I'm coming home early to go to bed. I usually don't get to bed until 12 P.M. at night, but I'm catching up on my sleep. I was out late yesterday afternoon." I walked on, muttering to myself.

There was a screech of brakes as I sauntered across the street and I looked around at a trailer truck a few feet to my left. An irate driver leaned out of the window and yelled at me. "Hey, bud, ya wanna get killed?"

"Yes," I said, musing on the point for a minute, "yes, I believe I would, now that you mention it. If it's not too much trouble, would you mind driving your truck ahead just a little, and then maybe back and forth once or twice just for good measure?" I lay down in the middle of the street, in front of the truck, and waited for the driver to carry out his half of the bargain.

"Get the hell out of the way!" screamed the truck driver. "I've got to get this truck moving!"

"Oh, I don't think I'll be much hindrance," I said. "I'm tall but I'm light and I don't have a very big stomach. You'll hardly notice."

"Move, move, or I'll call a cop!" the driver bellowed.

"Well, we could try that," I said, "but it would be in all the newspapers and I'd rather shy away from publicity. The other way it would look more accidental."

He came back a few minutes later with a policeman.

"What do you think you're doing?" the officer demanded, glaring at me.

"I'm lying in the middle of the road, waiting for the truck to run over me," I said, pointing at the truck to make sure he saw which one I meant. I smiled at him to show I bore no grudge at the tone of voice he had used, which had been rather abrasive.

"Get up," said the cop.

"Not until he moves his truck," I said. "I was here first."

"You can't lie in the streets," said the policeman, raising his voice just a little. "It ain't legal."

"I'm in a one-hour parking zone and I've only been here ten minutes," I said. "Besides which that meter over there is busted."

By this time a small crowd had begun to collect and a few cars behind the truck were beginning to blow their horns. "Look," said the policeman, glancing around a little nervously, "get up, or do you want I should run you into the station?"

"I'll gladly move, Officer," I said, "if you can show me an ordinance on the statute books of New Haven, Connecticut, or the United States, which prohibits lying in the street. I feel I am within my rights. I should like to see the man move his truck, first."

The crowd was growing rather large and eight or ten cars had piled up behind the truck, all blowing their horns. It was beginning to raise quite a furor. I rolled over on my side and waved at the people in the cars who were waving at me.

"Get up, get up," shrieked the policeman, waving his arms about frantically. "I'll charge you with disturbing the peace if you're not up in five seconds!"

"Oh, silly, silly officer," I said, wagging my finger at him. "How can a body possibly be disturbing the peace when he is merely lying calmly on his back? It's the truck driver. If he weren't here, the cars could get around me."

"But he can't get around you," wailed the policeman.

"He could have in the beginning," I said.

The cars were lined up for several blocks by this time and the din was beginning to get deafening, like all dins seem to get eventually. The policeman leaned down and whispered in my ear, "Look, Mac," he said, "take this five bucks and please, please go away. Please get up."

"My name's not Mac," I said, "but it's the thought that counts. I will accept your offer." I took the five-dollar bill and got up and walked toward the *Record* office. It looked like a pretty fair day. *Yale Record*

THE CAT AND I

At the age of six, I was celebate, unsullied, untouched by female hands. From my first birthday I had insisted on talcuming my bottom unaided; from my second, forbade my mother even to test my bath water. The frequency with which I was parboiled did not faze me; I stuck to my principles.

It was the first woman I met—the obstetrician—who founded and confirmed me in my misogyny. Having, as I suspect, botched the job, she vented her inadequacies on *me;* all helpless as I was, and naked, she held me up to the gaze of all in the room and struck me in a distinctly humiliating spot. The research she did before she entered me as *Male* on the birth certificate, I shall not detail; there are things better left unsaid.

My hatred of women did not deter them—relations and visitors—from hovering over my crib and sweet-talking me. Did I cry, they exclaimed: "How sweet!" I, therefore, as far as I was able, did nothing but stare straight ahead, scornful, inscrutable. One woman—one only—chucked me under the chin. This attempt to corrupt me I resisted to the full extent of my powers; I had the satisfaction of seeing my mother forced to pay for the woman's spring hat, which had become a sodden mass.

My first steps I took unaided, avoiding the double indignity of being helped by my mother and photographed by my father, whom I despised as an associate of that female world which attempted to dominate my life. I had tried to like him, suspecting a potential, though craven, ally, until one morning I saw him kiss my mother as he left for the office.

That afternoon I pulled down their wedding photograph and vandalized it beyond description.

At five, I found my first friend, a lean tomcat I trapped in a deadfall in the back yard. He had a wonderfully full vocabulary and seemed to be my kind. It was his own idea to bite my mother, and the recompense of one sardine he received had not been, as alleged, promised in advance.

As my sixth spring approached, I noticed that my chum behaved curiously; he disappeared at sunset and showed up in the mornings, considerably gayer. I marked his route, followed him, discovered all, and, in a fit of rage, murdered him and his corespondent in their love nest—the neighbor's garage.

The sight, however, must have stirred primal springs in my being. Yesterday I felt a strange urge. Donning the tanned skins of my erstwhile confederate, and his paramour, I attacked the maid, whooping; she was stronger than I, but mistook my attentions until it was too late.

I left the house forever, yesterday, on the eve of my sixth birthday. From now on it is the pack and me, from alley to alley, loving and leaving behind. *Columbia Jester*

HOMECOMING

BY HARRY REASONER

As you stand on University Avenue and watch the Homecoming parade, or dance to the rhythmic strains of the Homecoming band, you may wonder how all this—"Minnesota's best Homecoming, and the World's Largest"—came about. It's a cinch one man didn't do it *all,* you say to yourself.

And you are right, as usual. The secret of Homecoming is a thing called a committee. A committee, briefly, is a homogeneous group of men and women charged with the responsibility of mimeographing releases for *The Daily*. A committee functions through a chairman, called "Chairman," and various subcommittees, called the "subcommittees," with subchairmen, or "algae."

To illustrate how committees help make a Homecoming a success, *Ski-U-Mah* engaged a business major named Jones as a staff statistician to delve into the facts of last year's Homecoming. Jones discovered some interesting figures on the importance, or impotence, of the committee system in guiding the activities of the vital, throbbing university. Here are a few:

No. of students in university	15,742½
No. of committee chairmen	17,325
No. of committees	38,567
No. of students on committees and not chairmen ..	2

In spite of this, we had a good Homecoming. It was discovered afterward that the work was done by a man named Smith. The apparent discrepancies in the above figures, by the way, are explained by the fact that some students served as chairman on as many as fifty committees, and thus were counted fifty times by our statistician, who, as we have said, was a business major, and not very bright.

So much for generalization. What you want to know, of course, is, "How do I get on the Homecoming committee?" Let us say this: if you rid yourself of a few common misconceptions, you can easily succeed on this committee. First, it is wrong to suppose, as some youngsters do, that committee service involves any *work*. Absolutely not! The only work involved in committees is in the "filing." You see, children, when a function chairman is appointed, the first thing he does is to announce through *The Daily* that "filing is now open." Then he mimeographs little application blanks. This being a great democratic university, anyone can file. The chairman takes these sheets, considers them carefully, and then distributes the subchairmanships among his friends and fraternity brothers, or algae. Then all those who have filed that he doesn't know personally or "have a note about" he puts on the Heat and Light committee.

Shortly after the committees are all named, meetings are called. Many freshmen on committees for the first time, and unlearned in these matters, actually attend these meetings. This is a mistake and should be avoided. Nobody goes to the first few meetings. After a while members begin to get little carboned notes from the chairman, reading in a more or less standard fashion, as follows:

Dear Joe:

Well, fellow, I guess it's about time we really got logging on Homecoming, so I have put Midge in charge of a special committee to realign the committees. Ike will help her out, and Bill is in charge of publicity on this angle. He'll pick the staff later in the week. Joe Snyder is chairman of contact and he wants all you fellows on Heat and Light to really get on the ball and help him out, seeing as Ed has more or less got Heat and Light lined up. We are really going to log now, so be sure and be at the big general meeting, 330 Union, tomorrow at twelve-thirty.

Randy Backlund, Chm., 1941 Homecoming

P.S. See you there. Need any more stationery?

About all we can really hope to cover in this short discussion is a few elementary things. Certain facets of being a big committee man we will leave to your imagination—like the matter of expense accounts and secretaries. But let us remind you of this: it is a well-established fact that even the chairman of the Freshman Week Subcommittee on handling and orienting Burmese transfer students doesn't really require more than thirty staff lunches or three Chi Omega pledge secretaries.

So, you see, it's simple. You just get on a few committees and start logging from different angles. In a few months' time we guarantee you won't be able to walk from Folwell to the Union without seeing at least one person, or algae, that you know. *Ski-U-Mah*

WILLIAM WITHERHEAD'S WOE

BY AL REYNOLDS

I hadn't made it. There was no use trying to rationalize, trying to make it seem of little consequence. It was too late now. I would be graduating tomorrow, but it would be a day of mourning, not one of rejoicing and celebration. The bitter tears splashed indecently down my cheeks and wrung my soul dry as a hot soda cracker.

There had been four years to show my talents, four years to proclaim the majesty of my superior scholarship, but it had come to naught. The unchangeable grade sheet shouted the horrible truth so blatantly that I felt Macbeth's deed was but a minor action compared to mine.

I hadn't made Phi Beta Kappa.

I would never be a member of the select few, a monarch among men. But I had tried. Oh, yes, I had tried with a desperation that would have amazed a bulldozer. There, on the grade sheet, I had proof of it. Yes, see, right there, Winter Quarter of '51, an A in Geography. That was proof, wasn't it? True, it was only a 2-hour course on early nomadism in North Dakota, but it was definite proof I was Phi Bete material.

I tried to find the reason for my momentous ignorance. I knew others that had made it. There was that cute little thing from Bellevue who walked around the campus in mukluks and a tarboosh. I had sat behind her in an American history class. True, she had thought the Boston Tea Party a takeoff from a Westchester Glee Club, but she had made the grade. Also the lit major who thought Omar ran a wine works in Southern California. My tears flowed like the Tiber at flood.

But I, William Witherhead of Burnt Creek, North Dakota, would be a nonentity. And what of my sons? Would they not disown their father when they learned the dastardly truth? Oh, the world is a desert of woe when one is realistic. But then perhaps there would be no sons, not even marriage. For there is, I believe, a level which even the most tolerant female will not sink to. I would see Dawn and tell her of my defeat, I would beg forgiveness.

I phoned her and twenty minutes later we were parked in a quiet little spot near Green Lake. She sat there, soft and suggestive, waiting to receive my caresses. But I had no right now. I was a fraud, an impostor. I was like an automaton as I started my story.

"Dawn," I said, "there is something I must tell you."

"Oh, please, William, let's not talk. Don't waste these moments, just love me," she urged.

Her sweet red lips were partially open, her eyes closed. Beast that I was, I almost kissed her.

"Dawn," I persisted, "you must know. I didn't make Phi Beta Kappa." There, it was out, I'd struck the knife home.

Her eyes slowly opened wide. Her mouth closed into a hard grim line. "William," she said, "don't talk sacrilege. You're not serious?"

"Yes, I am," I answered, and awaited the feel of the lash. It soon came. I felt her fingernails tear down the side of my cheek.

"You monster," she hissed, "you disgrace to mankind, you deceiving wretch! I give you my love, I tell my parents you are a fine red-blooded American boy, and you do this to me!"

I said nothing. What can the guilty say? Tears of rage formed in her eyes and once more the Tiber overflowed its banks. I remained meek and submissive as she opened the car door and kicked me out into the night. A rib cracked gently as she gave one last thrust with her high heels.

I tried to find solace on First Avenue. The dimes dropped into the machines but the writhing little nudies left me dead, indifferent. I slunk into the dark corner of a dingy tavern and tried to submerge my wretchedness. I had downed only a small quantity of the brown stuff when I felt a warm bare arm steal quietly over my shoulders. I turned slowly and looked at the young thing beside me. Her blue eyes were friendly.

"Lonely?" she asked, her voice a husky and soft intimate sound.

"It's no use," I said, "I didn't make Phi Bete. I've lost the key forever." It's the skid-road now, I knew, why fight it?

She leaned toward me until I could almost feel the sweet, intoxicating perfume which wafted gently against my nostrils. Fifty per cent Seducée Moi, fifty per cent Budweiser. "That's okay, honey," she said, "so you lost your key. I know them landlords, they're worse than Republicans. So you stay with me. I ain't one to turn a gent out in the street." She leaned closer to me.

She hadn't cursed me or berated me in any manner. Apparently she was too far gone in the joyous liquid to realize what I had said. I left the tavern, returned to the dormitory, and put my miserable frame into the sack.

It was noon and I was contemplating the Aurora bridge when I saw Pa's big white Stetson coming toward me. Pa was under it. Pa was a big man. I looked at the huge hand which would smash me when I told him of my failure.

"Pa," I said, "there's something I must tell you. For what I have done there is no forgiveness; I ask none. I . . . I didn't get Phi Beta Kappa."

He raised his hand and I bowed my head to receive the blow, but instead I felt a light pressure on my shoulders. "Don't take it so hard, son, there are other girls. You shouldn't monkey with them furrin dames anyway. Come on, let's go home."

I would go back to sheep herding. I would live a life of repentance, my sheep would have the best of care.

"By the way," said Pa, "we sold all the sheep. No time for them. The diesels scared them, too. They're drilling on anything that's flat. Twenty wells so far. Brings in about $25,000 a month. You'll get ten per cent as soon as we get back. Little graduation present."

I vaguely remembered something I'd read about oil at Williston. I would accept the gift. Yes, I would need it on my road of atonement. Confess and you will be saved. I saw the light now. I would confess to all. It meant much traveling, many years of toil. It would mean Montreal, New York, London, Paris, Rome, wherever a city might house a listener.

And, perhaps, if the gods are kind, I shall one day hold my head high and walk among men. Until then, pretty little blue-eyed lass, I have a confession to unload. *Columns*

PARTIES, BANQUETS, AND BRAWLS

BY DON GROSSFIELD

The most important part of a good party is the choice of a female companion. Follow these simple suggestions and pick up your one-way ticket to frustration.

HAIR. Long on head and short on cheeks. You should be able to run your fingers through it without running into cockleburs. If you *should* find cockleburs, look again. You may have a date with a cocker spaniel.

EYES. If you have any kind of pride you will want your date's eyes looking at you and not at each other. They should be one, or at the most two, colors. Tartan plaid is definitely out this year.

TEETH. Preferably a full set. If not, the missing teeth should be located in the back of the mouth. Of course, there are those who like to neck with girls with missing front teeth. It all depends on whether or not you prefer passion to beauty.

BUST. This can not be overemphasized. Well, it can be but avoid girls who do; they may also be lying about their age.

WAIST. The primary function of a waist is to separate the bust from the legs. If it doesn't, get another girl.

LEGS. If you enjoy dancing, go out of your way to find a girl with legs. If you're the possessive type and don't want your date to walk out on you, find one without any. Legs should taper gracefully down to the ankles. However, they should stop there.

Now that you have a date, you have to select the proper beverage. Too much has already been written on this subject. It's really quite simple. Following is a simple guide.

BEER. Cheap as hell but your date will probably get sick before she gets drunk. Unless you'd rather clean up than make out, avoid it.

GIN. Now you're talking beverage. Known the world over as an aphrodesiac, it mixes well with grape juice, orange juice, and Schmulka Bernstein's Fermented Beet Borscht.

RYE. Powerful stuff. The same can be said for Scotch, Bourbon, and TNT. As a matter of fact a mixture of all four is guaranteed to have any effect you want. To carry it one must have asbestos pockets. It'll completely ruin your flask.

CHAMPAGNE. Hah!

Party's over. You are at the entrance to her dorm. In order of preference, here are the things you can do.

KISS HER. If she's not worth kissing

HIT HER. If you feel that this is not payment enough for the time you've had

STRANGLE HER. If even this is insufficient

FIX HER UP WITH ME. *Sundial*

DR. SCHILPP AND THE STRANGER

(The scene is in front of Deering. Dr. Paul Schilpp is swinging along rapidly when he is intercepted by a person wearing a long white gown and sandals.)

STRANGER: My dear sir, whence come you, and whither are you going?

SCHILPP: Eh?

STRANGER: I said, whence come you and——

SCHILPP: Excuse me, I have to meet my class in Fisk.

STRANGER: You are a teacher?

SCHILPP: No, I am a professor.

STRANGER: Excuse me, I had not appreciated the difference. What do you profess?

SCHILPP: Eh?

STRANGER: I said——

SCHILPP: Oh! Philosophy.

STRANGER: By the gods, what good fortune is mine today! For indeed it has been a long time that I have sought a man who could teach me this thing. Please to tell me what it is that you teach and what will happen to me if I associate with you?

SCHILPP: Did you want to enroll in my class?

STRANGER: But first, my friend, please to tell me what it is that you would teach me.

SCHILPP: Philosophy A4.

STRANGER: Is that Pythagorean philosophy?

SCHILPP: Eh? I don't understand you.

STRANGER: I fear that it is I who do not understand you. You will agree that philosophy is love of wisdom?

SCHILPP: It meant that originally.

STRANGER: The meaning has changed?

SCHILPP: Considerably.

STRANGER: You mean that men do not love wisdom any more?

SCHILPP: Not at all. It's simply that there is so much wisdom nowadays that one man cannot embrace it all

STRANGER: Then men can only love a little wisdom at a time.

SCHILPP: No, that's not what I said. They can understand only a little wisdom at a time, but they love it all.

STRANGER: You mean men love things they do not understand?

SCHILPP: Well, if you will come to the lectures in Philosophy A4——

STRANGER: Please to tell me, what part of wisdom is Philosophy A4?

SCHILPP: Plato's *Republic.*

STRANGER: By the dog, sir! It has been founded at last?

SCHILPP: Not exactly.

STRANGER: But you are planning to found it?

SCHILPP: I said we study Plato's *Republic.*

STRANGER: You are not planning to found it?

SCHILPP: No.

STRANGER: Then why are you studying it?

SCHILPP: Because it's prerequisite to all the upper-division courses.

STRANGER: Alas, I do not understand these marvelous words; but doubtless I shall grow wiser under your leadership. You speak of Plato's *Republic.* You teach the youth the course of studies outlined therein?

SCHILPP: No.

STRANGER: Your students know nothing of gymnastics, music, plane and solid geometry, astronomy——?

SCHILPP: They study all those things in other departments.

STRANGER: But what do you teach?

SCHILPP: I just told you; Plato's *Republic!*

STRANGER: Do you teach the youth to be virtuous?

SCHILPP: Dammit all, I'm not the Dean of Students!

STRANGER: Then the youth go to the dean to learn virtue. But what do they learn of you?

SCHILPP: Now, look here, you, you——

STRANGER: I merely ask——

SCHILPP: Who are you, anyway?

STRANGER: I merely ask for information so——

SCHILPP: You're one of those Chicago poets, that's what you are. Let me pass!

STRANGER: Sir, a word——

SCHILPP: Look out or I'll hit you over the head with my brief case!

STRANGER: Then you will not share your wisdom with me?

SCHILPP: If you mean, can you get into my class, the answer is no. Now get out of my way.

STRANGER: But I merely ask for the privilege of associating with you, so that I may learn what——

SCHILPP: I haven't got time to stand here talking with you. Haven't I made it clear to you? I'm not a sidewalk politician, I'm a philosopher! Good-by, sir! *Pelican (University of California)*

DAFFYNITIONS

ADULT—One who has stopped growing, except in the middle.

AIR CASTLE—A dwelling where the kitchen and laundry are omitted but the garage included.

AMERICANISM—Voting to set the speed limit at forty-five and demanding a car that will do ninety.

COLLEGE—A thing hard to select because you can't be sure whether a large or a small university would make your father wiser.

COLLEGE DEAN—A man who doesn't know enough to be a wise professor but who is too smart to be a president.

DISCRETION—A comb that experience hands us after we have lost our hair.

EDUCATION—That which enables you to get into more intelligent trouble.

FALL—Season in which we connive to secure tickets and fight our way into the stadium to see football overemphasized.

IGNORANCE—That which everybody has some of, only in different subjects.

INTELLIGENCE TESTS—Describing a spiral stairway or an accordion without using your hands.

LEADER—One who sees which way the world is going and then steps in at the head.

PHILOSOPHY—The science which enables us to be unhappy more intelligently.

PSYCHOLOGY—The science which tells us things everybody already knows about human personality in language which few of us can understand.

TEACHER—A person who swore he would starve before teaching and has done both ever since.

WILLOWY MAIDEN—Skinny girl with a wealthy father.

YOUNGER GENERATION—A group of persons alike in many disrespects.

The Skiff (Texas Christian University)

THE GLUKE

BY JAMES G. MC NAMARA

Captain Dwinch surveyed the scene before him with supreme satisfaction. This ship was his first command, and as he stood on the bridge—his own bridge—his emotions were not unlike those of a newly crowned king. Down on the deck below, his subjects, swarms of sailors, were scurrying about loading supplies, laying fresh paint, and making all the other preparations necessary to ready a ship for a long cruise. The spectacle would gladden the heart of any skipper.

Suddenly the captain's practiced eye fell upon one defect in an otherwise perfect picture. There, in one of the small boats, lay a sleeping sailor, apparently unmindful of the activity around him.

To Captain Dwinch a misdemeanor of this sort was inexcusable. There is a time and a place for everything and this was obviously neither the time nor place for sun-bathing. A messenger was hastily dispatched to summon the errant "swabbie."

Within a matter of minutes Gunther Padoo, the offender, was standing at rigid attention on the bridge, receiving a sound berating from his "old man." At last the irate captain gave the boy a chance to explain.

"Do you have anything to say for yourself?" he asked.

"I'm a specialist, sir," was the unruffled reply.

"And what kind of specialist would be privileged to sleep while everyone else is working?" demanded the captain.

"I am a glukemaker," Gunther explained confidentially.

Now here it must be noted that Captain Dwinch was not a graduate of the Academy. He had risen from the ranks and was not, by nature, a scientific man. Most of the latest developments in naval warfare were unknown to him, for he had not time to read the numerous technical manuals issued by the War Department. He vaguely supposed that a gluke had something to do with radar. However, rather than betray his ignorance, he dismissed the glukemaker, who immediately reported to the boat and resumed his nap.

The captain was considerably disturbed by this incident, and that night he spent several hours poring through every book and magazine which might possibly yield the key to this puzzle. All to no avail.

The following day found Gunther, the glukemaker, again dozing comfortably in the sun while all his shipmates were hard at work. To know that his machine was not running at a hundred per cent efficiency was a bitter pill for the captain to swallow, and he resolved that something be done to remedy the situation posthaste. All efforts to solve the problem by research had been in vain. It was evident that only one avenue was left open.

Thus, our hero was again sent for by the captain. This time the interview took place in the skipper's private cabin and the atmosphere had become almost congenial.

"To get right to the point, Padoo," began the captain, "I need a gluke and I want you to make it for me." Then he paused to see what effect this order would have on the sailor standing before him. Gunther's expression remained inscrutable as always.

The captain continued. "You are to make out a list of materials you will need and I'll see that everything is taken care of."

At this point Gunther interrupted. "Sir," he said, "the first thing you must do is assign me some section of the ship where I may work in absolute secrecy."

This the captain agreed to do. It would be a small enough price to pay for such a wonderful object as this gluke must be.

The list submitted by the glukemaker served only to lend a greater air of mystery to the project. Certainly no clue could be obtained from such motley articles as two hundred pounds of sheet metal, fifty feet of anchor chain, several electric motors and old vacuum cleaners, five cuspidors, ninety funnels, eighteen doorknobs, hundreds of feet of lead pipe, and a multitude of nuts, bolts, wheels, and gears. It was, on the whole, a highly improbable assortment.

Nevertheless, a twenty-four-hour guard was set up around the fantail and Gunther set to work with a vengeance. Each morning he disappeared behind some screens, not to be seen again until sundown.

This industry impressed the captain no end, but after a number of weeks his patience began to wear very thin. So it was with a great deal of rejoicing that he received the news that the long awaited day was at hand.

The next morning all hands fell out in dress blues and were lined up in formation on the fantail. When everything was ready, the captain, his eyes glowing with anticipation, instructed Gunther to produce his masterpiece.

With the help of a working party assigned for the occasion, Gunther managed to wheel into the center of the curious group a huge, shapeless mass covered with a tarpaulin. This was removed to reveal a grotesque monstrosity, the like of which had never been seen by anyone present. It was a many-sided affair, perforated with portholes, and sticking out from it at crazy angles were dozens of funnels, knobs, gears, and dials of every description. Surrounding the main body was a maze of lead pipe and rubber hose. In short, it looked like the work of a village idiot.

Finally, after a stunned silence, Captain Dwinch regained his composure enough to sputter, "But what does it do? Make it work!"

With this, Gunther gave a signal to his crew. Throwing a snappy salute to the skipper, he addressed his men crisply, "Okay, men . . . This is it!" The great hulk creaked, lurched, and lumbered slowly toward the rail.

"Look out," yelled Captain Dwinch. "It's going over the—"

His words were cut short by an immense splash as The Thing was pushed over the side. And, as it sank slowly to the bottom of the sea, it gave out a series of belches that echoed all over the ship. "Gluke! Gluke! Gluke!" *Goblet (Lehigh University)*

CLASSIFICATION OF RECENTLY DEVISED COLLEGE DEGREES

BY L. J. D. RICHARDSON

A.C.: *alieno capite.* "By impersonation." Not often resorted to, but a sound method.

B.C.: *blanditiis candidate.* "By the candidate's blandishments." Sometimes effective in degree examinations with many viva-voce parts.

C.C.: *codicillis celatis.* "With the help of notes secretly introduced into the examination hall." A time-honored and very popular class of degree. It is sometimes alternatively expanded as *codicillis clandestinis,* in the same sense.

D.C.: *dentium cute.* "By the skin of the teeth." A very common category . . . It is of greater value than a degree *l.c.* (*vide infra*) where the narrow shave may be much closer.

E.C.: *examinatoribus clementibus.* "By the kindness of the examiners." Sometimes also called *examinatorum commiseratione.* A class of degree often attempted and supplicated for by sanguine candidates, but few are successful.

F.C.: *favente casu.* "By a fluke," "with luck."

I.C.: *interventione caeli.* "By a miracle."

L.C.: *latitudine capilli.* "By a hair's breadth."

N.C.: *naso coti* (or *naribus coti*). "With nose to the grindstone."

O.C.: *ocellis compellentibus.* "By dint of a pleading eye." A strictly feminine form of degree.

P.C.: *perperam conlatus.* "Conferred in error."

Q.C.: *quis credat.* "Who can believe it?" The degrees after commencement become crystallized as degrees *quis credidisset.* (Who would have thought it?)

R.C.: *repetitione candidaturae.* "By going up again and again." A tedious . . . but popular category of degree.

S.C.: *stipendiis condonatis.* "With remission of fees." A long-established distinction of honor.

T.C.: *tutore conixo.* "By the strenuous efforts of one's tutor." A not uncommon, but unreliable, method of taking one's degree.

U.C.: *universa consternatione.* "To the horrified surprise of everyone."

T.C.D. (Trinity College, Dublin, Ireland)

EVERYBODY'S OFF ON SOMETHING

PATRICIA J. WOODS

I counted the twenty-six lampposts (twenty-five if you're going in a westerly direction) on the Great Neck railroad station every day for four years. It wasn't that the lampposts meant anything to me or that I felt toward them any proprietary affection. In fact, I came to hate the sight of them and tried to concentrate my attention on things inside the train. But count those posts I did, perseveringly and at length with considerable skill. During my high-school days they formed a very important part of my mania and therefore an integral part of my life.

The trouble with me is, I count everything in sight—beams in ceilings, oak trees on the left-hand side of a street, letters in words, and books on shelves. I can give you a fair estimate of the seating capacity of most churches I have ever knelt in. Counting seats and their actual and possible occupants is an ideal way to spend time during a dull sermon—if, of course, the church hasn't an interesting array of statuary and candlesticks. Candlesticks, however, are very difficult to count accurately because they are usually lurking beneath flowers. Accuracy is very important in this mania of mine, for from it stems my satisfaction in a finished performance.

I'm sure I'm not the only counter. I've seen other people on trains perusing the signs in a feverish and dogged way, counting letters and lines. I've noticed people look intently out train windows at scenery that only an inveterate counter could be interested in. I've seen other people gaze fleetingly, but rapturously, at all sorts of trivia, counting and counting. However, I've found counting from trains highly unsatisfactory and would never recommend it to anyone new in the field. One enters the train; it pulls out slowly. Ah, he thinks, this is fine; I can keep up with the posts (or lights or switch boxes). And then the train picks up speed, and he can't; and the numbers won't pop into his mind as quickly as the objects appear. He is frustrated; he broods; he becomes restless. He turns his attention to the ads, or the stripes across the shoulders of the coat on the woman two seats ahead, or to the number of people reading various papers.

When I go to the theater, I dread the thought that someone will sit ahead of me in checked or striped clothes. I know I shall stare ahead if the play is dull and probably work myself into a frenzy by trying to be certain whether there are forty-five or forty-six stripes from shoulder to shoulder. Even if a play is good, I find myself counting the number of actors on the stage or the number of pieces of furniture.

I have, like all people with manias, one pet delight, but one which, unfortunately, I do not have much opportunity to indulge in. I take great pleasure in counting the fingers and toes on statues and on figures in paintings. I have found quite a few supernumerary digits, more than you would have thought possible. I have never found one on a work by any of the masters, but I shall continue skulking around museums in case even the great have been napping.

What all this will lead me to, I shudder to contemplate. Perhaps I am a frustrated mathematician, and I shall one day fulfill my manifest destiny and perform amazing feats with numbers. I can also see a far less appealing future for myself in various institutions if I persist in this avocation, but there I should be happy, perhaps, for there would be bars or perhaps a screen or a grillwork containing infinite infinitesimal spaces which would keep me happy for years. Or maybe I shall become a highly proficient cog in mass production, counting rubbers or tooth-paste tubes as they leave conveyor belts. Maybe I shall become the star counter of Dr. Gallup's service and count the number of people who have done or thought numerous and various things. Anyway, I have thus far written 823 words, containing 3417 letters. I know, because I've been counting them right along.

The Sector (The College of St. Elizabeth)

THE WOLF

His name was Wolf, and he was just the type that people tried to keep away from their doorstep.

On this particular night, the Wolf "crashed" a rather high-class party. The Wolf was dazed because he was not used to attending socials where all the lights were on, and the people actually danced.

The Host noticed the Wolf's discomfiture and went over to him. "What's the matter? You don't seem to be enjoying yourself."

"Say, mister," the Wolf whispered, "would you object if I kissed one of the girls?"

"No, of course not," answered the Host, and walked off.

The Wolf smiled; maybe it wasn't such a bad party after all. He walked over to a little redhead and asked, "Wanna kiss?"

She looked at him for a minute, arched her thin brows, and then slapped him angrily. But this did not stop the Wolf. He approached a blonde, tapped her on the shoulder, and said, "Wanna kiss?"

The blonde didn't even take time to arch her eyebrows, but walloped him with a left that would have put Babe Didrikson to shame.

But the Wolf was still undaunted. He started toward another young lady, but the Host cut him off and took him aside. "Say listen, I said I didn't object to your kissing the girls, but for heaven's sake use a little tact. Start a conversation and lead up to it, if you must, but use some tact."

The Wolf nodded his head in the affirmative. "Watch my tact, just watch it!" he said, and once again started out for the cute brunette in the corner. He tapped her on the shoulder and said, "Did you see the World Series last fall?"

"Yes," she replied.

"Do you wanna kiss?" asked the Wolf.

Sour Mash (University of Kentucky)

DEAR JAMES

BY BETTY KOSTER

September 14, 1953

Dear Jimmy Honey,

Golly, hon, it's been only 2 hours and 37 minutes since you left, and gee whiz I miss you so much already. Don't see how I'll ever live the next two months until you come up to see me. Oh, Jimmy darling, I love you so very much. Have to rush off to some screwy little test they're giving us, so good-by for now, honey.

Oodles and oodles of love and kisses,

Suzie

September 17, 1953

Dear Jimmy Honey,

Just got your wonderful little letter 45 seconds ago, and I was so excited. Please don't worry at all about me dating any of these stupid boys up here. You were all wrong when you said that there were three boys to every girl here. All of my girl friends tell me that it's just the reverse. Anyway, honey, you know I think only of you. Love ya.

All my love and always,

Suzie

September 22, 1953

Dear Jimmy,

Boy, they sure keep us busy here. You should see the adorable green hat and sign I got to wear. I've met more people because of it. No one believes that there really is such a town as Ickeyvilleburg, but I make sure to tell them all about it, and you, of course, too. Stop worrying about me dating any of the boys, as we aren't even allowed to speak to them. All of the girls are very careful to follow customs exactly. We never break any rules, as the hatwomen don't like it.

All my love always,

Suzie

September 30, 1953

Dear Jimmy,

We had what they call turnabout day for customs. Met the nicest kids—girls, of course. I hope you won't mind if I go out this weekend with a hatman who stopped me though. I had to accept him, as there's a special college ruling that you can't refuse a date with one of them. He's an ick anyhow. My classes are all awfully hard, and I spend every minute studying, but it's fun—studying, I mean.

Love always,

Suzie

October 5, 1953

Dear Jimmy,

Being that I am always perfectly honest with you, honey, I'll have to tell you that I was forced to accept dates for this weekend with two seniors. You see, honey, there's some sort of silly ruling that a girl can't refuse a senior. You can imagine how badly they would feel if a lowly freshman turned them down.

Love always,

Suzie

October 12, 1953

Dear Jimmy,

Just had to tell you about the lovely fraternity houses they have here. When we get married, we'll have to build a home just like them. I especially like the basements, as they have the cleverest little room that adds so much atmosphere. I think they call it the cave or some silly little name like that.

Love always,

Suzie

Dear Jimmy,

I wish you wouldn't worry about me, honey. You know I love you very much. I am sorry that I have to tell you this so late, honey, but I'm afraid you can't come up for Junior Weekend. You see, I just found out that no imports are allowed on any of the big weekends, and also it's only for juniors. You know how badly I feel, but I don't want to break any rules.

Love always,

Suzie

November 13, 1953

Dear Jimmy,

Golly, they have the most divine dances here. I told you we freshmen weren't allowed, but I wore my real long earrings, so they thought I was a junior. Wasn't that clever? Don't be mad, honey, as I thought about you all evening. They had the most delicious orange punch at the fraternity house. Honestly, I'm just crazy about fraternity houses.

Love always,

Suzie

November 20, 1953

Dear James,

Just thought it best to tell you why I'm not coming home for Thanksgiving. I'm afraid I met the nicest boy last week. He's an Alpha, and they have the nicest house. Well, to make it brief, we eloped to Tyrone yesterday. I hope you're not mad, but he's so cute. Don't forget to keep writing me, as I want your friendship to last forever and ever. It's platonic now you know.

Love,

Mrs. Chix Betadelt

P.S. Isn't that the cutest little name you ever saw? I just love it.

Froth

A FRESHMAN'S CREED

Years of research by Northwestern's psych department have shown that every campus group is plagued with its own superstitions and popular beliefs.

The freshman class—an unusual bit of collegiate life—is no exception; it too has its peculiar outlook on life.

It has been indisputably proven that every freshman at NU is firmly convinced:

That college life is not as simple as explained in the student handbook.

That there is basically very little difference between a freshman and a senior.

That a gentleman never receives any other grade than a C.

That football really matters.

That any reasonably intelligent student can make Phi Beta Kappa if he studies.

That you can really be happy at NU without a car.

That President Snyder once set fire to his mother.

That this year Northwestern will have a winning football team.

That LA is really the best school on campus.

That the Evanston police harbor a purple hatred against all NU students.

That any student who flunks out of Northwestern can always go to Illinois.

That if you don't pay your bills within ten days, your connection with the university will be severed.

That there are at least thirty student suicides each year which are suppressed by the university.

That this year Northwestern will have a football team that will win at least one game.

That the opposite sex is keen.

That Harris Hall is the Midwestern headquarters for the Communist Party.

That this year Northwestern will have a football team.

That students in Tech seldom see daylight.

That Cooley's is really a "blind" for a bookie joint.

That every English professor is a frustrated novelist.

That Northwestern coeds are basically women.

That one could starve to death waiting for service at the Huddle.

That the Backstage is the "North Shore's smartest rendezvous."

That NU is a rich man's school.

That the funniest sight one can see is that of a professor falling down the stairs.

That this year Northwestern will have a football.

That most college men are "smooth."

That the Kappa's talk only to the Theta's and the Theta's talk only to God.

That although an occasional student flunks out of school, life must go on.

That *Daily* editorials dictate the policy of the university.

That every fraternity and sorority has its share of "closet cases."

That all beauty contests are either fixed or else the judges are blind.

That an instructorship at NU is equal to an assistant professorship at any other Midwestern university.

That open houses sure are lots of fun.

That anyone who does not subscribe to the *Parrot* is lacking in school spirit.

That gaining social poise is far more important than storing away vast reservoirs of knowledge.

That they—the freshman class—are entering the four best years of their lives. *Purple Parrot (Northwestern University)*

A THUMPING FINE IDEA

BY MARALYN WASHBURN

Jerry and the creep were sitting in the lounge when I walked in. I turned to run, but it was too late. Jerry grabbed my coat and shoved me into a chair. He doesn't like to suffer alone.

"I was just looking for you!" he shouted. "Have you met my cousin Orville?" I extended a hand—gloved—toward the creep and got a handshake with all the vitality of a dead fish.

"Ha' ja'do," sneered Orville.

"Orville is from Harvard," Jerry explained. Orville was looking the place over, sniffing delicately.

"Nice little school you have heah," he said, yawning. "But I will say it's a trifle dull!"

"Orville craves night life," Jerry said. "I told him I might be able to talk you out of some of your phone numbers . . . the ones you write in red ink!" He winked at Orville, who leered nastily.

"Phone numbers?" I've been going steady so long there'd be cobwebs on my fraternity pin if my babe didn't change her sweater every day. Jerry grabbed me and shoved me toward a quiet corner.

"I was afraid you'd be difficult about it," he said. "Excuse us, Orville. I've got to persuade him a little." When we were out of earshot, Jerry told me the deal.

"This is just to make it look good," he said. "I've got it all figured out. Do you know the Tri Phi sorority house?"

"Who doesn't?" That's the highest-browed outfit on the campus.

"Well, they've been looking for a janitor for three weeks now and they're getting so desperate they shove a broom at any man who walks in the door. I'll call Kitty—she's living at Tri Phi now—and have her tell the housemother that Orville's applying for the job." The light began to dawn.

"And you want Orville to think——You'll tell him——?"

"Just write out the address. I'll take it from there." Orville looked up expectantly as we came back. Jerry handed him the address with another wink.

"We decided it was too late to fix you up with a blind date," he said, "but this is better anyhow. Clean, quiet, comfortable, right on the campus . . . and no strings attached." Orville's eyes got very big.

"Oh, I say!" he spluttered. "I didn't know colleges did this sort of thing!"

"Progressive education," Jerry told him. "Now, this is a very high-class house, so be discreet. We'll meet you back here for breakfast—if you can make it!" Orville was about to leave by jet propulsion.

"I say, chappie, you are top-hole! But these—ladies, shall we say—are they really quite—uh, sporting?" Jerry, bless his heart of stone, didn't crack a smile.

"Top-hole!" he said fervently. That did it. Orville sprinted for the door, and Jerry and I collapsed.

According to Kitty, the housemother pounced on Orville the minute he poked his nose in the door.

"My dear boy!" she beamed. "You don't know how happy I am to see you!" She hustled him up the stairs.

"Can you start right away?" she asked. Orville's eyebrows hit his hairline.

"Why—why, yes, I had planned to!"

"Splendid! I've had ads in simply all the papers, and the girls have even asked their friends to help us out, but you're the first one who's come!" Orville looked back toward the door, but Kitty and her pals had formed a scrimmage line across the foot of the stairs.

"You'll be paid by the hour——"

"PAID?"

"Why, yes," said the housemother anxiously. "Isn't that satisfactory? The college makes the rules, you know, but if you'd rather have a salary, I'll try to arrange it. Now as to your duties. You'll take care of the top floor first—the girls up there have been nagging me for days!—then the second, and then the first. When you finish with them—it shouldn't take more than two or three hours, if you hop right along—go around to the kitchen and help the cook. The poor woman's nearly crazy!"

Orville turned pale. "Now listen . . ." he said nervously.

The housemother shot him a hard look. "Not trying to back out?" she said menacingly.

"Well, as a matter of fact—yes," said Orville.

"Watch him, girls," snapped the housemother. "I'll be right back with his uniform."

"Uniform?" panted Orville.

Kitty giggled.

"Sure! You wouldn't want to get all dirty, crawling around on the floor!" The girls started to close in, and Orville made one last try for freedom. He hit the line, straight-armed two of the babes, and dived through a window. He landed running.

Jerry slapped his knee and howled. It had been two weeks since Orville's visit and he still had a fit every time he thought about it.

"Oooh, hoo, oh ha, ha ha! I bet he ran till he hit the Atlantic! Oh, haaaa!"

"Jerry, old man," I said, "this letter came for you today. It's from Orville." He shot me a stricken look and tore open the envelope. His face got whiter and whiter.

"Is he going to sue?" I asked.

Jerry groaned and buried his face on his hands. I grabbed the letter.

"I say, old chap," I read, "I appreciate your trying to show me a good time and all that, but you really should have warned me. If

I had only known the situation, I'd have wired home for help! . . ." I looked up at Jerry.

"I don't get it," I said.

"Read on," he told me. I read on.

". . . So I'm going to make up for my beastly behavior at once. I'm bringing my fraternity brothers down next month, for the week-end. I'm sure we'll have a jolly good time! They've even agreed about the uniforms . . . think it's a thumping fine idea, as a matter of fact. Well, I must toddle. See you soon! Orville. P.S. There are fifty of us. Will we need more?"

Jerry's already gone, and I'm just waiting to see if I passed my physical. I hate to be a coward and take the easy way out, but they say that Korea is really lovely in the spring.

The Spartan (Michigan State College)

WHAT'S TO LAUGH?

So the editor glares at me and says, "Don't just sit there; write! Be funny!" So tell him I can barely scrawl and what's funny anyway? Se he says if I can't be funny in a story to get him some jokes with plenty of kick in them. So I get him some jokes. So he says let's pretend you're writing a Master's thesis on humor and you have these jokes for data: sit down and write me all about why they're funny or not and what makes them jokes.

Your guess is as good as mine, but here's what I got.

A psychology student was visiting the state hospital and asked an inmate his name. The answer was, "George Washington."

"But the last time I was here you said that your name was Abraham Lincoln."

"That," came the sad reply, "was by my first wife."

This joke is funny, but it's kind of hard to analyze. If you think about it for a while, you'll find that the real punch is obvious: inmates of the state hospital aren't allowed to marry!

Then there's a slightly harder one:

1st Senior: "Busy?"

2nd Senior: "No, you busy?"

1st Senior: "Nope."

2nd Senior: "Then let's go to class."

This one leaves us with several distinct possibilities. Maybe they don't have a class that period. Maybe they're not Seniors. Maybe they're not going to class. Maybe they *are* busy after all. But the real kick is more obscure: it's Sunday, and school is not in session.

Some jokes get their kick out of a play on words, or pun. One of the best available we will borrow from your friend and mine, Wm. Shakespeare. He sets the scene in ancient Greece and proceeds to establish a situation in which two sounds emerge from off stage at the same time: a military battle cry on a trumpet, and the raucous laughter of some unidentified females. The next line must have stopped the show, even in Elizabethan times, when the actor placed his hand to his ear and said, "Hark! The Trojans' trumpets!" The punch is quite apparent: even in Elizabethan England everyone knew that the Trojans didn't have trumpets!

Now try this one yourselves:

A beautiful blonde is standing on a street corner in Tampa, Florida, waiting for a bus. A wolf pulls up in a Buick and says, "Hi, gorgeous! I'm going west!"

To which the sweet young thing replies, "How wonderful! Bring me back an orange!"

Give up? Well, it's not too easy, but if you remember the friendly rivalry between Florida and an extreme western state, you might realize that nobody in Florida would ever want an orange from any other place. Ripping good, what?

Of course, you shouldn't get the idea that jokes are stereotyped according to topic. Check this one, also on hitchhiking:

A hitchhiker was standing by the road waiting for a lift, and finally a flashy convertible stopped for him. Conversation with the driver was practically at a standstill until the chap behind the wheel produced a fifth of gin and offered it to his passenger, "No, thanks," he replied, "I don't think I'd better."

The driver suddenly became enraged and, pulling a revolver from his pocket, leveled it at the rider and said, "Drink up and drink up fast, or I'll shoot!" The passenger quickly downed a few gulps and handed the bottle back with shaking fingers.

"That's better," said the driver with a satisfied sigh. "Now you hold the gun on me."

We're all familiar enough with the warning, "If you drive don't drink, and if you drink don't drive," to get that one, but it's still pretty subtle, huh?

So the editor takes one look at the story thus far, and says why don't I include some new jokes. Okay, I say, but first, what's a new joke? He looks at me with pity in his bloodshot orbs and says a new joke's a new joke and what's the matter with me, anyway. So I says what's the matter didn't you ever hear that there's nothing new under the sun? So he looks at me real hard and menacing and says get the hell in the shade then, but write some new jokes.

But it's not that easy. Stop and think a minute—what's a new joke? A new joke, in case you don't have the answer yourself, is one which you've never heard before. Hence, the cards who always start out: "Stop me if you've heard this one . . ." or: "Have you heard the one about . . .?"

So about this time I remember one that's a panic. Stop the presses if you've heard this one, but how about . . .

The group of buddies hanging onto the bar having just one more for the fifth time, when an old friend walked into the room, stepped across the room, up the wall, across the ceiling, down the other wall, and out the door. There was a moment of stunned silence, and then: "What do you suppose is wrong with him?"

"Yeah, how about that? He didn't even speak to us!"

So I read this little gem over and I roared with laughter. The more I read it the funnier it gets. Suddenly I look up and there stands the editor, with about ten other people. They're practically drooling vinegar, they look so sour. Okay, I tell the editor. You aren't amused. So what's to laugh? *Kitty Kat*

HAVING WONDERFUL TIME

BY RALPH ESTLING

"Studying?" Conrad asked gaily. Charley had an even dozen books arrayed on the desk before him, a pencil in his hand, a headache, and a bad temper. He didn't answer.

"I asked if you were studying," Conrad reiterated, a little louder than before.

Charley put the pencil down, closed his eyes, and carefully placed his forehead against the palm of his hand. Then he opened his eyes and smiled at Conrad.

"Why, no," Charley said quietly. "As a matter of fact, I was going through these books underlining every eighth word on each eleventh line of every twenty-fourth page. I do this so that when people ask me what I am doing, I can tell them I am underlining every eighth word on each eleventh line of every twenty-fourth page. Now, there are some people who prefer to underline every *seventh* word on each . . ." Conrad left.

In five minutes he was back, eating a peanut butter and jelly sandwich. He looked at Charley.

"Studying?"

Charley told him to perform certain physiological acrobatics. Conrad sat down and began licking his fingers. "In many ways," he said, "you remind me of Joey Schultz."

Charley said nothing.

"Joey Schultz was a pal of Willy Schleimann. You remember, I told you about Willy Schleimann. He used to design buildings without any doors and rescue drowning pigeons at Malibu. You remember Willy Schleimann."

Charley remembered.

"Well, sir, Joey Schultz was a lot like him, only a little more eccentric. He worked a whole summer so he could buy a car. When he learned to drive he got restless and disappeared. I didn't hear from him for three months and then I got a postcard from Montgomery, Alabama. He had a great idea, he said. He was going to stand on his head in front of the state capitol and get somebody to take his picture. Then he was going on to Phoenix and do the same thing there. When he'd stood on his head in front of every state capitol building, he'd send the pictures to *Life*. Joey always wanted to have his picture in *Life*.

"In a couple of weeks I got a letter from Little Rock. He'd been to Phoenix and now he was heading to Sacramento. I wondered why he was skipping all over the country like that but then I realized he was doing this alphabetically, starting with Alabama and then going to Arizona, Arkansas, and now California. Sure enough, inside of five weeks I got postcards from Denver, Hartford, Dover, and Tallahassee. In Tallahassee, he wrote, that when he gave his camera to some guy to take his picture standing on his head in front of the capitol, the guy skidooed with it. It was too bad because Joey still had the Dover snapshot in it and he had to pick up a new camera and drive back up to Delaware again. He was kind of disgusted, he said, because this was messing up his schedule. He had to come all the way back down to Florida again.

"But after hitting Atlanta and then Boise, he made good time. He breezed through Springfield, Indianapolis, Des Moines, and Topeka in five days. I didn't hear from him again for over four months. When he did write he was in Charleston, West Virginia. He was just about through, he said. He'd be in Madison, Wisconsin in two days and in Cheyenne in four more days. Then he was coming home. He was glad, he said. He was pretty bushed. That was the last I ever heard from him.

"The week after I got the postcard from Charleston, I picked up a copy of *Life* and almost keeled over when I saw forty-eight photos of a guy standing on his head in front of each state capitol. Only, this guy *wasn't* Joey Schultz! It was somebody else altogether!

"I don't know for sure, but I can guess what happened. Joey crawled into Cheyenne on schedule all right, looked at the latest issue of *Life,* saw pictures of this other guy standing on his head in front of the state capitols, and—well, I don't know. He was kind of a temperamental guy and—well, you know . . ."

"Through?" asked Charley.

"That's all," Conrad sighed.

He wandered out of the room. Charley heard the porch door slam. Then it slammed again and the loud clumping of feet heralded his roommate's quick return. Conrad bounded into the room, waving a somewhat battered letter.

"It's from Joey!" he yelled. "He's in Addis Ababa! Where the hell is Addis Ababa?"

"Abyssinia," Charley said.

They looked at each other and then a photograph slipped out of the envelope and fluttered to the floor. Charley picked the snapshot up. It was a picture of someone smiling as he stood on his head in front of a large, impressive building that could have been a palace.

Pelican

THE NIGHT OF THE GREAT CRASH

BY CBF

Harry was only batting about .500, but the rest of us had successfully crashed almost every party to which we hadn't been invited. It had become more or less of a game with us, and when we heard about the Smyth party we couldn't resist. It was a real challenge; the Smyth family seat was some thirty miles from Boston, our scouts told us, and entirely surrounded by walls and watchdogs. But Joe was invited, so that this was a "point" rather than "blind" operation.

Joe let the five of us out and drove down the road, turned through the brilliantly lit gates, and went on up to the house. He returned in about fifteen minutes with the word that Jim had succeeded in getting in with the orchestra, as planned, an hour or so earlier. Then he gave his return ticket to Tom, which took care of him, and then split about half of his identification papers up with Neil. This was for "documented outrage," a device whereby Joe was to return, say he had lost his check, point out his name on the list, and get in. A few minutes later Neil would appear, calmly give Joe's last name, and of course be told that the name was checked off, and that he was a liar, and that he might as well run along. At this juncture, Neil would draw himself up and present Joe's bursar card and driver's license, etc., and be admitted by a suddenly humbled man at the gate. They all slipped away into the night, and, by a prearranged dot-dash blinking of the light in the men's room, signaled us, perhaps twenty minutes later, that they were inside and ready to pull us in if they could. Bad Luck Harry, as we had taken to calling him, shook hands and we separated into the night.

I arrived at the front door and saw two of the boys standing by. I caught their attention and made a dive-bombing motion with my hands, our signal for a maneuver known as the pass out. They promptly came out onto the lawn, taking checks as they went out. We all disappeared behind a hedge. I pulled my tie out of its bowknot, mussed up my hair, and we reappeared a moment later, my two cohorts carrying me. At the gate one of my bearers said to the man at the gate in an urgent, confidential voice, "Miss Smyth's cousin. Be an awful scandal if anybody sees him this way." The man nodded quickly and even helped carry me to the men's room. Six minutes later, hair combed and tie tied, I made my way toward the champagne. A few thoughts about Harry crossed my mind, but I stopped worrying about that, and in fact, about anything, when I saw a truly lovely girl appear on the dance floor. Such a creature. She was being cut in on right and left. I watched her for several minutes. She seemed quiet, fixing each of her partners with a Mona Lisa smile that I found provocative. I walked across the dance floor toward her, intending to cut in. At the last moment my courage failed me and I walked on. I looked over my shoulder and was electrified to find her staring after me, wistfully. I faced about. She smiled at me. My heart pounded. I had to dance with this girl. I marched over, weak at the knees, and cut in on the woman of my destiny. I swept her into my arms—and Harry's voice said, "Take me out to the car, sport. My tux is out there and I can change back into it. And for God's sake don't forget to take the pass-out checks with us." I stared at the creature of my desires. Harry lifted a corner of his lovely blond wig, displaying his crew-cut, and winked at me enticingly. "I wasn't in the Hasty Pudding show for nothing," he said sweetly. And, for the second time that night, I was carried past the gate. *Harvard Lampoon*

THE PIT FALL

BY CCO

Harry, my good friend, is extremely sensitive; he would chafe and worry if a Portuguese poodle snubbed him in the street, even if there were no particular reason why the Portuguese poodle should be expected to recognize him.

To be chafed and worried about some trifle like this from September through January, however, is absurd. I told him so.

"What in heaven's name is the matter, then?" I asked softly, on being told that the matter was of great consequence. "Why do you study the pavement so fixedly? You will ruin your posture."

Harry paused before replying. We were standing in front of the Harvard Provision Company.

"Let us drown our sorrows and our posture in one fell swoop," said Harry balefully, raising his head from his breast to glare at the bottles in the window.

"Oh no, you don't, Harry!" I cried, leaping forward. "Think of your loved ones, man."

"Aaaaaagh!" said Harry shortly, shaking loose the hand I had laid on his arm. "That," he went on, "is just *it!*"

"Harry, lad!" I cried. Some people on the other side of the street stopped and looked askance. "Harry, what have you done? Does a felony long since committed weigh on your conscience?"

Harry laughed mirthlessly. Then he faced me and looked me in the eye. "Do not fear, or be surprised," he began, "if I ask you questions and merely require you to answer, without interruption."

I nodded.

"If you were *told* to read such and such a book, approach such and such a girl, see such and such a museum, especially by your family, what would you do?"

I assured him that I would, in most cases, hurl myself into the Pit before I complied. He seemed pleased.

Harry's eyes burned, a frightful foil to his face, which was the color of chicken à la king.

"IF," he began—while more people joined the group across the street, looking askance at us—"IF your uncle and your father had told you to go up to the YARD, and look up——"

"Oh, Harry, Harry," I said, out of my senses with concern, "what have you done?" I laid my hand on his arm.

"I HAVE FAILED TO SEE, VISIT, OR ENTERTAIN AT ANY TIME, THE FRESHMAN SON OF A FRIEND OF THE FAMILY!"

Frozen for a moment, I composed my face into a mask, stepping away from him.

"No Pit is deep enough for you, then," I said, and cursed him out of my path.

I crossed the street to join the group who were looking askance.

Harvard Lampoon

A NEW TUNE

BY KEN DUNCAN

"Young man, don't you do anything but have fun? Don't you ever open those books I pay good money for? Surely, if you had made an attempt to learn, you'd have to get better marks than this. This report card is a disgrace to the family, to my training, to . . ." Bill backed away from the sheet of paper his father was brandishing. Without saying a word, he just stood and stared off into space with the same expression he might have at a dull movie. After a few minutes of silence his father became impatient. "Well," he said, "don't you have anything to say for yourself?"

Bill's eyebrows rose, wrinkling his forehead, and his lower lip jutted out. "Nothing right now," he said, letting his face relax. Focusing his attention on something a little to the right and behind his father, he shoved his hands into the rear pockets of his levis and relaxed.

"You have nothing to say?" Mr. Bagdon said loudly, and then, softening his voice, made a sort of mandatory appeal. "That term in college cost me several hundred dollars. Don't you think I'm entitled to something for my money? Some small token? An excuse?"

"Yes, sir," Bill said, after a respectful pause, "you deserve an explanation, and a good one. That's why I don't want to give you any spur-of-the-moment answer. You deserve something that has been thought out."

After sessions of sadness, righteous indignation, pathos, and almost every other form of after-report-card experience, Mr. Bagdon didn't know what to say. He slid forward in his chair and let the back prop his head so he could watch his calm son. "Perhaps one could ask for the simple truth," he said with a shade of sarcasm, "or is that too much to expect from a could-be college junior?"

Bill's forehead dropped and his chin rose, making his eyes, nose, and mouth squeeze together. "If I knew why I get poor grades," he said, "I'd do something about it. But since I don't know why, I have to keep dreaming up some new tale to tell you. And now I've run out." He stopped and looked at the floor, but before his father could think of something to say he looked up again. "If I repeat a used one, like getting a raw deal from the professors, it would be a flop. That's why I don't have anything to say right now—I'm waiting for an inspiration.

"I've given up trying to find the easy way to get good grades, and this term I just tried hard work. That wasn't easy. I wasn't too successful, but my marks are a little better than last time, and I'm determined to keep working." Mr. Bagdon stared at his son with new interest. "But I spoiled that excuse when it wasn't true," Bill continued, "so I have to find something else."

Such truth and complete sincerity overwhelmed Mr. Bagdon, and he smiled forgivingly at his son. Looking at the report card again, and nodding slowly with new understanding, he said, "Yes, now that you mention it, this is better than the last one. It isn't all D's and C's this time. You have one B. That is better my boy—encouraging." The great relief that follows great anger took hold of Mr. Bagdon. "Yes, sir, that is a good mark, a B—a B in Psychology." *The Spartan*

NYNHH

I thought I'd never get on this train, especially after that wretch kept us until five of . . . and why the taxi driver had to go all the way up to the Quad after stopping at Seelye I'll never know. Oh well—I'd better get some of *Ulysses* read . . . only four hundred and seventy-eight pages to go. The only good thing about carrying this around is that the most interesting people talk to you about it . . . that character who got on at New Haven last week . . . in the drama school and the clutches of the most divine neuroses . . . not gray flannelish; as a matter of fact, sort of dusty looking but very intense and intellectual . . . you'd never think he came from Des Moines. . . . A lot of Holyoke girls getting on . . . nice-looking suit if you like pink plaid . . . really, at times James Joyce gets awfully basic.

Springfield . . . I just know that man is going to sit next to me. He weighs three hundred pounds and wheezes. He's headed this way. Why can't he sit up there next to Pink Plaid? No, she came prepared and is surrounded by all her little buddies. It's a sure thing his hips and mine won't both fit.

"No, this seat isn't taken." Right on my hat! "You really didn't hurt it." Bergdorf Goodman's has slews of them and they'll be glad to give me one in return for two months of my allowance. Maybe he'll get off soon. Oh no—his ticket says New York, and he'll go to sleep in five minutes. What if there's a fire? I'll be crammed in and helpless and they'll find me dead—a victim of corpulence. That's really quite tragic. *Ulysses.*

I do wish Pink Plaid would stop that laughing. There's nothing in the least funny about this trip . . . it's fairly grim, if you ask me. Go on, dearie, knock yourself out.

That's right, fellah, make yourself right at home on my shoulder. The great earth mother, they call me. Come on, Gargantua, shift!

"Excuse me, please." Back to the smoking section. Why does that little girl keep staring at me? Now she's sticking her tongue out at me. Delightful child.

"Oh no, I'd be glad to watch her while you go to the ladies' room." Watch *her*? She hasn't taken her beady little eyes off me since I came back here. She's singing to keep me from getting suspicious. I wish she'd look out the window or something. Why doesn't her mother come back? She got off at Hartford just now and plans to leave the little monster with me for life . . . I have a nice kind face. What will they say when I bring home a nameless child? Here she is.

"I didn't mind at all—she's a darling child." Dracula was, too. I've got to get this book read. . . .

That perfume next to me is asphyxiating me.

I wonder how long it will be before that man asks me to turn the page. You *can* get it in the Modern Library edition, if you're that intrigued.

"Yes, it is quite interesting. . . . I'm reading for an English course. . . . No, not Mt. Holyoke, Smith. . . . Do you really think they're all Communists? . . . I don't think . . ." I might as well settle down to hear about how his wife's cousin's daughter approved of the New Deal in 1936. . . .

We must be getting near . . . wonder if I packed my blue scarf . . . it's starting to rain and it's going to last till tomorrow, I know. If there's one thing I loathe, it's being gay and collegiate when I'm turning blue. Why don't I know any nice arty men who hate sporting life and like to sit around warm bars, discussing the Theatuh? Fred is very sweet, really, but you just know he's going to be a back-slapping garter-snapper in about ten years. Oh, for a good neurotic esthete. I'd better get back to my seat and Gargantua.

Pink Plaid is still merry. She probably gets pink cheeks and curly hair in this weather . . . and I know she's always rushing around being a good sport about things. She'll cheer the team on, this afternoon, by God, and insist that everyone sing college songs and play Colonel Puff tonight.

Falstaff is asleep again—on top of my hat.

"I'm sorry to bother you, but I'd better get my things. Thanks very much for getting it down . . . oh, it's slipping . . . oh, dear, I hope you didn't hurt yourself . . ." My roommate's perfume is going to look pretty down the front of my taffeta dress. You'd better move to one side, Buster—we won't both fit between the seats.

Pink Plaid is waving to her date . . . smiling a big happy smile. I hate people who look healthy and as if they have all their work done for next Wednesday. There's Fred's roommate . . . must have left his other head at home.

Stop pushing, ladies, there are enough dates to go around. Your suitcase is abrading my shins, dearie. Oh, there's Fred.

"Hello—how *are* you? The trip down was lovely. . . . Yes, isn't it too bad it's raining? But it'll probably clear up in a little while, and even if it doesn't it's sort of nice. But it's so nice to see you again!"

Campus Cat (Smith College)

A JIGGER OF WRY

BY WILLIAM B. PALMER

Someone once said that the essence of written humor is the trick played on the reader's mind when the mental picture it has built up is suddenly and unexpectedly twisted in grotesque fashion. In other words, it's a switcheroo, with the mind playing the sucker. Like this:

We sat there, she and I, with the light from the fireplace dancing in our eyes. Then, without speaking, she scooped up her mud pie and placed it on the coffee table at our feet.

"What will it be like when we're married?" she whispered, wiping her soft, muddy hands on my sweater. I drew her closer.

"If all goes well, darling," I said, "we'll buy that small estate in Greenwich, raise a few kids, and keep cows on the sun porch." She smiled, gave my hand a pat, and then slipped away to stir up the fire, which was melting the soles of my sneakers. Her live body, silhouetted against the dying flames, threw a soft shadow across the room, and I wanted to tell her how I loved her.

"You know how much you mean to me," I said, offering her a cigarette. She threw it in the fire and set up her hookah.

"I know," she said, "and sometimes, when I'm alone here in the house, I start wondering about us." She struck a match and her eyes shone as she lit my mustache. "You dear," she purred, "you're too good to me. You're considerate, loving, and you look so handsome with your mustache burning that way." I took a drink and put out the fire.

"Come on, let's go out on the terrace," I suggested, helping her to her feet. She took my hand, and I led her through the french doors that opened out on the patio. We stood there and gazed out over the city lights.

"Goddamn fly just bit me on the arm," she said, swatting away at the elusive insect. I put my arms around her, and she caught me behind the ear with her fist.

"Got the little beggar!" she exclaimed. "Tsetse," she said, and flicked him over the balcony. The moon was just appearing over the horizon, and I began visualizing the whole area bathed in its pale light. Down below us, darkness hid everything but the hundreds of white lights and neon signs on the main street. I glanced at her as she stood there by my side, spitting peach pits over the edge.

"Your mother thinks we should have a simple wedding," she said, "but I've always dreamed of a cathedral ceremony, with hundreds of guests and a huge reception in the downtown armory." She picked a radish from the flower box and gazed fondly at it.

"You shall have whatever your little heart desires," I murmured, toying with her sideburns, "but must you insist upon growing radishes in the flower boxes?" She smiled, and a slight breeze rippled her auburn hair. The moonlight had drained the color from her cheeks, giving her an unearthly, ethereal appearance, and I saw that her eyes were wide open.

"Your eyes remind me of two billiard balls," I said, leaning against the railing. She lowered her lids and began chewing on a scallion.

"I know I'm a silly fool for asking," she said, "but tell me, have you ever loved another woman?" She placed her hand in mine.

"Let go of my hand," I cried, "you're hurting me," and I kicked her in the shoulder. We clutched at each other, and she began unraveling my sweater.

"Knit one, purl two," she chanted, and I held her close to me.

"Why must we always quarrel so?" I asked, wiping the tears from her eyes.

"Because we are lovers," she said, wiping the tears from my eyes.

"Come on," I said, "let's go back inside," and I led her through the french doors and into the living room. We sat down at the piano and I romped through "Flight of the Bumble Bee."

"You're tender," she said, tucking a scallion into my breast pocket. I wanted to tell her how I hated scallions, but this was her night, and I didn't want to spoil a minute of it.

The moonlight had filtered through the french doors and was covering the floor with its almost artificial light. Suddenly, she broke from my grasp and ran to the fireplace, turning her back to me.

"There's something I must tell you," she said in a quavering voice.

"Yes?" I said, throwing the scallion into the wastebasket.

"The fire is out," she sobbed, throwing herself on the sofa, so I broke up the coffee table and started another fire.

At daybreak they found us standing there on the terrace, eating scallions and watching the sun come up.

And now I'm beginning to wonder if maybe there isn't something more to written humor than merely playing a trick on the mind. Maybe it's got something to do with plot, and keeping your head when those about you are losing theirs. Yale Record

THE GROCERY-STORE FABLE

BY BOB LEMON

Once upon a time there lived a man named P. Pamonondus Putney, and he was an upper-middle-class ectomorph. Which means, in plain language, that he made a good dollar and was thin. Now you may think, if you fancy you know something about psychology and the art of classifying people, that when you say a person is an upper-middle-class ectomorph, well, that's about all there is to say about him, but that just goes to show how wrong you are. Because P. Pamonondus Putney was not as simple as all that.

In the first place, P. Pamonondus Putney was a married upper-middle-class ectomorph.

There, that changes the picture some, doesn't it?

In the second place, P. Pamonondus Putney was a nearsighted married upper-middle-class ectomorph.

And in the third place, P. Pamonondus Putney was a nearsighted upper-middle-class ectomorph who went on grocery-store errands.

Go ahead, catch your breath. I'll wait.

Now to you and me and all the rest of us simple, down-to-earth, classifiable folk, going on grocery-store errands may seem as easy as a plain old schizophrenic neurosis, but to individualistic P. Pamonondus Putney it was a horse of a different color, as you shall see.

One day Pamonondus was sitting in the living room reading his favorite upper-middle-class book when his wife walked in.

"Pamonondus," she said, "go down to the grocery store and buy me a can of beans."

Pamonondus got up and went down to the grocery store to buy a can of beans.

"My name is P. Pamonondus Putney," he said, "and I would like a can of beans."

"Self-service," said the clerk.

Five hours later Pamonondus came back. His face was worn and haggard, but in his hand was a can of beans. "Third shelf from the top," he said, "aisle four, under 'Mayonnaise.'" His wife took the can from him and read the label. Then she hit him with a wet dish towel, as she was wont to do when she was annoyed. "Stupid!" she said. "I wanted *string* beans not baked beans!" So Pamonondus adjusted his spectacles and picked up his can of beans and went back to the grocery store.

"My name is P. Pamonondus Putney, and I want a can of string beans not baked beans."

"Self-service," said the clerk.

Seventeen hours later Pamonondus came back. His shirt was torn and there were circles under his eyes, but in his hand was a can of string beans. "Second row from the bottom," he said, "aisle two, section two, under 'Condiments.'" His wife took the can from him and read the label. Then she hit him with a scalloped tomato, as she was wont to do when she was annoyed. "Stupid," she said, "I wanted Murphy's string beans, not Growser's! And now I want a can of baked beans, too." So Pamonondus wiped off his spectacles and picked up his can of Growser's string beans and went back to the grocery store.

"My name is P. Pamonondus Putney," he said, "and I want a can of Murphy's string beans not Growser's and I want a can of baked beans, too."

"Self-service," said the clerk.

Two days later Pamonondus came back. His necktie was gone and his pants were ragged and dirty, but in his hands were two cans. "Back of the store," he said, "behind the third counter, under 'Scouring Pads.'" His wife took the can from him and read the label. Then she hit him with a fricasseed chicken breast, as she was wont to do when she was annoyed. "Stupid!" she said, "this is not a can of baked beans, this is a can of spaghetti noodles, and you forgot the mustard." So Pamonondus picked up his spectacles and his can of spaghetti noodles, being careful to leave the can of Murphy's string beans on the table, and went back to the grocery store.

"My name is P. Pamonondus Putney," he said, "and you have evidently changed the baked beans from the third shelf from the top, aisle four, under 'Mayonnaise,' where they were, and I would like to know where they are now. Also I forgot the mustard."

"Self-service," said the clerk.

Four days later Pamonondus came back. His clothes were shredded and he was cut and bruised and there were big bags under his eyes, but in his hands were a can of baked beans and a jar of mustard. "Eighth row from the top," he said, "in back of the dill pickles, aisle three in the cellar, under 'Wines and Beers.'" His wife took the can and the jar from him, read the labels, and smiled winsomely, as she was wont to do when she was pleased, which wasn't very often. "Pamonondus," she said, "you have done very well. You have got me a can of baked beans and a jar of mustard. But while you were gone

I decided that I want a can of stringless string beans and that I would rather have Growser's than Murphy's after all." So Pamonondus picked up his can of string beans and went back to the grocery store.

Five days and 13 hours later he came back. His shirt was gone and his pants were in tatters and on his face was a five-day growth of beard and in his eyes was the look of a wild man, but in his hands were three great big boxes. "Here," he said, "are forty-three cans of beans. There are plain string beans, stringless string beans, beanless string beans, stringless and beanless string beans, green string beans, blue string beans, red string beans, chocolate-chip string beans, butter-rum string beans, Growser's string beans, Murphy's string beans, Whittlebey's string beans, Sirango string beans, Ile de France string beans, Horton's Corner string beans, baked beans, wax beans, soy beans, toy beans, and four cans of unidentified substance because the labels are missing. And they come from all over the goddamn grocery store and you will have to put them all back one by one because I ran out without paying for them and I'm not going to give you any money." And with that he rushed out and threw himself in the ocean together with five cans of Tuttle's Extra Large Seedless Green Olives which he had taken just for sport.

And that was the end of poor old nearsighted married upper-middle-class ectomorphic P. Pamonondus Putney.

MORAL: Going on grocery-store errands is enough to drive a man to the drink. *Yale Record*

PRINCETON'S GREATEST HOAX

THE INCREDIBLE STORY OF A FABULOUS PRINCETONIAN ADELBERT (BERT) L'HOMMEDIEU X. HORMONE

BY HARVEY SMITH

All but one of the four hundred-odd members of Princeton's famous "War Baby" class, the class of 1917, were born in the middle eighteen nineties. The sole exception, a redhead named Adelbert L'Hommedieu X. Hormone, didn't see the light of day until some forty years later; on January 17, 1936, to be exact.

Yet Bert, as everyone called him, is a year or two older than most of his classmates, has been married four times, sired an even dozen children, is grandfather of double that number, has packed more fantastic adventure into his lifetime than all the Tarzans lumped together, and is almost as well known to his contemporaries as Dick Kazmaier is to the present generation.

Many of these thousands of contemporaries have stated publicly at one time or another that they remember Bert well in college. Some, including men of unimpeachable character, have claimed to have known him intimately. None, however, not even I, who know him best of all—has ever laid eyes upon him.

Here, recorded for the first time, is the explanation of this seeming anachronism—the complete story of how the nonexistent Hormone came into being, and why he seems destined to live forever in the annals of Old Nassau.

In 1936 I was secretary of the class of 1917. To fully comprehend what follows, it should be stressed at the outset that a Princeton class secretary's primary function is to provide the Princeton alumni magazine with a steady flow of news about his classmates. "Our worthy Senator Claptrap has returned from a junket to Alaska . . . Good old 'Pinky' McVickar, much to the distress of Seattle spinsters has deserted the ranks of bachelordom at last. Congratulations, 'Pink' . . . Doc Ezra Wright is the father of twins. Nice work, 'Doc,' we didn't think you had it in you." That sort of thing.

Class secretaries of other colleges have the same primary function, but theirs is a comparatively easy task inasmuch as most alumni magazines are monthlies. What makes the going tough for a Princeton class secretary is that the Princeton alumni magazine is a weekly. That means meeting a deadline every seventh day. And with classmates not overly co-operative in supplying news about themselves, the secretary sometimes is hard put to find anything to write about. Also, it is an irreparable blot on the class's escutcheon to have the *Weekly* appear without any class news. Some classes haven't missed an issue in over half a century.

Of course, an experienced secretary bridges the newsless gap with various dodges—listing names of classmates who haven't been heard from in a long time; asking for addresses of same; appealing to delinquent members to get behind the treasurer and cough up the class dues; recalling highlights of bygone gridiron epics; wondering if the class remembers who was voted most likely to succeed, etc., in senior year; even resorting on occasion to reprinting in full the church calendar of a clergyman classmate. One secretary, in desperation, reprinted all the verses of *Old Nassau,* on the grounds that the Yale game was only a week away, and the class should know all the words.

There comes a time every so often, however, when even the most ingenious secretary has exhausted his entire bag of tricks and is faced with the ignominy of a blank column in the *Weekly;* a fate, to a class secretary, worse than death. That was the plight in which I found myself when faced with the deadline of January 17, 1936.

During the day I had called every classmate I could get on the phone and it was always the same answer, "Sorry, old man, I wish I could help you, but I can't think of a thing." Neither could I. My wife had long been in bed, and I had sat in front of my typewriter staring at a sheet of blank paper for hours. I had scratched my head endlessly but nothing came out of it. Then, suddenly, whoever it is who watches over class secretaries, tapped me on the shoulder.

It is impossible to explain the working of the creative process. This, as I recall it, is about what happened. "Why not invent a classmate?" I asked myself. Having sown the seed, I proceeded to invent one. My class was already middle-aged by then. Why not have this classmate do what so many middle-aged men would like to do if they weren't tied down by a family, business, lack of money, and inhibitions?

Well, what would they like to do? I knew what I'd like to do. I'd like to see at first hand—in the flesh, so to speak—some of those luscious Balinese girls the magazines had recently been boosting circulation with. I figured that if that's what I, a more or less average member of the class, would like to do, that's what most of the class would have a yen for. So I put him (I hadn't yet named him) right smack in the middle of Bali, literally surrounded by scads of satin-skinned beauties. Even those of sterner moral fiber than the average would get a vicarious kick, I reasoned, out of reading about a classmate who actually lived in Bali.

How would a member of the class of 1917 ever wind up in Bali unless he were a missionary? And I didn't want my by now full-born classmate to be a missionary. He would have to be the adventurous type, who had wandered more or less around the world and done everything no conventional Ivy-Leaguer would hardly dare dream of doing. So I gave him a background that never would have stood up in the pulps, let alone the Princeton *Alumni Weekly*. I was all steamed up by now and I laid it on with a thick brush. After all, I had only a single column to fill and if this was going to be a hoax, which was what I intended it to be, I planned to make it a super-duper hoax to end all hoaxes. To make absolutely sure, in my own mind, at least, that there could be no question about it, I gave the classmate the utterly fantastic name of Adelbert L'Hommedieu X. Hormone; Bert, for short. Hormones had just begun to be popularized at the time, and the name Hormone seemed just right for my mythical classmate. Furthermore, it warned anyone who might otherwise swallow Bert, that he was an out-and-out phony.

I had one final creative job to do. In order to make Bert at all credible, I had to make him a bona fide member of the class of 1917. I couldn't, of course, make him a member who had graduated with the class, as all members who went through four years together, knew each other fairly well, certainly by name. I solved this problem by putting him among that vaguely remembered group who enroll with a class and drop out at the end of the freshman year. You have a hazy recollection of them when their names are brought up. You think you remember what they looked like and what they did, but you're not one hundred per cent sure. There was a little-known man in our class with red hair who left the middle of freshman year. So I had Bert leave college at the end of freshman year and made him redheaded, both to make possible an identification with the little-known redheaded classmate and because red hair seemed a natural for Bert, who now seemed as real to me as though we'd taken our entrance exams alongside each other. I went to bed conjuring up visions of what a whale of a time Bert and I would have if I ever got to Bali.

Here, word for word, from the January 17, 1936 issue of the Princeton *Alumni Weekly,* are the fruits of that enchanted evening:

"Like a voice from the dead came a recent letter from Bert Hormone —the first time he has been heard from since leaving college (at the request of Dean McClenahan) at the end of the freshman year. Very few of the class knew Bert, as most of his leisure hours were spent in Trenton—doing social service work, he said, when hauled before the dean. Those who roomed in Edwards, however, will have no difficulty recalling his unruly thatch of flaming red hair or his endless supply of Limericks, acquired from cowhands on the King Ranch where he'd spent his boyhood.

"Bert writes from Bali, where he has been living for the past ten years. His letter, enclosing a dozen candid-camera shots of Balinese Lorelei, has had to be deleted considerably, for family consumption, but enough of it remains to give you an idea of life in the island paradise where brassières are as rare as icebergs:

"'I won't bore you with my wanderings since leaving Princeton.

I'll just mention a few highlights,' Bert writes. 'In the fall of '16, following a night with a crowd of Limey sailors in a Marseilles bordello, I woke up to discover that I was a private in the Foreign Legion. I almost got dusted off in front of Verdun but managed to squeeze through and stayed with the Legion after the war, putting in two years in Africa. Perc Wren put me in his book, *Beau Geste*. After that I knocked around the Malay straits for a while, then shipped on the square-rigger *Eric Jorgensen*, carrying a load of grain out of Sydney. I lost two fingers while making fast a topgallant in a blow off St Paul Island. Lloyds paid me a thousand pounds and a Dutch bookseller (who, by the way, introduced me to *This Side of Paradise*) told me the best place in the world to spend it was in Bali. So with that stake I came out here and unless I go completely balmy here's where I'll be when it's time to cash in my chips.

" 'Bali's all you read about in the steamship ads and plenty more that never gets in print. . . . I wish I could get some of you '17ers out here for a reunion. Boy, would we whoop her up for old '17! We got a bar out here that makes the Nass seem as lively as the Union League Club the night Roosevelt got elected. I own it! Lock, stock, and 200-odd barrels of the finest banyan rum that ever wet a human gullet. I've got a floor show of Balinese belles that would make what I remember of the Follies chorus look like Miss Spence's girls putting on *Peter Pan*. And I've got a jazz orchestra of two natives, three Chinese, and a beachcomber from the Argentine who get fined two yen every time they stop playing . . .

" 'The only time I've had a real chance to open up for any Princetonians was three years ago when two lads from '21 dropped off a Dutch tramp. I won't mention their names because they might have gotten married since. Did we bust this island wide open! We started off at my place—Bert's Bar, they call it—with four or five Hormone specials—absinthe, lime, banyan rum, and a dash of Pollen's Dry Sec—and the lid was off. We taught the band to play "Going Back" and the gals to sing "She Works in the Jam Factoree" and "Annabelle Jerome" (they've been regular request numbers ever since); along about midnight we organized a P-rade and all the natives joined in, singing "Going Back" and whooping her up for Nassau Hall. Then someone got the idea of driving to South Bali to the sacred nutmeg grove where they were holding the annual festival—Lament for the Virgins. That's where we made our mistake. The natives take these things seriously and we didn't. I, of course, should have known better, and if the chief hadn't been a pal of mine we'd all have been kaputt. As it was, eight of us woke up in the hoosegow, the two lads from '21 were deported, and I lost my license for six months. But it was worth it and if ever anyone steps into my place and announces he's from '17 all I can promise is that Bali ain't seen nothing yet.'"

I knew that I had done a workmanlike job of making Bert real, but I didn't think that any but the dim-witted would believe that he actually existed. All that I had set out to do was to fill a column of a single issue of the *Weekly,* and although I expected to be complimented on having brought off what the book reviewers call a tour de force, I thought that Bert would die a natural death within a few days. Although I say it who shouldn't, being one who firmly believes the sun rises and sets on Nassau Hall, what followed made me re-evaluate the gullibility not only of my classmates and contemporaries but of the Princeton administrative staff and faculty. With the sole exception of my classmate and ex-partner, who could read me like a book, the entire Princeton family swallowed Bert hook, line, and sinker and came up yelling for more.

The *Weekly* hadn't been out but a few hours when the phone started ringing, asking for more dope on Bert. The first call was from a former class president, a Phi Beta Kappa man, and successful lawyer, for whose intuitive intelligence I had a most high regard. "Tell me something about this Bert Hormone," he opened. "I've been going through the class records and can't find anything on him, yet I sort of remember him. I think he roomed under me in Edwards. Wasn't he a tall guy, a little stooped?"

My first inclination was to tell him to stop pulling my leg, but his voice was as sincere as though arguing before the Supreme Court, so I replied as seriously, "Yeah, very tall, well over six feet, but he wasn't stooped. In fact he carried himself straight as a ramrod."

"I know he had red hair—curly, wasn't it?"

"Very."

"Boy, what a life he's led. When do we leave for Bali?"

Having made the decision to make a liar of myself, I stuck to it. The more questions that were put to me, the more real Bert became to me. After a dozen or so phone calls I knew exactly what he looked like, how he dressed, ate, drank, and slept, his habits, likes, and dislikes. I could read his mind almost as well as my own.

At a class dinner a few weeks after Bert's debut, the chief topic of conversation was Bert, and I was deluged with questions. Fortified by more than my usual quota of martinis, I answered them all dead-pan. If I had a bear by the tail, I might as well swing it. And swing it I did. I built Bert up to Herculean proportions.

Following the dinner, I had a nightcap with one of my closest friends, now head of one of our biggest corporations. In no time at all the talk got around to Bert. "He's not only had one of the most amazing careers I've ever heard of," my friend said, "but he can write like nobody's business. If you could write like that, Smith, you'd be in the chips in no time at all."

"Boy! I wish I could," I said with a straight face. Up until then my friend had been only lukewarm about the few things I'd published.

My biggest kick came, however, from my wife. She had always looked with a jaundiced eye on my literary endeavors. She read what I wrote only from a sense of wifely duty, and damned my efforts with praise that was so faint as to be almost indiscernible. She was, however, an avid reader of the 1917 column in the *Weekly*, mostly to learn which of our friends were having children. I hadn't told her anything about the Hormone hoax and was thinking about something else when she laid down the *Weekly* and said, "That's the most interesting letter I ever read."

"What letter?"

"From your classmate, Bert Hormone."

Coming from her, that was the highest praise of my writing I ever received, then or since. A wonderful aura of self-satisfaction surrounded me. I only hoped it wasn't visible. "Tell me more about him," she asked, and I did. And how!

The pay-off—at that time—came a few days later when the office of the secretary of the university phoned me to say that they had searched all the university records and could find nothing on file pertaining to my classmate, Adelbert Hormone. Could I tell them something about him. I said I'd be glad to and explained (by then I'd become a really accomplished liar) that the reason his name was not on the record was that it had been the custom when we were in college to expunge from the official record any mention of an undergraduate who had been expelled, and that, unfortunately, the dean had given Mr. Hormone the heave-ho in no uncertain terms.

Could I tell her (my caller was the secretary's secretary) the reason for his expulsion? "Well," I said, "I'd rather not. It was because of something I can't very well discuss with a lady." Maybe, I told myself when she hung up, I had more than a bear by the tail. Maybe I'd created a Frankenstein.

Naturally, interest in Bert subsided somewhat after a few months, but I knew he was more than just an overnight sensation from the fact that almost every time I ran into a Princeton contemporary he would ask if I had heard from him again. I knew also that I would never again have to worry about being faced with a blank column in the *Weekly*. Whenever I got in a tight spot for news thereafter, good old Bert happily would come through with a letter or cable, or a classmate would come to my rescue with a report that he had run across Bert in his travels.

A few days ago, for example, I came across a letter from Scott Fitzgerald written from Hollywood. "I'm out here with Metro," Scott wrote, "doing a script for Robert Taylor and Joan Crawford. Lots of old Triangle men here—Jimmy Stewart may be in my picture and Brookes Bowman of 'Love and a Dime' fame is on the Metro lot. No news of classmates—only a note from Sap Donohoe at Coronado and a short visit with Bert Hormone, whom I haven't seen since Triangle days. He came out here with the Federal Theatre project (this was while Bert was on his way from South America to Tahiti), was spotted by Selznick, I believe, and took a test for the part of Rhett Butler. The rumor is that they wanted someone with a more roguish face and Bert still has the same bland innocence of twenty years ago."

Gradually, as I painted Bert with a thicker and thicker brush, the hoax became apparent to an increasing, but by no means large, audience. For several years following Bert's debut, hardly a month went by that I didn't receive letters from Princetonians I had never heard of, inquiring about the old rascal. One venerable grad of the nineties asked if I could tell him the best steamship service to Bali. The biggest blow to my faith in my fellow alumni landed when a nationally known industrialist asked me for Bert's address. His letter (among my most valued Hormonana) categorically stated that he and Bert had been together in Paris in 1918 and he wanted to write him. "Try the American Consul at Papeete," I wrote back without the slightest twinge of conscience.

As I look back on the Hormone saga, it was fully ten years before Bert became widely—and I think, reluctantly—accepted as purely fictional.

I knew from the beginning that I had too valuable a property to kill the goose that laid the golden egg by having him suddenly develop into a rabid correspondent, so I let him lie dormant for a while.

In December he bobbed up again, this time in Tunisia, hobnobbing with a tribe of Tuaregs, of all people. He began by saying that he was delighted to know that three classmates who roomed in his dorm recalled him after so many years. He went on to tell who the Tuaregs were (all of his letters were incontrovertibly authentic. The Encyclopedia Britannica and other sources took care of that) and dwelt at considerable length on the charms of the native women. "Many of them blue-eyed and blond, tall as Coldstream Guards, graceful as Burmese panthers, slender, but with just enough of what it takes."

Bert lingered among the Tuaregs longer than he had anticipated, hinting, not too subtly, that he may have been influenced by the Tuareg custom of women seldom marrying before they were thirty, yet being permitted to take as many trial husbands as they wished before they resigned themselves to one. "They generally take plenty," Bert wrote. "Nor did I ever hear any of them complain about having to wait until thirty or thereabouts before settling down to monogamy."

This, of course, was meat for middle-aged grads, and I could almost hear their wails of anguish when Bert went on to say that a sheik had laid him open with a saber because he was giving the sheik's favorite too big a play. Fortunately, Bert fully recovered after six weeks in a Cairo hospital, and the way was left open for further adventures by his P.S. "Just had a chance to join an expedition to South America (I'd just read a fascinating article about the beauty of the white Indians of the upper Amazon). Will drop you a line from there. Otherwise will see you in June." Bert served as reunion bait for quite a few years.

En route to the upper Amazon, where he went in quest of the elusive white orchid, Bert wrangled a pass to Devil's Island to reune for a few days with two former Foreign Legion pals who were doing time there. He didn't have much to say about his Amazon adventure except to report that he had entered into a *mariage de convenance* with the daughter of the white Indian chief, who in due time bore him a red-headed son.

In response to my request some years later that he record his wives and progeny for the class records he wrote that he had had four wives: Renée Martin-Cochand, former *première danseuse* of the Russian Imperial Ballet, whom he had married in France during World War I; Geertje de Vries, a half-caste daughter of an oil-company official, whom Bert had married in Bali ("There was a girl!" he commented); Agrippina, the white Indian; and Taua [You and Me], whom he married in Tahiti, resulting in his being dropped from the Social Register. "Taua," the editor of the *Papeete* (Tahiti Weekly Chronicle) wrote me, "is without question the most beautiful, accomplished, and charming Polynesian in Tahiti, or for that matter, in the entire Society Islands archipelago."

Bert said that he didn't know how many grandchildren he had, as it had been some time since he had heard from his two oldest children: Renée, the wife of Alain du d'Badonviller Lamorinière and L'Hommedieu X. II, who studied paleontology at Brasenose College, Oxford, and who at the moment was an aspirant in the French Army. "I do know definitely," he reported, "that I have an even dozen children," and enumerated the two by Renée and ten by "There was a girl!" Geertje. Two of the ten were twins and the oldest, George Washington, was working in Bali as head of the research division of a brassière manufacturer. Apparently he didn't count the redheaded son he had left on the upper reaches of the Amazon. At any rate he didn't mention him.

That Bert's quixotic life was the product of heredity, with quite a bit of exotic and erotic environment thrown in, was revealed when *Le Mirage* of Paris reported the death of his father at the age of seventy-nine as a result of wounds received in a duel. *"L'affaire d'honneur,"* *Le Mirage* reported, *"a eu lieu à la suite d'une tentative de viol faite par le colonel à la jeune et charmenta femme de son adversaire."* *Le Mirage's* French was flawless, I had a professor of French at Columbia write it.

The editor of the chronicle revealed an interesting sidelight on Bert's marriage to Taua. "Many Tahitians, when they reach middle age, adorn themselves with the most elaborate tatooing, a record of their life up to that time," he wrote. "They are very proud of this tatooing and none was prouder than Mara, Taua's mother.

"When Bert first asked Mara for Taua's hand, she looked on him with much favor until she discovered that he didn't have a single example of the tatooer's art on his body. Then she refused to consider him. It took Bert a long time to find out that he couldn't have the daughter unless he got himself tatooed to Mama's satisfaction. At first he indignantly refused, but the thought of losing Taua broke down his resistance. He suggested an anchor on his forearm, and later, an American flag with rampant eagle. But Mara would have neither. She brought out a faded photo of a Yale football player of the Golden Nineties, taken on the Yale fence, and pointed proudly to his big block "Y" on the Eli's chest. (Bert later learned that the Eli had once been her husband and that she revered everything about him, particularly his gridiron exploits with which he regaled her constantly.) Mara delivered her ultimatum. Either he had to have a "Y" tatooed on his chest or no Taua.

"That was too much for Bert, who, as you doubtless know, worships your alma mater with a devotion which I, a Stanford graduate, find quite inexplicable. He was on the horns of a dilemma if ever anyone was, and almost had a nervous breakdown as a result. Finally his friends came to his rescue. Not to bore you with the details, they got him stinko on *namu enata,* the illicit cocoanut brandy of the islands. By the time Bert came out of his coma forty-eight hours later, his hirsute chest bore a six-inch blue block "Y" and across his abdomen was a gold watch chain and dependent from it a Phi Beta Kappa key.

"None of us dared be on hand when Bert was to make the shocking discovery that for the rest of his life he was to be 'a Yale man through and through,' but I will say that he took it like a Hormone. I guess it was the thought that at last Taua was to be his. He was in better spirits than I'd ever seen him when he came into my office a few days later and opened his shirt almost proudly. 'I'm the only Princetonian who ever won his "Y",' he said, 'and the only man fired from Princeton who afterwards won his Phi Beta Kappa key.'"

Bert's marriage to Taua turned out to be an idyllic union. They hunted and fished and swam in their lagoon and had built up a profitable business taming and raising sharks and selling them to owners of Hollywood swimming pools. But the morning after our class dinner in 1947 I was so disgusted with what had happened the night before, I made up my mind to do away with them both.

Bert's account of their life together, which had appeared in the *Weekly,* a short time previously, had inspired the dinner committee to engage a professional to impersonate Bert at the dinner as the guest of honor. "Bert Hormone will positively appear," the ballyhoo read. Although most of the class by this time knew that Bert was legendary, they all loved him and went for the gag in a big way. The dinner, despite the fact it was held in Philadelphia, brought out more classmates than any in our history. But at least one classmate still thought

Bert was real. He vigorously protested that it was an insult to the class to have a person with Bert's moral standards as guest of honor. The committee overrode him one hundred per cent.

The impersonator was supposed to have familiarized himself with Bert in advance by reading my book (I had put Bert between hard covers by then), but I doubt if he more than glanced at the pages. He not only made a complete botch of his assignment, but told stories which left a bad taste in everyone's mouth. The gag fell flat as a pancake. To make matters worse, I had been elected to introduce "Bert" and give him the necessary build-up.

As a consequence, I decided the next morning to have Bert and Taua killed by one of their sharks gone berserk. On further thought, I decided not to. I'd just let him live on in Tahiti. Their marriage was too happy for me to break it up. But I never heard from him from that day on. Not until a few months ago when I received a postcard from Princeton, Indiana, saying that he was on his way to reunion, but it had been so long since he'd been in the U.S. he'd landed in the wrong Princeton. This was followed by cards from Princeton, B.C., and Princeton, Kentucky. I have no doubt before he finally reaches "the best old place of all" he'll have visited all the Princetons in North America. And that he'll pick up new experiences along the way.

Something tells me that someday when I walk into my reunion headquarters, the lovable old redhead will be sitting with feet on the table, a mug of beer in either hand, surrounded by classmates demanding to hear more about Bali and Tahiti.

Bert may forget that night before he's through. But I never will. Nor will thousands of other Princetonians. Good old Bert! The best friend a class secretary ever had. *Princeton Tiger*

THE CLICHÉ EXPERT

BY DAVE BURNS

Q: Mr. P. Charles Arbuthnot, campus cliché expert?

A: Just call me Charlie.

Q: You are, Mr. Arbuth–er, Charlie, an expert on undergraduate patois?

A: I'm in the know. I've been around. I'm no simple tool.

Q: Excellent. Then, with your permission, I shall test your competence in the field by putting a few questions to you.
A: Shoot.
Q: How are impending final examinations affecting you?
A: I've had it. This is bottoms. I'm really locked.
Q: Locked?
A: I've clutched. I'm all tensed up.
Q: Then I take it you don't expect to make a high grade?
A: I'm completely faked out in my two departmentals, but I'll be damned if I'll grind.
Q: How about your other course?
A: I've had two guts all lined up, but they backfired.
Q: Why?
A: Too many curve breakers.
Q: I see. Have your courses all been this difficult?
A: I'm no gut hopper, but this term is the worst. What with the ole theess and all I've really been screwed.
Q: How?
A: To the wall.
Q: What happened?
A: I thought I was gonna rack on midterms, but my shovel broke—I forgot I'd even cracked a book.
Q: Did everyone do so poorly?
A: Oh, there are always a few greasy grinds.
Q: Grinds? What do they do?
A: They're curve breakers. They clobber the exams and suck around the profs so you can't even keep an average.
Q: What kind of average?
A: A gentleman's average.
Q: You don't study much, I presume?
A: I stay loose. I hit the flicks, goof off a little, quaff a few brews with the boys.
Q: Where?
A: Down at the Nass, Goldie's, or the Peak. Sometimes we hit the K.I.
Q: Do you do this often?
A: I throw a small blast now and then. I'm not *completely* out of it.
Q: Then you have time to relax occasionally?
A: That's what I said. I take off on weekends. Maybe get tanked.
Q: What do you mean?

A: You know. Drunk, stewed, clobbered, gone, liquored up, oiled, stoned, in the bag.
Q: Do all your parties include liquor?
A: Are you kidding? A dry party's no party at all.
Q: You like liquor?
A: A blast is pretty sad without a little booze. It's rather weak. Not too real.
Q: Do you all have dates at your parties?
A: No. Some guys get flushed, shafted. But that's better than being stuck.
Q: Stuck?
A: With a pig, a drag, a beast.
Q: Oh. Are all dates like that?
A: Not mine. I get a nice babe down, see, stacked, warm, hot to go, a game girl.
Q: And?
A: Then some bird dog moves in.
Q: What does he do?
A: Feeds her a big line, beats my time, tries to make out.
Q: But if this doesn't happen?
A: Then I'm golden, man. I go ape. I'm in like Flynn.
Q: What happens then?
A: It's *real*. That is–if I don't drop the ball.
Q: Well, to return to examinations—–
A: Exams! Eat the bird, will ya?
Q: Excuse me! I was just wondering what you were planning to do.
A: I'll just have to shovel the old bull, that's all.
Q: Well, Mr. Arbuth–er, Charlie, how would you describe the house parties?
A: It's the cry! The latest!
Q: What will you do until then?
A: I'm gonna flake out.
Q: What?
A: Pat the pad, sack out, lay in the sun.
Q: Hmm. You've been a great help, Charlie. Just one more question: You do plan to participate in house parties?
A: You some wise college *fellow?*
Q: I mean girls and everything. You do like girls?
A: The greatest, man! The greatest ever! *Princeton Tiger*

THE MUSE PSYCH

BY BUD NYE

Franklin ran up the steep wooded paths, smiling, smelling the clean spring air, listening to the songs of the birds. He was on a kinesthetic debauch, with a little olfactory and auditory fun thrown in.

At last he came to their meeting place, a little grassy platform high on the hills, sheltered at the back by thick pines, and overlooking to the front and west the long river valley. Beyond, the river and the rolling hills stretched to the horizon via interposition and the blue-haze phenomenon.

"In a Pleasantness-Unpleasantness Rating Scale," Franklin mused, "this place would score plus one hundred with me."

Soon came faint rustlings. They grew in volume and intensity by the second; and as the sound waves struck the receptors in his internal ear, Franklin made a precise wave-phase and complexity discrimination (almost unconsciously) and localized the sound to his right and below him. He looked down the path, and he saw her. Eustacia ran to him, laughing gaily and breathlessly.

"Whew!" she cried, "I feel deep pressure and dull pain amounting almost to an ache in the tendons, muscles, and joints of my legs. What a climb!"

"You're late, darling. What happened?"

"Oh, I got tied up with a couple Introvert-Extrovert forms from the Testing Bureau and couldn't leave until I got them correlated."

"Well, anyway, you're here. Let me look at you," said Franklin in a neat bit of recall.

He perceived with a minimum of saccadic eye movements 'Stacia's brown hair, rosy cheeks, girlish figure; but more than that, these visual experiences called up a host of rich associations, all of which he had integrated into a dear pattern symbolized by the word Eustacia. He realized now that she was no longer just a pleasing arrangement of lights and shadows, of tints and shades. He loved her.

"Eustacia," he murmured, setting up a low frequency vibration in his vocal cords.

The timbre of his voice produced in Eustacia a conditioned emotional response. She sighed and closed her eyes.

They kissed.

" 'Stacia, let's get married," said Franklin, going rashly subjective.

Eustacia drew back, frowning a little.

"But, Frank, you know the results of our Self-Rated Personality Tests. We would have to make so many adjustments it just wouldn't be us. I'm sorry; I like you a lot."

"But 'Stacia," he protested, "you know that disparity doesn't mean much." Frank drew himself up. "Why, its test retest reliability is only eighty."

"Well, that's enough . . ."

"And besides, neither of us is really atypical in any sense. We're both well within the norms on the Prissman-Jelinck Attitude Scales. And they've both got a much higher reliability."

"I know, I know," she said impatiently. "I know!"

"Darling, we could have such fun together. You've always been curious about olfactory differentiation. We could go on together, man and wife, subject and observer, to the very heights of experimentation in the field. Without you, 'Stacia," he said reverently, nursing his anticipatory metabolism step-up, "without you, I am a–I am a . . ."

He groped for a four-letter word descriptive of the individual stripped of learning incentive, of goal set, of all the refinements of the innate drives that culture demands of and provides for the carrying on of life. He settled for h-u-l-k.

"I am a hulk. An empty hulk."

"I know," she inserted impatiently.

"Well, then, darling, let's get married."

"I'm sorry, Frank, but we have our separate lives to live. It has been established by Pillwiddler Somstoosen in a study of 5000 divorces in the professional classes that opposed interests cause 97.5 per cent of the breakups. It's far too great a risk."

Frank glowered. "I'd like to know his method of recording the cases. And I'd like to compare the divorces with the successful marriages in the professional classes."

"Don't let's talk about it any more, Franklin."

"Pshaw!" said Frank, disappointed. "Why do you think I hung around to be your lab assistant in all those manual-dexterity demonstrations–so I could set the state record on the Minnesota Form Board Test?"

"No, Franklin. I knew you liked me. But can't you––"

"And besides, I set the record way last year. No one's come close since."

"That's just the trouble. You're vain and conceited. You know as well as I do that the charm of your apparent personality arises chiefly from secondary cues—your clothing, status, and possessions."

'Stacia was on the verge of tears. To avoid them she stimulated the cutaneous pain receptors of Franklin's cheek with a sharp left, following it with an anger-motivated right cross to the nose.

"You beast!" she screamed. "I hate you. I hate you! I hope I never perceive you again!" She turned and ran sobbing down the path.

Frank sighed. The afternoon, he concluded, had been an orgy of uncontrolled variables. He tried to reassure himself that none of Eustacia's hasty conclusions would prove valid and that she would be her same old objective self when next they met. Yet he couldn't keep out the disquieting thought that the afternoon's results were significant.

As the fiery sun sank in the west, and Franklin's retina experienced a gorgeous display of positive and negative afterimages, a brooding melancholy enveloped him.

His tear ducts secreted rather unmanfully. He cried. *Ski-U-Mah*

ROTTEN FOUL

John Ackworth Manley woke up one morning feeling rotten foul and hating everybody. He looked at the clock on the desk and then over at his roommate, who was sleeping heavily in a tangle of bedclothes. He was supposed to wake him at seven, Manley remembered. He went over to his roommate's bed, grabbed a leg sticking out from under a plaid blanket, and pulled him on the floor with a great thump.

"You wanted to get up at seven, damn it," said Manley, "so get up." His roommate, who was one of the gentlest people who ever lived, sat up on the floor staring at him.

"That's right. That's just like you," said Manley angrily. "Sit around for half an hour looking out the window and playing the radio until I want to take a shower and then run in the head and take a shower yourself." Manley leaned down and ferociously ripped off his roommate's pajama coat. "Now get the hell in there and take a shower *now*." With a few jerks and pulls Manley got the rest of the pajamas free from his roommate, who stood, naked, staring at him, his mouth open. "Go ahead," Manley said, giving him a push toward the door.

When his roommate had gone, Manley stood in the middle of the room brooding for a minute. His head was throbbing. He picked up the phone and called his almost-fiancée at Smith. "So what if I did get you out of bed, fats?" he said into the phone. "By the looks of you, you ought to be out weight-lifting, instead of lying around in bed all day. . . . I just wanted to tell you that I won't be up this weekend after all. . . . No, it's not because I have to study (this a falsetto mimic). . . . It's simply because I can't stand your stupid laughter. . . . Who's being funny? . . . God, don't start talking like your mother. . . . Yes, I would insult your mother, but why bring the Civil War into this? . . . What? . . . I know you were a perfect fool when you got engaged to me, but I didn't know it at the time."

He hung up, got dressed, and went over to his club for breakfast. While he was eating at a corner table by himself, having snubbed all the members, the leading candidate for the club's presidency came over and sat down. "Well, John," he said brightly, "all ready for the election tonight?"

Manley put down his fork. "Brinkwood," he said slowly, "I wouldn't vote for you for the president of this club if your running mate were one of those red-rumped, blue-faced baboons you see in the zoo. So please stop bothering me and go eat your soggy toast elsewhere." Manley finished his fried eggs and went out. It was time for his English class. He had planned to cut it, but now he decided to go.

Old Lindlump, the professor, was discussing Milton. Manley listened for a while, then he raised his hand. "Yes, Mr. Manley?" said Old Lindlump, smiling benevolently. "Old Lindlump," said Manley, "I just wanted to tell you that you fascinate me no end. I have never before met a man who, every time he opened his mouth, could be so consistently wrong on every possible subject." Manley got up and went toward the door. "I don't know why I've stood it so long. I suppose it's because I couldn't bring myself to stop staring at your fantastically silly face." He closed the door behind him as the class gazed in silence.

Manley went home and took a nap. His roommate was reading a book and listening to the radio when he came in, but Manley gave him a look and he went out. When he awoke it was lunch time and he trudged over to the college dining hall. He was feeling fouler than ever. His roommate was sitting by a window, chewing on a grilled cheese sandwich. Manley went over to him with his lunch and sat down next to him in silence. "Gee," said his roommate, "you have liver and onions. They had grilled cheese sandwiches when I went through the line."

Manley looked at him. "You'd prefer liver and onions to grilled cheese sandwiches?" he asked coldly. "Er . . . I guess so," said his roommate, a little afraid of the look in Manley's eye. He took a sip of milk and added, "I like liver and onions."

"So you like liver and onions, eh?" said Manley, his voice loud. "So you like liver and onions?" He picked up his piece of liver and pushed it flat and hard in his roommate's face. Then he wiped his hands on the napkin and walked out of the dining hall.

Later in the afternoon, when Manley entered his adviser's office, he found him leaning back in his chair and staring at the ceiling. "And how are we feeling today?" he asked smilingly when he saw Manley. Manley suddenly flipped over the fire extinguisher that hung on the wall and set the hose steadily on his adviser. "Cripes!" yelled the adviser, trying frantically to shield himself from the blast with his hands.

Manley went to a movie and then went home. His roommate had gotten a birthday cake from his mother that morning. Manley set the cake in the middle of the floor and then stepped on it. Then he went to bed. "I hope to hell I feel better in the morning," he said, setting the alarm and remembering he had to wake his roommate. *Yale Record*

SISSY AFTER SEVEN

BY C. R. K.

Buttolph laid his plans carefully. He went to considerable expense to get the necessary equipment, but the prize was well worth it: the fair Ursula, a blonde he wished with extreme fervency to keep in his room past the seven o'clock limit set and firmly enforced by Dean Godoctopus and his minions, the proctors.

Buttolph's room was on the second floor of Holder, certainly not a location favorable to his success, for it is well known that a Man in a Hat stands guard in the court to prevent the very thing that Buttolph proposed to do. Buttolph's acquaintances did not consider him the type to carry through his scheme, for he was bookish, practically a teetotaler, and definitely not a party boy at all. His courtship of Ursula produced some wonder, for she hailed from Dixie, drank like a fish, and was dumber than hell; she was often described as a "Southern always-fried chicken." But her charms were unmistakable, and Buttolph was wished every success.

Buttolph's chances were lessened (in fact the odds against him went up to 8-1 at Jack Honore's) by the fact that he broadcast his intentions so much that the Watchdogs got wind of "something funny going to happen in Holder on Saturday evening." Around quarter to seven on the suspect date a disproportionately large number of them gathered in the court, dodging stray highball glasses and whiffling with impatience.

In an empty classroom of Dickinson, Buttolph, with Ursula (who did not understand what the hell was coming off but was game anyway), made his last minute preparations. Modestly turning his back, he bade her change into a pair of a friend's gray flannels, sports coat, shirt, and tie. Her hair was concealed beneath a boater, and her dainty feet were shod in white bucks, specially bought and carefully dirtied for her by Buttolph. An acoustic device placed in her throat turned her slightly hysterical giggle, which a proctor can detect at three hundred yards, into a throaty masculine chuckle. Her perfume, which would betray her sex to Mike's Men even if they had bad colds, was neutralized perfectly by a compound which Buttolph had spent a whole afternoon brewing in Chem Lab. This done, she smelled typically Princetonian—a blend of cheap gin and McCosh '50. Finally, he covered her soft chin with synthetic five o'clock shadow, another Chem 335 concoction. The stage set, they walked fearlessly out onto the campus. If Ursula could not pass for a Charlie, she certainly looked at least as masculine as a Harvard student.

As they walked toward Holder, Ursula caught on, bright little girl that she was. She looked at Buttolph queerly, patted him on the hand, and gurgled, "Honey, bettuh men than you have tried this. But you can't fool a proctuh. If you can do it, youah the smahtest boy in the world, an' I'm all foh you." "I can, I will, I MUST," replied Buttolph, and they stepped through the arch into full view of the proctors.

Manny, Moe, and Jack looked, listened and smelled. They turned away, satisfied, and focused their attention on a lad in the twelfth entry who was hanging out a window by his heels. Buttolph and Ursula entered the former's room. Buttolph's roommates were gone. The foiler of the proctors locked the door and eyed Ursula smugly. She looked at him with a light in her eyes that few sophomores have ever seen. "You did it," she whispered. "You dahlin'."

Buttolph paid no attention to her. Turning away, he began to beat his chest and utter victory cries. "Away, woman," he shouted to her as she grabbed him. "You had nothing to do with this. It was I, I,

Orlando Buttolph, who has proved that Man is smarter than Proctor. I'm a hero—the savior of humanity. It is I, I who——"

This was more than the scorned Ursula could take. Choking with rage, she tore off her shirt, tie, and boater, and raced to the window. Before Buttolph could stop her she flung it open, removed the frog from her throat, and shrilled into the courtyard below: "PROCT-TUH!! Make this nasty boy let me out of heah!"

While Manny, Moe, and Jack, uttering small screams of delight, dragged the power-drunk Buttolph off into darkness, the outraged Ursula returned to Dickinson to retrieve her clothes. Buttolph was summarily expelled for behaving in an impolite and ungentlemanly manner.

MORAL: The sex-after-seven rule is a bad rule and should be changed. *Princeton Tiger*

INSIDE THE ATOM

Ladies and Gentlemen: This evening we are gathered here to witness a vivid demonstration of atomic power and its effects. By the use of models, Dr. Brown, my assistant, and I shall attempt to show you exactly how atoms of U-235 are split and how their energy is released.

Now in this hand you see an atom of U-235. Actually, it is not really an atom but a large, inflated balloon. Atoms, of course, are much smaller and in one hand alone I could hold as many as one hundred atoms. That should give you an idea of their minuteness.

Covering this atom—or balloon—are a number of small spheres which are known to science as "electrons." Actually they are only ping-pong balls glued to the balloon, but for all practical purposes we shall refer to them from now on as electrons. When I shake the atom, you notice that it rattles. This is due to the presence of a proton—or golf ball—in the interior of the atom—or balloon. Now you know all there is to know of atomic structure.

Atoms are generally held in place by what are known as "molecules." For this reason Dr. Brown, representing a molecule, will thus hold the atom in his two hands. Molecules are constantly in motion, and they are extremely sensitive to heat. To illustrate this conclusion I take a match in one hand, inserting it into Dr. Brown's shoe, I ignite it. Notice that Dr. Brown hops violently from one side of the room to the other, bumping into desks and tables and thus illustrating the effects of heat upon a molecule. In scientific circles this reaction is known as the Brownian movement.

But let us now concern ourselves with atomic power and its attainment. In order to release this tremendous energy we must first split the U-235 atom. This is accomplished by the use of many hard particles which are known to science as "neutrons." Fortunately I have a bag of these neutrons at my disposal which I shall pass among you of the audience for your inspection. Of course, these particles are not really neutrons but merely green peas; nevertheless they duplicate closely the shape and color of the actual neutrons.

While you in the audience are examining these atomic projectiles, I shall introduce the instrument by which the neutrons are directed into U-235 atoms—the cyclotron. This, which you see in my hand, is not actually a cyclotron but a common ordinary slingshot. A cyclotron is somewhat larger than a slingshot and is run by electricity. You—in the back row—would you refrain from throwing neutrons at the blackboard? Thank you.

And now for the supreme moment. Mounting this table I take my cyclotron in the right hand and the neutrons in my left. Dr. Brown, as the molecule, will race from one end of the room to the other, holding his atom between his hands. As he rushes by I shall attempt to split his atom with my little neutron. You may begin, Dr. Brown.

Here he comes and I hurl a neutron at the atom with my cyclotron. But I miss. He returns, and I hurl still another neutron at the atom. But I miss.

At this point I should like to comment on the difficulties we scientists have faced in releasing atomic energy. I believe this experiment reveals better than words the extraordinary hardships and the frustrations we face from day to day. You may resume your Brownian movements, Dr. Brown.

Here he comes, I hurl my neutron—but I miss. He returns, I hurl my neutron, but—whoops! Dr. Brown has slipped and fallen upon his atom! Dr. Brown! Are you all right? Oh dear, you've broken your glasses. But I see you have split the atom.

Well, ladies and gentlemen, that seems to conclude our little experiment for tonight. In it we have seen Dr. Brown fall down and break his glasses and thus present *undeniable* proof of the destructiveness of atomic energy. Multiply the destruction of Dr. Brown's glasses a hundred times and you will have some idea of the tremendous power of the atomic bomb. And with that disturbing thought before us I conclude this lecture on atomic energy. Thank you. *Sundial*

CAT-ASTROPHE

This is a story of the survival of one little kitten—and there were three. They were named very much alike; one was Phtt, one was Phtt Phtt, and the third was Phtt Phtt Phtt.

Little Phtt became very ill and the doctor said he would die, and sure enough he did. A very sad day. It must have affected the others very much, because Phtt Phtt immediately got sick, and the doctor said it was too bad but he would die too. And he did. And that made things worse because dead cats around a place don't smell at all nice.

Well, you might have known it would happen. Phtt Phtt Phtt also became very ill and the doctor's diagnosis was unchanged: "Phtt Phtt Phtt is going to die too." But Phtt Phtt Phtt wasn't going to do any such thing. He sat up and said "No, I'm not,"—and didn't.

There's no arguing this outcome. It is clearly a case of the survival of the Phtt-est.

ORLANDO WAS A GENTLEMAN

A true gentleman is always polite, and Orlando Olsen was a gentleman. Even under the most trying circumstances his manners were above reproach. Lord Chesterfield himself couldn't have been more noble, more chivalrous.

He was taking Rosaline Roberts home from the library. She was a freshman and he had known her only a week.

"Would you like to go to our house dance next Saturday night?" he asked.

"Oh, Orlo! I'd be so delighted," she beamed. "But Orlo," she added thoughtfully, "my mother won't let me go out in the evening without her."

"Why not bring her along?" he proposed gallantly.

"But she is a little lame and it tires her to walk far," Rosaline continued.

"We will send a taxi for her." Orlando was not to be defeated by adverse circumstances.

"But she doesn't like to go out in the evening unless she goes out for dinner also." Rosaline was despondent.

"It would be only an added pleasure to take your mother and yourself out to dinner before the dance," said Orlando. Romeo couldn't have done better.

They walked on some time in silence.

"Orlo. I've a confession to make," said Rosaline.

"What is it my dear?" from Orlando.

"I can't go to your dance," she sobbed.

"Why?" he asked.

"I can't dance."

A true gentleman is always polite even under the most trying circumstances. Orlando Olsen was a gentleman.

"That is perfectly all right. You can come any way. It's not your fault that you don't dance. Neither does my room mate. I'm making this date for him." *Orange Owl (Oregon State College)*

THE CURSE OF THE RUMPLETWITS

One fine spring afternoon in the early years of the eighteenth century, Baron Rumpletwit was spurring his roan mare down a shadowy path on his country estate. Suddenly, a gypsy woman, old and picturesque, appeared from the underbrush and grasped his bridle. The baron casually tossed her a shilling.

"Only a shilling?" screamed the hag. "Only a shilling? Curse ye for your parsimony, Baron Rumpletwit! Curse ye and your son and your son's son, and every man-child born in your castle to the seventh generation! The gypsy's curse be upon ye!"

The baron paid no attention and cantered cheerfully home. Little he did dream of the future that was in store for his descendants. From then on the castle was mantled with the dread shadow of the curse of the Rumpletwits.

The baron lived on to a contented old age. His son and his son's son also lived peacefully and happily till they died of old age. And so it went for six generations.

The seventh descendant of the old baron, Luther Rumpletwit, was a handsome lad, popular and well liked by all who knew him. He was brave as well and had no fear of the dire curse of the Rumpletwits. In fact, he hadn't even heard of the dire curse of the Rumpletwits.

Luther Rumpletwit, too, died of old age. The gypsy was sore as hell.

Harvard Lampoon

OH, WHAT A BEAUTIFUL MOURNING

BY D. D. S.

Brriing! went my alarm.

I opened one eye.

Brriiing!!

I shut it.

Brriiiing!!

I turned over and put the pillow over my head.

BRRIIIIIIING!!!

"Hell!" I muttered, as I reached over to turn it off. "Sno use!"

"Hey!" hollered my roommate from the next room. "Time to get up! Your alarm went off!"

"Ugh!" I muttered. I looked out the window. Rain. Fog. "Ugh!" I repeated.

My roommate walked in. "Hey, you don't look so good!" he said.

"I don't feel so good," I said. "Parties all weekend, girls, more parties, more girls, fun, whoopie——" I groaned. "And now Monday morning. And a splitting headache. And rain. Look at that stinking rain!" I groaned again.

"Yeah," said my roommate, "and you got a test today, too. Remember?"

"Oh no!" I bellowed. "This is too much!"

I got up, dressed, put on my raincoat, and walked out the door. It was miserable out. Everything was miserable. "I think I'll kill myself," I thought, as I plodded along.

I stumbled over to Nassau Hall and started climbing the stairs. A professor came by.

"Good morning!" he said. "Going up to the tower?"

"Yes," I said. "I'm going to jump off."

"Can't say I blame you," he said, and walked away.

I got up to the tower and stepped out onto the roof. I looked all around below me. People were walking along like little ants all over the walks. Occasionally someone would look up at me, nudge his companion, and point. Then they would both stare for a moment, and walk on.

"Humph!" I thought. "Take it lightly, will they?"

With that, I went over to the bell and grabbed the cord. "I'll show 'em!" I muttered. I pulled it as hard as I could, and the bell started ringing nice and loud. I kept it up for about three minutes and then went back to the edge of the roof.

People were still just walking around as if nothing was happening, only they were moving faster.

This flustered me. But then I realized. "So they think it's the eight-forty bell, do they?" I muttered. "Well, I'll show 'em!"

All of a sudden I noticed my roommate below me. He looked up. "Hey, come on down!" he shouted. "You'll be late for class!" Then he walked on.

Desperate now, I started hollering. "I'm going to jump! I'm going to jump! Any minute now! Look, everybody, look!" I waved my arms around and jumped up and down.

One or two people stopped and looked up at me. I kept on yelling. Slowly a mob began to assemble. "I've got 'em now!" I giggled with glee.

A couple of proctors walked out in front of everybody and waved to me. I waved back.

"Hey, come down offa there!" one of them yelled.

"No!" I shouted. "I'm going to jump!"

"Don't be funny! Get down offa there!"

Cars began to stop along Nassau Street, and people were cramming their necks out the windows to see me. Horns started honking, sirens started blowing, people started screaming. I felt wonderful.

"Aw, come on!" said the proctor.

He pointed a flashlight up at me and started shining it.

"Idiot!" I shouted. "It's daytime!"

"Well, we always carry these things," he shouted. "Now, get down from there will you? Please? Pretty please?"

"Nope!"

I looked behind me and saw a couple of cops reaching out. "Come one step closer and I'll jump!" I said. "Just one step!"

I looked back at the people beneath me. There was a priest walking toward Nassau Hall. Things looked official.

All of a sudden I heard a voice behind me. It was a girl's voice.

"Come on, honey," it said. "Come away from there over to me."

There was a sexy blonde stretching her arms out to me.

"Damn bribes!" I muttered.

I looked down at the mob. Firemen were rigging up a huge net underneath me. Police were standing all over the lawn blowing their whistles and waving their arms through the air.

There in front stood the dean. He was looking up and grinning.

"Okay, bud," one of the proctors suddenly hollered. "If you want to jump now, jump!" He pointed to the net, which was all stretched out below me.

"Nope!"

"What?" he gasped.

"Nope! I've changed my mind."

The proctor looked bewildered. "But–but——"

"Sorry," I said. "I will not jump. You can all go home now."

"But the ladders, the nets, the cameras——" he sobbed. "All the work we've done, all the people–everything, everybody all ready . . ."

I looked down at the dean. Frowning. He was frowning!

Just then one of the cops behind me took a step forward.

"I am taking a step forward," he announced.

"It's no use," I said. "I am not going to jump!"

"But–but you promised," he said. "One more step, you said, and——" He broke down into uncontrollable slobbering. "You promised," he whimpered, "you promised." He sobbed profusely. I felt like sort of a heel.

All of a sudden I saw the blonde.

"Come on over to me big boy," she sighed. She was holding out her arms.

"Come on, big boy. Come on over to me."

I smiled.

Maybe it wasn't such a rotten day, after all. *Princeton Tiger*

CHEMICAL ANALYSIS OF A WOMAN

SYMBOL: Wo.

ACCEPTED WEIGHT: 120.

OCCURRENCE: Wherever man is found.

PHYSICAL PROPERTIES: Boils at nothing, freezes in a minute, melts at less than room temperature with proper treatment. Very bitter if neglected or improperly used.

CHEMICAL PROPERTIES: Great affinity for gold, platinum, silver, and precious stones. Violent reaction if left alone. Able to absorb great amounts of food matter. Turns green when placed beside better-looking specimens.

USES: Highly ornamental. Useful as a tonic in the acceleration of low spirits. Useful as an equalizer in the redistribution of wealth.

NOTE: Probably the most effective income-reducing agent known to man.

CAUTION: Highly explosive in inexperienced hands. Very complex and results in many unexplainable actions. Highly unpredictable; should be watched at all times. *Cornell Widow*

MR. BLANDINGS IMPROVES HIS DREAM HOUSE

BY JACK UPHAM

NOTE: Hollywood recently tried to depict the story of Mr. Blandings on the screen, but unfortunately, the story had to run the customary gauntlet of censors, publicity agents, and "box-office" mad producers. Thus, by the time the story reached the public eye, it had been so prostituted that it had little or no bearing on the significance of the original theme. Therefore, I should like to reconstruct the basic story.

The architect heaved a weary sigh, removed his glasses and stood up, pointing to the mass of charts and plans arrayed on the table. "Well, I guess that's it, Mr. Blandings," he said. "You couldn't ask for a better house."

Mr. Blandings scowled as he studied the master chart on top of the pile. "Mmm—yes. Just one thing."

"What's that?"

"Bathroom!"

"Bathroom?"

"Yes, bathroom. Carl, this may seem silly, but I have always regarded the bathroom as being the most important part of the house."

"Well, here's the bathroom on the second floor," Carl protested, pointing to the chart. "All of the latest styles in modern comfort will be observed."

"I realize that," said Mr. Blandings, "but my bathroom's going to be really different. Every time I'm in a bathroom, I get to thinking. I think of the goal I set a long time ago. I vowed that if I was ever in the position to build the house of my dreams, I would build a bathroom all my own! I've had many ideas for improvements and I've remembered them all, in anticipation of the day when I should build the perfect bathroom!" His eyes glowed at the prospect of revealing his secret triumph for the first time. "First of all," he said, "I want it partitioned."

"Partitioned?" the architect was bold to say.

"Yes—divided into three parts—washing, bathing, and toilet, each with separate doors. Just think of shaving in the morning with an unsteamed mirror! The shower will be in another room!" His face fairly shone as he went on, "The wash basin must be adjustable for height, with full-length mirror behind it."

"Marvelous idea," commented the architect, "what's it for?"

"Well, you have to stand close to the sink, so that you won't splash any water. If you're looking in the mirror, how can you still be close to the sink? And, when you're trying to stay close to the sink and shave, you have to look in the mirror! Then, if you made it to accommodate me, my youngest son wouldn't be able to reach it! What's more, think of being able to take a shampoo in the sink without getting the bends or stomach cramps! That reminds me—I want a faucet in the middle about eight inches high. I never could get my head under the faucet in any sink!" Blandings paused to catch the architect's reaction to this, lit a cigarette, and continued, "I want a small button near the soap dish that will ring a bell near the towel rack so that I can find it with soap in my eyes, and I want a small cylindrical container with a wringer at one end—for the toothpaste tube. In my house, everyone wants to squeeze the tube a different way—with this, I can save arguments."

"A stroke of genius!" Carl gasped.

"There should be a little spigot at the bottom of the soap dish to drain out the soap goo that drops down. It's really ideal for washing your hands in a hurry. Oh—and I'll want two lights—one on each side of the sink. Then maybe when I shave I can cut my sideburns both to the same length. One side's always in the shade with just a single light. Put a plug on each side, too—I use an electric razor and I don't like wires across my face."

"They never do make 'em with enough wire," the architect said.

Mr. Blandings nodded agreement. "When you put in the toothbrush rack, leave a space for name plates. When my wife buys new brushes, it takes me a month to find out I've been using the wrong one. And then, you'll have to build a medicine cabinet at one end. It ought to be about eight feet by six, with two-foot shelves on each side."

"You call that a cabinet?"

"You've never seen *our* medicine cabinet. My wife keeps it stocked with everything from elephantiasis serum to splints for a dislocated esophagus! You'd better build another closet behind it for the overflow from the medicine cabinet. The last time I looked into our cabinet at home, she was using a part of it for her discarded shoes and hats. They, alone, should warrant a separate closet!"

"Closet and storeroom," muttered the architect, making some notes on a pad. "This'll take up a lot of space. You'll have to build an extension."

Mr. Blandings, as he often did, pondered a moment. "Tell you what to do," he said thoughtfully, "build an extra wing on the back. Upstairs, the washroom; downstairs, the bathroom and toilet—the *real* toilet. In case someone hasn't time to come down, a small one upstairs. You'll have to connect the whole business with the bedrooms upstairs and the kitchens downstairs. Put in a back hall and stairway here, with a door leading outside."

"Leading outside?"

"Sure. After all, you never can tell where you might be. The stairway will be handy in case you have unexpected company and you want to take a quick shower. You can get downstairs without being seen. Oh yes—I want a guest bathroom!"

"A what?"

"A guest bathroom. You know that whenever a guest uses a bathroom, he or she always feels uncomfortable about using the guest towels. The things look too delicate and fancy to use! Yet the wife insists on putting them up—might as well be sure they *will* be used. We'll have a special bathroom with nothing but guest towels! On second thought, build two bathrooms—one for men and one for women. You know the difficulties involved in holding a mixed party at a house with only one guest bathroom."

"Boy, you sure have it all figured out!" Carl said. "What about the shower?"

"You'll have to put in a bathtub *and* a shower. I like showers; the wife doesn't. Ask her about the bathtub, but *I'll* tell you about the *shower*." The gleam returned to Mr. Blandings' eye. "I want a sort of rheostat control on the outside that I can adjust for temperature and velocity. And instead of a single shower head, I want a bank of shower nozzles all along the side of the booth. Then I won't have to duck and twist every which way to get showered all over. On the other side, I'll need a shelf at chest level with places for four bars of soap. On the average, I drop the soap three times in the shower. This way, I won't have to bend over and pick it up until I drop it a fourth time. Then there ought to be a place in the remotest corner of the shower where the soap on the floor can slide so it won't be stepped on."

"Good precaution," Carl said.

"Up above the shower heads, I want a small shelf for a metronome and a couple of clips to hold sheet music—I sing in the shower—and for this reason, too, I think perhaps you had better soundproof the room. I sometimes get up early."

"Very thoughtful."

"Besides the shower—and the tub—on the floor, I want a section of corrugated rubber tiling so the bath mat won't slip, and I want the rest of the floor made out of some porous material that will conduct heat. You can run a few heat ventilator outlets under the floor—then it won't be so cold to step on."

"Cold—feet——" Carl said as he made more notes in his book. "This will run into real money, you know."

"How much?" said Mr. Blandings. "Let's see," said the other, studying his notes. He made a few brief calculations, then concluded, "Altogether forty-five thousand."

"Wait a minute! Before, you told me twenty-five!"

"That was before you added your bathroom," the architect said. "That'll cost you twenty thousand alone."

Mr. Blandings frowned, stroked his chin and frowned again. Suddenly he said, "I've got it! Tell you what you do, Carl—forget the house! JUST build me the bathroom!"

Jackolantern (Dartmouth College)

BLIND DATE

Are you so homely that you always look at the reverse side of a pocket mirror to keep from scaring yourself to death? Do you sleep with your face in the pillow just to be kind to burglars? Do men dodge you when you walk down the street instead of Packarding or Rolls-Roycing you? Are you knock-kneed, cross-eyed, pigeon-toed, and hawk-nosed? Do you have to pretend that every day is Halloween before you have the courage to go downtown? Are you the kind of girl that jealous wives like their husbands to go out with? Are you lantern-jawed and droop-lipped? Do you pray for rain so that you can hide behind an umbrella? Are you sweet sixteen and never been kissed? Do your hands dangle below your knees and does your pair of shoes equal one cow? Are you called to the phone every five minutes to turn down a side-show offer? Do you protect yourself from Peeping Toms by leaving the shades up?

Now, then, take stock of yourself. Get a toe hold in the carpet and crack the mirror with a good stare. Are you the female described above? If so, sister, I'll pay you fifty dollars spot cash for an answer to this article. All you have to do is to drop me a line and tell me the hiding place of that dizzy, long-eared bum who dug you up for me in a blind date last Saturday night.

Punch Bowl (University of Pennsylvania)

DEAR MR. OLMSTEAD:

BY WALTER PETERSON

102 Hamper
November 10

Supt. of Building and Grounds
Parkhurst Hall
Dartmouth College
Hanover, N.H.
Dear Mr. Olmstead:

Ordinarily I would not be reporting such a trivial thing, but it should come to your attention, because I believe that you can help me.

My radiator cheeps. It does this constantly—that is to say, it does it all night. Naturally, if one is to maintain his average, he must sleep.

Your help in this matter will be appreciated.

Sincerely,

John S. Bakin '56

November 17

Dear Mr. Olmstead:

While your suggestion to wear ear muffs in bed has proved a great help, there have been other complications. Since I wrote you, I have explained to Smitty the janitor, Capt. Gaudreau, the UGC Judiciary Committee, and several others, that I am not keeping pets in my room. I do not like pets.

Any further suggestions will be welcomed.

Sincerely,

John (Canary) Bakin '56

November 24

Dear Mr. Olmstead:

It is now cheeping and beeping.

Enclosed, please find bills. I hope you will give my request for reimbursement prompt attention, as I cannot afford to buy ear muffs for everyone on this floor.

Would you also be so kind as to explain to Dean MacDonald that I don't get much sleep. I really meant no offense to Professor Scarlett.

Sincerely,

John (Mr. Doze) Bakin '56

December 3

Dear Mr. Olmstead:

You will be glad to know that both the cheeping and beeping have stopped. However, a curious thing happened last night, which I'm sure will interest you. Last night, I found myself repeatedly awakened by water dripping on my forehead.

This I believe was due to the steam escaping from the radiator after your repairs and condensing on the ceiling above my bed. I need help.

If I may anticipate, please do not suggest a raincoat, as my father is already disturbed about the unexpected bill for 14 prs. of ear muffs, which he found enclosed with your note.

Sincerely,

Drips Bakin '56

Infirmary
December 14

Dear Mr. Olmstead:

I'm sure you will be happy to know that I am not letting worries over the radiator retard my recovery, although as I explained to Miss Dunn, I do have trouble falling asleep without the cheep, beep, and splash to which I had grown accustomed.

The boys across the hall tell me that your crew has been in to investigate in my absence, and I must admit that I am disturbed about the reports that they have harvested my mushroom crop. As the bard said, "sweet are the users of advertising," and I had hoped to use the mushrooms to pay for the rubber sheeting you were so kind as to suggest as an economy measure. I saved $12 over the price of 12 raincoats.

Sincerely,

John (Sniffles) Bakin '56

102 Hamper
December 19

Dear Mr. Olmstead:

Just a word before I take off for the vacation to let you know that I appreciate your interest in my case. However, I'm more than a little worried by what Smitty, our janitor, tells me.

He said that the chewing gum is just temporary, and that over vacation you intended to get some baling wire and make it permanent. I know advice from me is out of place, sir, but can't we let well enough alone? The mold on the walls is starting to dry up, and I feel it should be given a chance.

I was very interested to hear that you are also interested in growing mushrooms. I always wondered about the basement of Crosby Hall. Frankly, I don't think the damp does them a bit of good, but the current crop is doing okay.

Please, sir, consider leaving the baling wire.

Merry Xmas,

John S. Bakin '56

January 15

Dear Mr. Olmstead:

I am very sorry to be continually bothering you; however, something very interesting has happened since you put in the baling wire. The three rooms directly above me have not been getting any heat. Please help me, since it has been very cold and there is scarcely room in my single for the occupants of the other three rooms.

Your suggestion that I replace the mushrooms with celery was admirable, since I understand a dark, damp place is best for growing the delicate variety that has the best market. However, in the present emergency my sprouts have been trampled, and I wonder if you know of something hardier.

As ever,

John

Infirmary
January 21

Dear Mr. Olmstead:

Thank you so much for having the bunks installed along the walls. It has added greatly to our comfort, although I wish someone had told us that the radiator was removed to make way for the bunks. While we have all recovered from exposure, the doctor tells me I have an advanced case of rheumatism. I didn't know extreme cold could do anything like that to a person. Oh well, as the French say, *sail on gay*.

Thanks anyway for your further kind suggestion, but I doubt the economic value of tundra grass, and it is probably too cold anyway. I think I will give up the idea of trying to grow anything.

Faithfully,

John

January 25

Dear Mr. Olmstead:

You must help me. The ACTH treatments have already cost $90 and Father says he will not pay the bill, since he feels the college is in some way responsible for my condition. If I don't pay up soon, I will be sent back to my room.

Even a small refund on my room rent would help.

Hastily,

John Bakin '56

January 31

Dear Mr. Olmstead:

I am truly sorry about the skating rink, but I insist that I had nothing to do with it, being in the infirmary at the time, as Miss Dunn will verify. Undoubtedly some of the boys on my floor wanted to have a skating party for Carnival. I am also sorry about Smitty's broken hip, although he should have known he didn't have to go in to empty my wastebasket.

I appreciate your writing Father about the ACTH, for now he is coming up to see me.

Have a happy Carnival,

John S. Bakin '56

February 12

Dear Mr. Olmstead:

You will be happy to know that my problems are solved. I am having no more radiator troubles, and my health is improving steadily. Furthermore, Father is no longer quite so angry about paying for the ACTH, and the doctor says I may be able to stop taking treatments sometime.

The University of Miami has accepted me without taking finals and I am majoring in plant culture. I have some very rare onions and quite an interesting mushroom which I will have to send you someday.

Sincerely,

Toadstool Bakin '56

Dart (Dartmouth College)

JUST PLAIN HARD TO TAKE

BY LINCOLN

"Hello," I said as I pulled up a chair and sat opposite David Lopeheart. He sits by the window in the far corner of my political science class. I see him now and then around the College, a thin, stooped fellow who looks disinterested in everything. The dining hall was emptying; I had been the last person to come through the supper line. I grinned and thought of Charlie back in the shower with our clock fifteen minutes slow.

"Oh, hello," he said through a mouthful of food. His eyes were a little red and bulged; he looked as if he were half-way between a roaring binge and a hangover.

"Sort of early in the day to have a jag on, isn't it? Who's the girl?"

"No girl," he said. "It's my roommate." He sunk down toward his food and pushed a few potatoes through the side of his mouth. "Sometimes I get so disgusted I can't take it any more. Never a kind word for anybody. Cheats his way through every course he's taken here. Never studies; just sits around the room in his underwear, smoking and biting his fingernails and staring at the wall and laughing at his own private dirty jokes. You'd think the way he mopes around here that he'd just lost his last friend or his girl, but as far as I can make out, he hasn't got any friends, and I know he hasn't had a date since he's been here. He's always got a great story, though; last weekend he went into New York and came back with a bra. Still had the Macy's tag on the strap. He had a tremendous tale cooked up about some girl he met at the Big O who really went for big, husky guys like him. And I've never seen such a sloppy specimen of humanity in my life."

He was gesticulating broadly and had raised his voice quite a bit by this time. A couple of my friends at a corner table turned and looked at me quizzically.

"He's got the same routine about the army," Dave continued. "He wasn't in the army; he couldn't even pull caissons. His old man squeezed him into some cushy job with the Merchant Marine—so he tells us he's landed on every beach from North Africa to Iwo without batting an eye. You can see what I mean; having to room with a guy like that really gets on your nerves. His stories aren't even *funny*. He just puts them together to make people think he's an operator. He fools a few guys, but not me. He was a pilot in Italy till a few guys who were *really* pilots in Italy heard his story. Then it was the Bulge and Okinawa. You know how it is—I was in the Solomons myself and it makes me sore.

"Then when he gets away from here, he's a wheel on the RECORD and the *News* and fraternity row; that's when he can get time off from the track team."

I could see this was going to go on unless I were able to break him off. "What's your roommate's name?" I asked.

Without replying, he rose from the table. "I've gotta shove," he said. "Have to wash up so I can take some girl over to the Vernon dance tonight. Might see you there." I promised myself to avoid it at all costs.

As Dave shuffled slowly down the line of trays, Charlie came in, all decked out for his date, and sat in the chair Dave had just vacated. "Let me have your coffee," he said. "I have to put *something* down before we go out."

I pushed it toward him and nodded at Dave, who was then leaving the dining hall. "Do you know who that guy rooms with?"

"Who, him?" Charlie looked at the hunched figure retreating through the door. "He rooms alone, why?" *Yale Record*

SUTURE FANCY

BY GEORGE F. GITLITZ

May I please have your undivided attention, everyone, I'd like to tell you about my operations. You—you there—with the martini and the this-is-where-I-came-in expression, reaching for the corner of the page—not so impatient, please—yes, I *know* Irvin S. Cobb wrote about operations and that you've read him—yes, yes, I've read him, too—yes, of course, but, you see, Cobb *missed* the main act—don't you understand, he was asleep, fast asleep during the whole business—oh, I know he had a big dream, but that was nothing—that's right, now you're beginning to see, he missed the *operation*, the crux of the whole deal—yes, of course . . .

Here's the thing, I don't *have* operations, me personally, I mean—no one *has* them unless he's crazy or his doctor's a crackerjack salesman or he has to have a baby by Caesarian section or he's tired of his gall stones or something like that—no, I *watch* them. Now don't get me wrong, you won't see me walking around the campus with a straw, hoping someone will cut his finger, or spending my nights in a coffin with a wooden stake through my heart, it's just a diversion of mine. I'm a pre-med, it's instructive, it's interesting, I know a doctor who gets me into the hospital at home on my vacations, so I watch operations. Some guys collect things—me, I watch operations, see?

Surgery—ta ta ta ta—martial music—flashing steel—terse, whispered commands—masked faces—complete darkness except for a dazzling light above the limp, white-sheeted form on the table—Danny Kaye reaching for his fountain pen—tick, tock somewhere in the room—pulse, pressure, respiration, suture—if that's not the average guy's conception of an OR, I'll eat the oxygen mask, because it was certainly mine before I was taken to see my first gastro-jejunostomy. But oh, the shock of it all! No, not the kind you might have expected—they didn't have to scrape me off the floor and bring me around with spirits and make me put my head between my knees—it was their attitude that got me. There they were, some poor devil's very life in their rubber-gloved hands, and what do they do, they make small talk. Like women. Women.

I had no idea of what rituals to expect before they actually began—it seemed such a momentous occasion—a surgical operation—the very thought awed me. Would they say a prayer, invoke the Muse, what? The chief surgeon spoke, "How'd you make out in the game at the clambake last night, Ted?" Zzzzzt—my jaw dropped—in a twinkling he had slit the patient from stem to sternum—the first assistant's hemostats clicked in the red ooze. "Lost three, Bill, but I told Myrtle I won—you know, so she'll let me go next year, heh, heh." HEH HEH??? What was the big idea—this heh heh business? Didn't he comprehend the gravity of the situation? A man's life, think of it!! Soon they were inside the peritoneum. "Thought old Doc Winton would split when he rolled snake eyes for the third straight time." I was stupefied . . . "And was he plastered! He has a hemorrhoid at ten this morning, but I don't think he'll be able to tell one end of the knife from the other." His comrade winked slyly, "Or one end of the patient from the other." The nurses had hysterics.

I had to resign myself to it, and after a while even joined in with a squeaky, nervous, laugh of my own. After all, doctors were people, or at least resembled them. An hour and a half flitted by. The chief surgeon blurted out, exasperatedly, "I swear I don't know where the hell I am, Ted. This bird has his inferior mesenteric artery in six-hundred wrong places." This, I thought, was a fine kettle of fish. Didn't know where he was, eh? Maybe if he had done some reading-up on it the night before, instead of running off to the doctor's bake, he might not be flunking his practical quiz this morning, which flunk wouldn't go on *his* permanent record, oh no, on the patient's!! But while I fumed to myself, they safely located the vessel, and everything seemed to be going all right. They were even sweating, which gave me new confidence, for I figured that showed at least they were trying.

"I'm going to have to stop for a few minutes, Ted." The chief was taking off his gloves. "Cover it with hot wet tapes, and I'll be back as soon as I can. My wife gave me a laxative when I got home last night and—" He disappeared out the door. But I was ready for anything by this time, and swore I wouldn't let anybody dream that I was the least bit astonished. "Well," I tossed off flippantly, "I guess it happens to the best of us." The camaraderie of it all began to tickle me. It was like a friendly game of golf, complete with the caddy nurse ready to hand them their choice of irons for any difficult shot. They didn't even have to worry about slicing, in fact it was considered good form. The ball, of course, was the patient. He had to take all the licks, had to come along for all eighteen holes, couldn't enter into the conversation, and—well—if they lost him, there were always more. I wiped the cold sweat off my brow and waited the return of the pro.

Yale Record

TOW BARGAIN

BY C. HEIMSATH

Darling, are you happy?

Uh huh.

Isn't it wonderful to be up here in the white wonderland of nature?

Uh huh.

Isn't skiing a perfect personification and stimulation of all the most vital elements of human aspirations?

What?

Isn't skiing a perfect personification and stimulation of all the most vital elements of human aspirations?

Uh huh.

I just *love* being here in the out-of-doors. This is great; this is *life;* this is worth living!

Sit still, George.

To soar above all the earth! To be lifted out of the humdrum of all of life! This T-Bar is the greatest contraption. Just to think that with a few wires they can pull people up hills!

George, sit still.

A minute ago we were down there and now we're way way up . . . By Gad! Look how far up we are!

I know, George, that's what a T-Bar is for.

But we might fall. The wire might break—this is *dangerous!*

Relax, George.

Do these things ever break? *It's a long way down!*

(pause)

I'll bet they do break.

(pause)

I'm *sure* they break.

(pause)

Well answer me, they *do* break *don't* they?

No George, they don't break.

Promise? (pause) Darling? Darling?

Yes, dear.

What would happen if my skis crossed?

You'd fall off I guess. Now don't worry, George. Relax.

My skis feel as if they were crossing. (pause) I think my skis are going to cross. (pause) Help! My skis are crossing! I'm going to fall!

Your skis aren't crossed George. Stop worrying and look. Look at the view.

I don't wanna.

It's beautiful. It's nature's wonderland.

I don't wanna turn around.

You can see for miles.

I'm cold. Aren't you cold, darling? I'm cold as hell.

It's envigorating.

It's cold! I wanna get off. I don't like this anymore. Brrrrrr rrr.

We're almost at the top.

My feet are wet. I'm miserable way off here in the middle of nowhere. It's cold as hell.

It's nature's wonderland.

Oh shut up. I wanna go down now. Look how far up we . . . Gad!

(pause)

Brace yourself, it's time to get off.

(pause)

George!

(pause)

George!

(pause)

Help! Help! I'm down here in the snow!

I see you, George.

How do I get up? I can't move. My leg's broken. My leg's broken! Yes, I'm *sure* my leg is broken! Oh the horror of it all!

Can you move your legs?

Which one?

The broken one.

Sure, it doesn't hurt much. I'll make out. Go ahead, don't wait for me. I'll just die here in the snow.

Next to nature?

Oh shut up.

Now, George, get up and come up here.

No. I can take it! I'll take my fate like a man! I'll just freeze here and the dogs will eat my lifeless bones.

Well, goodby then, I'll see you later George.

Help! Help! Don't go! I'm a helpless cripple. It's cold here in the snow. My feet are wet. My blood runs cold in the sands of time.

Then get up.

Yes maam.

Now stand on your feet.

I'll try.

Now walk like this up to the station.

Darling. Darling, I feel better now. It's so wonderful having you here near me to help me. You love me, don't you?

Uh huh.

Oh darling, it *is* wonderful to be here with you. We really are in —uh—in—uh—a white heaven here above the fields and plains. We're together and all is beautiful! Look out there across the open handiwork of nature. Look out across nature and think . . . think . . . MY GAD! MY GAD! HOW DO WE GET *DOWN*?! *Yale Record*

ETC.

BY G. T. B.

cornelia agnes bedelia depew knew all there was to know about . . .
    life . . .
        and love . . .
            and S-E-X

and whenever someone mentioned that mrs somebodiruther had just received a visit from the stork, cornelia agnes bedelia depew just smiled a knowing smile, and winked a knowing wink, because she knew all there was to know about . . .

LIFE
AND LOVE . . .
AND SEX . . .

one day as miss depew was walking in the park she saw a MAN–
a man! said miss depew
don't get me wrong . . . miss depew had seen many a man in her day
BUT YES
but then this man was different from any man whom she had ever seen before
BUT YES
he was sitting quietly on a park bench feeding pigeons, but that isn't the point
BUT NO
for if one looked closely, and miss depew always did look closely at things especially men, one could see that this man was somewhat sans costume
NAKED
–i beg your pardon my good man, said miss depew, but you strike me as being somewhat sans costume
N*A*K*E*D
–you are very observant, said the man, for yes
I AM
–but why, asked miss depew, are you
N . . . A . . . K . . . E . . . D
–what, asked the man, have i to hide
miss depew smiled
A FRIENDLY SMILE
and winked
A FRIENDLY WINK
and said
WHAT A PERFECTLY CHARMING ATTITUDE
and immediately began to doff
HER CLOTHES–
HER CLOTHES––
HER CLOTHES–––
ALL OF THEM
–very companionable of you, said the man, im sure and he gave miss depew a friendly pat on her
DUFF
and gave her a well meaning slap on the

DUFF
—how dare you, said miss depew
but she wasn't angry
IN THE LEAST
and slapped him back, a friendly slap
ON . . .
THE . . .
DUFF . . .
but after some minutes of this, they decided they were getting
NOWHERE
that is to say
N-O-W-H-E-R-E
and they decided to give it up for better things to do
LET US
ventured the man
GO . . . TO . . . MY . . . APARTMENT
—a charming idea, said miss depew
A CHARMING
CHARMING
CHARMING
idea
and so they went
B*U*T
where sixth ave crosses chadwick blvd
THEY WERE STOPPED
tch . . . tch . . . tch . . .
BY a po-LEECE-man
—where do you think youre going, said the cop, as bare and
N-A-K-E-D
as the day you were born
—what, said they, have we to
BE ASHAMED OF
—ah, said the cop
OH!
a very commendable attitude
TO SAY . . .
THE . . .
LEAST
and immediately began to doff his clothes
ALL OF THEM

and gave them both a friendly
  PAT
and sent them on their way
when the apartment was reached, the man offered miss depew a drink
  WHISKEY OH!
when miss depew had finished her drink, he offered her another
  WHISKEY OH!
when miss depew was somewhat tight . . .
—id adore to, said miss depew, i simply l-u-u-ov- art
of any kind
  ETCHINGS OH!
especially etchings
  ETCHINGS O-O-O-OH!
—they, said the man, are in here, the
  B E D R O O M
—lead on, mcdough, said miss depew, and laughed a knowing laugh,
and winked a knowing wink,
for you see, cornelia agnes bedelia depew
  KNEW
all about life,
 and love,
     and—oh, yes, s-e-x
        ESPECIALLY S-E-X
so they went into the
  BEDROOM OH!
and then
  AND THEN
     A N D T H E N
cornelia agnes bedelia depew got the biggest, that is
to say the
  B . . . I . . . G . . . G . . . E . . . S . . . T
surprise of her life
  FOR THERE
on the wall
  WITH WHITE MATS . . .
     AND BLACK FRAMES . . .
        AND LOOKING VERY PRETTY
were twelve
  E-T-C-H-I-N-G-S
etchings? oh!

at that very moment cornelia agnes bedelia depew
LOST FAITH OH!
and realized she knew
NOTHING
about
LIFE . . .
OR LOVE . . .
OR . . . OH YES, S-E-X
and that changed her whole life
BUT YES
for she married the man, so that there would be someone
TO PROTECT HER
from the snares, so numerous, of
LIFE
and LOVE
and . . . S-E-X OH!
and they lived
BUT YES
nakedly ever after
AND HAD JUST OODLES OF NAKED
CHILDREN
for
what had they to hide? *Princeton Tiger*

A FRIEND INDEED

BY NEIL CHERNIAK

Little Mary Wiggins clapped her hands with joy and laughed so hard that her golden curls skipped merrily about her face when the Wiggins family arrived at the little red and white cottage they had just bought in the country. They were far away from the big city with its terrifying noises and here they would live forever and ever.

The first few days whirled by like a glorious dream. It was such fun for Mary to scale the tall elm that stood in the front yard. It was such fun to roll around on the smooth green grass, scamper up on the rough red rock, and wade in the gurgling brook while the sun beamed brightly upon her. It was such fun, that is, for the first few days.

But afterward it was different.

True, Mary still scampered, scaled, rolled, and waded, but it was no longer with real enthusiasm. For, after all, you can fool around in the country just so long. Besides, Mary felt lonely. In the city it was friends, parties, banquets, talk, eat, eat, eat, from sunup to sundown, but in the country it was different. There were no people to talk to except Mommy and Daddy, and you really couldn't call them people or banquets.

All this did not escape the notice of Mr. Wiggins.

"Our child is very sad," he said decisively. And off he went to the city in his automobile.

The next morning when Mary woke up, she found herself surrounded by toys. There were a jack-in-the-box and a doll and a box-in-the-jack and a llod. Although these would have brightened the heart of any other child, Mary wasn't cheered up even one bit. A toy isn't a friend. You can't cuddle it, talk to it, or . . . or eat it.

As the days passed Mary grew worse. She refused to go outside or eat the regular country fare, hot eggs and toast and butter, although they are very nourishing. Her little curls no longer skipped merrily about her face.

Mr. Wiggins said, "Our little girl misses the gay life of the city. I will bring her a gay city friend but not the terrifying noises of the city." And off he went in his automobile to the city.

When Mary woke up the next morning, there was her cute little plump little boy cousin. Mary bounded from the covers and grasping her little cousin by his chubby digits, rushed into the yard.

She played hard and played past breakfast time although she hadn't eaten in days. Mary nuzzled her cousin and her cousin nuzzled her. His fat little tummy shook happily.

Along about noon Mary remembered how hungry she was. The pit of her stomach ached and ached.

"Let's have a picnic," she told her cousin, and she dashed into the house. Soon she returned with a blanket and a cup and plates and knives and forks. They were going to have a jolly time.

"Are you hungry?" she asked her cousin. "I am. Let's eat."

She cuddled her soft, warm, cousin to her bosom. Then, setting a plate before her and daintily holding a knife between her fingers, she ate him. *Columbia Jester*

PRIDE OF THE AIR FORCE

BY SERGEANT H. K. BROWNING, JR.

Transcript of an interview between Lieutenant Roger Rudder, America's leading jet ace, just returned from Korea, the press, and Colonel Eager Beaver, Air Force Public Relations.

PRESS: Welcome home, Lieutenant Rudder. How do you feel about being back in the U.S.?

RUDDER: Pretty teed off!

COL. B.: Lieutenant Rudder means that his eyes were misty when the Golden Gate, one of the symbols of American Faith in the fight for freedom, loomed into sight.

PRESS: What is the first thing you are going to do in San Francisco?

RUDDER: Find a broad.

COL. B.: He intends to fly back to his home town and see his mom and all the other folks.

PRESS: Are they going to give you the Congressional Medal of Honor?

RUDDER: They damn well should!

COL. B.: Lieutenant Rudder's modesty disclaims any such high awards. Every man in battle deserves it as much as I, is what he said.

PRESS: How about the case of champagne that Colonel Weeval was going to give you for breaking Rickenbacker's record?

RUDDER: Awwww, he pooped out on it.

COL. B.: Lieutenant Rudder is a teetotaler. The price of a case of champagne was generously donated to Korean War Relief, at his request.

PRESS: How did you manage to shoot down all those planes?

RUDDER: I guess I'm just a pretty hot pilot.

COL. B.: Lieutenant Rudder is bashful and attributes all his success to a combination of teamwork, luck, and superior equipment.

PRESS: We understand that the Air Force program while on combat duty keeps you mentally and physically fit at all times. Is this true?

RUDDER: I don't know. Between noon and 7 A.M. I was either in the pad or full of Saki.

COL. B.: The calisthenics and rigid schedule keep our pilots in superior shape, is what the lieutenant means.

PRESS: We understand that the *esprit de corps* helps our pilots win a number of dogfights. How did you find the morale?

RUDDER: Cruddy! Nobody gave a damn.

COL. B.: What the lieutenant means is that spirit is one of the intangibles that gives us the upper hand in aerial combat.

PRESS: How about the Chinese?

RUDDER: Those meatheads? They don't know their rear from third base.

COL. B.: What the lieutenant means is that the quality of the Chinese airmen is declining.

PRESS: What about your mechanic; wasn't he pretty good?

RUDDER: That dumb SOB was born with his thumb in his mouth! It was a miracle I ever got off the ground.

COL. B.: Lieutenant Rudder is lavish in his praise of our courageous ground crews who work day and night to keep 'em flying.

PRESS: We understand that you are going to visit the factory where they made the F-86's you flew.

RUDDER: Yeah, if the bums aren't on strike. I'd like to get my hands on the jerk that welded his lunch bucket into the tail section of my ship.

COL. B.: He is proud of our American workers and the magnificent job they are doing to back the attack.

PRESS: We understand that you are going to teach gunnery for a while before going back.

RUDDER: Yeah, someone has to give the kids the ungarbled word. The stuff they taught me almost got my tail shot off.

COL. B.: Rudder is unqualified in his praise of the high degree of training that is given our pilots.

RUDDER: Sorry, boys, I've got to get out of here before the bars close and line up a dame for tonight.

COL. B.: Lieutenant Rudder can't wait to get back to a piece of his mother's apple pie, the girl he left behind, and the old Main Street where he played. *Stanford Chaparral*

PSYCHOLOGY 101 FINAL EXAMINATION

1. Let's pretend that Dr. Boguslavsky turned you into a little boy rat and put you all alone in a cage and didn't give you anything to eat or drink for twenty-four hours. At the end of that time, which of these would you like best to get your needle-sharp claws on?

a. a pan of water
b. a hunk of cheese
c. your mommy rat
d. a girl rat
e. Dr. Boguslavsky

2. A psychopath who has an Oedipus complex coupled with strong masochistic tendencies is most accurately referred to as:
a. screwy
b. loony
c. titched in the haid, like
d. all of these

3. Sigmund Freud:
a. wore a beard
b. had a bad mind
c. was quite annoyed at people crude who called him Frude
d. none of these

4. In a particular distribution curve the mean is to the right of the median which is to the left of the mode, even though the standard distribution is small. This means:
a. very little
b. nothing
c. not a damn thing
d. all of these

5. Which of the following statements is a dirty, rotten lie?
a. Rats are fun.
b. Psychologists are smarter than anybody.
c. Dreams really mean a lot.
d. The well-systematized, infallibly reliable SCIENCE of psychology is nothing more than mere ordinary "common sense."

6. If you were the dog Pavlov used in his famous conditioning experiment, what would you have done when old Ivan rang that bell in your ear?
a. salivate
b. propagate
c. micturate
d. regurgitate

7. Suppose you were a Freudian psychoanalyst and a gorgeous blonde

walked into your office and when she took off her overcoat she was absolutely naked. What would you do?

a. turn on my tachistoscope
b. give her a Rorschach
c. ask her to take a T.A.T.
d. test her Galvanic Skin Response
e. none of the above. *Cornell Widow*

PORTRAIT OF GENIE

BY D. D. S.

I was walking along the street the other day when I suddenly came to an old antique shop. When one comes to an old antique shop, one must go in it, especially if one is writing a story that starts out this way, so I went in it. The first thing I saw was a dusty old bottle on the shelf, and the next thing after that I saw was a dusty old man hobbling out toward me.

"Welcome to my little store," he said.

"What's that dusty old bottle for?" I asked, expecting him to say that there was a Genie in it, or something.

"There's a Genie in it, or something," he said.

I lifted the bottle up to my ear, and a voice came out of the bottle: "Let me out, let me out! Please let me out!"

"It wants to come out," I said.

"Well don't let it out in here, that's all I have to say. Can't have Genii running all about."

"Have what?"

"Genii."

"That plural of Genie, or something?"

"Don't be dumb," he said. "If you're going to open that thing, take it outside."

"Don't you want any money for it?" I said.

"Hell, yes!" replied the old man. "How much you got?"

I gave him all I had, about twenty-seven cents, which was more than the dusty old bottle was worth, but I collect bottles anyway, so it was all right.

When I got back to my room, my roommate was there. "What's that?" he said, pointing to the bottle.

"It's a bottle with a Genie in it."

"How much'd ya pay for it?"

"Twenty-seven cents."

"Cheap for a bottle with a Genie in it," he said. Then he left the room.

As soon as I was alone, I unplugged the bottle and out came a lot of black smoke which gradually shaped itself into a big fat man. He looked like an Arab.

"Are you the Genie?" I said.

"Whatja think I was, an illushun, or somethin'?" he said.

"I just haven't happened to have many Genii in my room before, so——"

"Many what?"

"Many Genii."

"That plural of Genie, or somethin'?"

"Don't be dumb," I said. "Now what about the three wishes I get?"

"Just make 'em, and I'll grant 'em," said the Genie.

So I sat down and thought for a moment and then I said, "Get me the most beautiful girl in the world!"

"Ya gotta close yer eyes a minute and a half, or I can't do it," said the Genie.

So I shut my eyes for a minute and a half, and when I opened them, there, sitting on my bed, was a big, voluptuous, sexy, blond girl. She was flirting with me and playing around with her stockings. Seductive music flowed through the air, the odor of perfume filled my nostrils. Then my roommate walked in.

"Who's she?" said my roommate.

"The Genie brought her," I said.

"All right, all right, I can take a hint," said my roommate, and walked out.

I turned to the big, voluptuous, sexy, blond girl. "Doing anything tonight?" I said.

"Huh?" she said.

"I said doing anything tonight?"

"I dunno," she said.

"How about a dance?" I said.

"I don't know how, ain't never learned," she replied.

"Movie?" I said.

"Huh?"

"Want to go to a movie?"

"No," she said, "I can't understand them."

"God, you're dumb!" I said.

"You said it!" she answered. "I sure am pretty, but God I'm dumb."

With that the door suddenly opened and two proctors stared in at us.

"What's she doing in there?" one of them said, shining a flashlight in my face for effect.

"The Genie brought her."

"Yeah, yeah, I said what's she doing in there?"

I could see there was no use arguing. Proctors are so set in their ways. So I said, "I wish you would both go up in a puff of smoke."

The two proctors went up in a puff of smoke, and I knew I now had only one more wish left.

At that moment the Genie came in through a window.

"Where've you been?" I said.

"Been over to visit my parents in Arabia," answered the Genie. "I didn't think you'd need me for a while, so I—"

Suddenly he saw the girl.

"Hi, baby!" he said.

"Hi, big boy!" she answered.

"Cut it out!" I said. "I'm frustrated enough as it is without you two carrying on!"

"You still got another wish left," said the Genie.

So I sat down and thought. "Can't think of anything else," I said. "I thought the girl would be nice, but she's too damn stupid!"

"I dunno 'bout that!" said the Genie. He was eying the girl suspiciously. She was eying him suspiciously. They just stood there eying each other. Silly stuff.

"However," I said, "there's a freshman issue of the *Tiger* coming up, and I can't think of a thing to write for it. Give me an idea!"

"Granted!" he said, and with that, he started to smoke up again. "Come on in, baby," he said to the girl, and suddenly the big voluptuous, blond, sexy girl started to smoke up too, and they both went into the bottle, quick as a wink.

I picked up the bottle and put it on the mantelpiece. Just then my roommate came in.

"Where'd she go?" he said.

"She's in the bottle with the Genie," I said, pointing to the mantel, and then I took out a piece of typewriter paper and started to type.

I am almost finished typing now. My roommate is over by the mantel, looking into the bottle. He is blushing all over. *Princeton Tiger*

SO YOU WANT TO GO TO MEDICAL SCHOOL

BY GEORGE F. GITLITZ

Pleased, I'm sure, Dr. O'Rourke–charmed, Dr. Jones,–Doctor–Doctor, how do you do–yes, thanks, I will–no, thanks, never touch them–what?–well, beer and occasionally a cocktail, but never–well–

Always wanted to be one, sir, ever since last year–sort of a divine calling–yeah, that's it–from Heaven–gotta help those sick people–poor people–public service, you know? Yeah–

Oh, you went to Yale, too, Doctor? *Sure,* I had Zilch for Zo–who didn't–ha ha–*sure* he told us that one–oh? When *is* your reunion sir? –yes, great place, Yale, nice the way the alumni stick together–my Dad's was last year–yeah–

I don't know, sir, it won't help the ground troops, much, and think of all those innocent South Koreans–always gotta think of the poor innocent people–the sick, the wounded–that's why I want to be a–

Sure I like 'em–oh, I don't know–Vassar, Wellesley, even from high school sometimes–personality that counts–oh, dancing, plays, opera, ballgames, even parked cars, sometimes–

I suppose it's all right for the English, Doctor, but over here we have to protect free enterprise–sure–oh, I'll be right behind the AMA if you'll only let me into your med school–of course money never meant much to me personally–sort of a mission with me, you know–but I suppose there are certain advantages–

Well, Doctor, I don't think we should blame Acheson for *everything*–

Majoring in English, sir–want to be a *cultured* doctor–too many uncultured ones around–no personal offense, sir–have to have *something* to talk about with your wife–

My tonsils, that's about all–good enough for the Army, heh heh–chickenpox, measles–

Petting? Why–why–well–sure, of course–

Nah, the sight of blood doesn't bother me a bit–just when it's mine–

Quant? Loved it, especially the labs–kept me from wasting too many afternoons on the tennis courts–easy to get into bad habits, you know –yeah, organic's fun, too–

A third cousin and two great-uncles by marriage–I guess medicine just runs in my blood–yeah, that's it, you might almost say it's hereditary–

A little swimming and squash, too—gotta keep in shape—"mens sana in corpus infinitum," I always say—

Yes, I realize you have some job picking 65 out of 2957—I'm afraid most of us applicants just don't appreciate what you're going through—

The Yale Record, sir, may I sell you a subscription?—sort of relieves the tension of studying, you know—

It's hard to say, Doctor, but Princeton's losing a lot of her forward wall, too—never can tell—

About seven hours a day, mostly in the Library—

Darn nice pool, yes—a lot of squash courts, too—

Pre-marital what?—well—I'll tell you—

Mostly classical, Doctor, although I suppose jazz has its place—

Oh, maybe specialize—don't know—maybe pediatrics—worked a couple of summers at a boys' camp—learned to love kids—damned shame when they're sick—yeah, kids—little tykes—gotta help the sick ones—maybe OB, who knows?—

Cancer? That's another thing—maybe I'll find the cure—have this vision, you know—maybe I'm the guy—just gotta have a chance—

No, sir, frankly I *don't* think movies are better than ever—

Yes, Doctor, I *have* heard the one about—

Well, Doctor, it's been my pleasure—Doctor—Doctor Jones, glad to have met—I certainly hope so—remember about cancer—I may be the one—yes, sir—thanks again—if I only have a chance—maybe multiple sclerosis—who knows— *Yale Record*

PIN CRAZY

"I think that your frat pin is just the most beautiful thing in the whole wide world," cooed the darling Southern gal. "Look, Alfie, how tonight's moon resembles the glowing crescent on your chest."

"That's no crescent. That's where I spilled my jello. My pin's over here."

Alfie opened his jacket and exposed the badge over his heart. Then he re-buttoned his jacket and walked over to the edge of the swimming pool. The moonlight fell squarely on the smooth water and bounced off in galaxies of diamonds sparkling in the night.

"Isn't it romantic out, Alfie?" Anna Belle snuggled against him.

"Look how that bright star seems to be kissing the moon. Just like your pin, isn't it, Alfie?"

"Yup."

"Alfie, is it true that the boys in your house wear their pins on their pajamas? If I had one—I would. The moon would never sink, nor the star go out, if . . ."

"It's not a moon, it's a crescent. Don't you think it's getting chilly? I mean we better go in now, all right?"

Anna Belle rubbed her soft, cool cheek against Alfie's. "How can you be cold with that wonderful pin sending its fraternal warmth through you. But, Alfie, honest, I'm freezing honest."

"Want my jacket?"

"No, Alfie, it's not your jacket. It's hard for me to explain just what," Anna Belle said, fingering his pin.

"I understand," said Alfie, seeing the true significance of her actions, "It's my pin you're after."

Gently he took her arm—and broke it at the wrist. "Never do that again," he said. *Star and Crescent*

A FABLE

BY DARYL MASECK

Once upon a time in the Province of O-Hei-Yo, there met on the campus of the Provincial University, two student officials. Quoth the gentleman to the lady, "Oh, lofty holder of office, what noble organization do you serve, and what are its purposes?"

"I" said she, "am High Potentate of the W.S.G.A., the Women's Self Governing Association. With freedom and liberty we determine what hours we shall keep, and where, when and what social functions we shall have."

"And I," said he "am High Potentate of ROTCSGA, the ROTC Self Governing Association. With freedom and liberty we determine the style and color of clothing we are to wear, when and where we shall go to class, and see that our chosen teachers speak to us with respect."

Whereat both laughed boisterously. *Sundial*

CONVERSATION PIECE

BY GOODMAN

"Hello, is Tony Anderson there? Oh, that you, Tony? This is Cameron. Cameron Carter. From the Dramat. How do you like Yale so far? Well, marvelous. In case you're wondering why I'm calling, we heard about you over at the Dramat and I thought you and I could get together for a drink sometime. What are you doing, say around fiveish? We need fresh blood like yours on the Dramat, you know."

"I won't be able to devote much time to the Dramat this year, Cameron. You see, I'm going to be an engineer, and——"

"An engineer! An engineer you say! Oh, I see. Yes. Well, to get down to the point, I want to hear all about you. So just tell me everything. Everything."

"Well, I worked on the show last year at Deerfield. And I worked with a stock company this past summer for a while, but I——"

"I know what you're going to say, so just don't. Good God. Don't tell me about stock. I know about it. And I love it. So don't tell me the hours were tough and that you didn't get to act. So you didn't get to act. Why, stock is the maternity ward of Broadway. That's what it is, the maternity ward of Broadway. Why, I was talking to Marlon just last . . . do you know Marlon? Marlon Brando?"

"No. No, I don't."

"Oh, there I go again. Off on a tangent. Aren't I terrible? Now, go ahead and tell me all about yourself. I'm really interested. Maybe it's a weakness. My being so interested in people. But, you know, the way I figure it, the more people you know, the more you know about life, and the more you know about life, the more you know about acting. That's just the way I feel about it. Of course, out in Hollywood they don't think like that. Good God! Everytime I think about Hollywood I am nearly sick. Sick. Really sick. Have you ever thought about Hollywood?"

"In what way?"

"You'd make piles of money, but it would simply RUIN your art! Not that I've seen you act, because I haven't, but I can tell, no, I can feel that you have the soul for it. And that's what's important. The soul. So a person has technique! Technique, for heaven's sake! So what? Too bad we're not doing Candida. You'd be great as Marchbanks. Ever played Marchbanks? You should. Do all the parts you can. Walk-ons and just anything. It all adds up. Experience. That's what counts. You want to be a good actor, don't you? So what do you do. You get experience."

"I've never acted."

"Oh. Oh. Oh, that so? Well, that sheds a new light on the matter. I thought you were an actor. Like I. You know, Claire, that's my mother, I always call her Claire, always have, as a matter of fact, well, Claire took me out to Hollywood when I was nine. They wanted to sign me right up. You know, like a male Shirley Temple. I could sing, dance, cry, God, I could do anything. They were dying to have me. Well, Claire said I had to get an education first. Naturally, I was simply livid at the time, and I said to Claire, I said, Claire, are you out of your head? But you know? She was right. Because I'll have so much more to offer now. And there's a time for everything.

"Where were we? OH! Go on and tell me more about yourself. You said that you didn't act. What do you . . . don't TELL me! You write! You write beautiful plays! I knew that's what it was you did! Ah, to write! It's the only thing. To express ideas in words. To spread all your feelings out on paper for people to read and hear and see. Ah, to write! That's really the only thing. What are actors? Puppets. Nothing more and nothing less. Puppets. They did one of my plays last year, you know. Wish you could have seen it. I never brag, but people went wild when they saw it. They simply raved and raved for months. It all took place in this man's brain. Very modern. But go ahead and tell me about your plays."

"I don't write either."

"Well what on God's sweet earth DO you do?"

"I, well, I always did want to be an assistant stage manager or something like that. The only thing I've done so far is pull curtain."

"Pull the curtain. Oh. Ah, I see. Well, what I mean is, that's fine. Uh . . . I . . . well, where would the theatre be if there weren't people to pull curtains? I ask you that."

"Yeah. I see what you mean."

"Well, you think about it, Tony. I've loved talking to you, and we'll have to get together some other time. I really have to go. 'By now."

"Good-by." *Yale Record*

HARDHEADED ARAGONESE

BY PHILIP SHAHIN

Long ago the Aragonese were known in Spain as the most stubborn of people. They prided themselves on this trait and came to believe themselves the most hardheaded people in all the world. In time, Don Fernando Lopez emerged as the most hardheaded of all the people of Aragon.

Directly opposed to the stubborn, hardheaded people of Aragon were the farmers of Navarre. They were gentle folk who cared more for their fiesta than they did for displaying the strength of their skulls. The most docile, easygoing, and agreeable of all these farmers of Navarre was Luis Antonio—and it was Luis who opposed Don Fernando for the hand of lovely Maria.

One day a group of the peasants of Aragon met in the village inn. Don Fernando, to impress Maria, began to boast of the hardness of his head. Finally, seeing that Maria was not impressed by his words, he offered proof. He would, he declared, drive a nail through the brick partition separating two rooms, using his head for a hammer.

The peasants were excited and bets were laid. A long nail was placed against the wall and Don Fernando started to butt it with his head. Onlookers were amazed to see the nail sink into the wall with each blow.

Suddenly, when only about an inch of the nail was left, its progress stopped. Don Fernando butted harder, but it was in vain. He banged ferociously, but the nail would move no more. Exasperated, facing defeat and ridicule, he shouted, "The nail must be through! Go to the other room and see."

His friends opened the door and gasped. There, tilted back in a chair fast asleep, with his head against the spot where the nail should have appeared, sat Luis Antonio, the easygoing and docile farmer of Navarre. *Caravan*

TRUE ANALYSIS OF A UTOPIA U. COED

If She's a

FRESHMAN	SOPHOMORE	JUNIOR	SENIOR
She blushes at naughty jokes.	She smiles at naughty jokes.	She laughs at naughty jokes.	She tells naughty jokes.
She says, "Oh, please stop that."	She says, "Oh, please stop."	She says, "Oh, please."	She says "Oh."
She wants to marry a football player.	She wants to marry a movie star.	She wants to marry a capitalist.	She wants to marry a man.
She thinks a college education leads to things social, cultural, and academical.	She thinks a college education leads to things social and cultural.	She thinks a college education leads to things social.	She thinks a college education leads to things.
She reads *What Every Girl Should Know.*	She reads *How to Win Friends and Influence People.*	She reads *The Art of Love.*	She reads *The Care and Feeding of Infants.*
She won't date a boy who has ever had a drink.	She won't date a boy who just had a drink.	She won't date a boy who has had over one drink.	She won't date a boy unless he drinks.
She thinks things learned in college leave one intelligent.	She thinks things learned in college leave one fairly intelligent.	She thinks things learned in college leave one intelligent enough.	She thinks things learned in college leave one.

She tells her mother everything.	She tells her roommate everything.	She tells her diary every-thing.	She doesn't tell a damn thing.
She likes to smooch.	She likes to smooch.	She likes to smooch.	She likes to smooch.
She thinks all boys are nice.	She thinks some aren't nice.	She thinks most aren't nice.	She thinks none are nice.
She drinks cokes on a date.	She drinks pink ladies on a date.	She drinks highballs on a date.	She drinks anything, anytime, anywhere.

Corn Shucks

PARDON ME, MADAM, I THOUGHT YOU WERE A TURNSTILE

My mother and father couldn't afford a baby, so they had me. I was born with my mother's features and my father's fixtures. Six days after I was born we moved out West. It was easier than explaining to the neighbors. We settled in a little town called Indian Head. It's on the other side of Buffalo.

Our family had more trouble than a soap opera. They could never afford to buy me shoes, so they painted my feet black and laced up my toes. But hardships have always plagued my life. Why, at the age of two I was left an orphan—and at the age of two what would I do with an orphan? And I can still remember the time I learned how to swim. I was one of a set of twins, and when we were born our father looked at us and said, "Let's drown the ugly one." And that's how I learned to swim.

At the age of four I had white hair. I had a nearsighted nurse and she kept putting the talcum powder on the wrong place. It was soon after this that I lost my parents. What a crap game! I missed Dad in particular. He's the one who really taught me how to save. All during my childhood he showed me how to put quarters in a little black box. I was seventeen before I discovered it was the gas meter. But I soon won them back. My parents, not the quarters.

Then I went to kindergarten. I didn't hate to go to kindergarten, but of course I was different from the other five-year olds. I was twelve. I was the only one who ever flunked kindergarten. Well, as a child the kitchen sink fell on my head and that would be a drain on anyone. But what fun I had playing crap while the teacher called the roll. And it was even more fun fermenting my Pablum. I became the boy bootlegger of P.S. 17. But the teacher caught me at it and told my dad. I can remember how he said, "Listen, stupid!"—he always called me Listen—and then took me up and introduced me to the Board of Education.

But I later made him proud of me. Our class gave a play called *The Life of Abraham Lincoln* and I was picked to play Lincoln. I was the only one in the fourth grade with a beard. But I didn't care. It was a good place to hide jelly beans. It was at this time that adolescence leered at me. Adolescence—that's the period in life when a girl's voice changes—from NO to YES. My mother began teaching me the facts of life gradually. She started with artificial flowers. I was at that awkward age. Too young to leave at home alone and too old to trust with baby sitters. Too short for transoms and too tall for keyholes. Too young to get a job and too old to be a juvenile delinquent. But I finally grew up—what other way *could* I grow?

Leaving public school, I went to City High, but they sent me home to sober up. It was at that time that my father told me not to go to burlesque shows because I'd see something I shouldn't see. So at the first chance I got I went to one and I did see something I shouldn't—my father. But I was really teacher's pet, which was a lot of fun. You wouldn't know unless you've petted with a teacher. She was a sweater girl but she certainly was a good teacher. I guess it was because she outlined things so clearly. Every time she asked a question I was the first one to raise a hand. By the time I got back the question was always answered.

Finally I got out of high school. I had been in the twelfth grade so long the pupils were beginning to think I was the teacher. So I enrolled in Arwhee Normal. It was really sad the day I left—everyone crying—they thought they'd never get rid of me. And I'll never forget those last words my father said to me, "Rover," he said—he always wanted a dog instead of a son—"you're going to go a long way." And to make sure, he nailed the door of the boxcar shut.

Then I entered college and soon I was rubbing shoulders with Ph.D.'s, LL.D.'s and B.V.D.'s. In fact, I always had my nose stuck in a book. I couldn't afford a bookmark. I was a two-letter man at college—then somebody told me about chlorophyll. Some fellows got to be quarterback on the football team but I was just nickle back on the bottle. Then came six-packs. My biggest thrill came when I joined a fraternity. The first night they had a beer-drinking contest. I didn't win it but I came in sickened. Webster says that taut means tight. Well, I guess I was taut quite a bit while in college.

But the greatest thrill I had at college was my love life. It was there that I met my first girl—Liverlips Latour. I can see her now, sitting on the campus with a straw in her mouth, siphoning gasoline out of a lawn mower. I went right up and tried to kiss her on the forehead but all I got was a bang in the mouth. Every time I'd kiss her she'd slap my face. I broke her of that habit though. One day she slapped my face while I was chewing tobacco.

Finally I did steal a kiss. That was like taking the bumper when I could have had the whole car. But it was the hottest kiss I've ever had. She forgot to take the cigarette out of her mouth. I remember how I used to clutch at her and she'd break away. Then I'd clutch at her again and she'd break away. My clutch was all right but my brakes were slipping. Each night I'd hold her and she'd whisper sweet nothing doings in my ear. It was getting so that every time I saw her I'd say, "Get thee behind me Satan—and push!"

What a girl! Her lipstick is kissproof; her stockings are runproof; and her breath's 96 proof. Some people read the Kinsey report—she just reminisces over it. One look at her and boys become men. Ten minutes with her and you can write your memoirs. I'm telling you, a girl like that can be your downfall—if you're lucky. Then I asked her to be my mistress, but she reclined to do so. She's descended from a long line her mother shouldn't have listened to.

But I had to forget my love affair. Dad had become a problem at home. He was wanted by Alcoholics Anonymous, dead or alive! He could really hold his liquor. Why, you couldn't get it away from him. So I quit school and went back home. The day I arrived Dad got so drunk he swallowed a dictionary. We fed him Epsom salts for a week but we couldn't get a word out of him. Another time he put his false teeth in upside down and before we could stop him, he chewed up half his head. Then we tried to reason with him. But he said if he gave up liquor, he was afraid he'd never be able to break himself of Sen-Sen. Then one night when we weren't watching, he sneaked out and drank a quart of shellac and died. What a lovely finish. *Gargoyle (University of Michigan)*

SINE OF LOVE

I saw her as a most beautiful conglomeration of ellipses, parabolas, and sine waves in perfect symmetry as she slithered into the living room. I sat confidently on the sofa sketching free body diagrams. I felt the firm pressure of her thigh against mine as she sat down beside me. I would judge its modulus of resilience to be about 0.034 in-lb. I felt her warm breath (approx. 102.4 degrees F.) on my cheek as she said, "Have I kept you waiting too long, Zerxes?" "Only 34 minutes and 16.2 seconds," I replied, as I subconsciously estimated the tensile strength of her sweater to be at least 4000 psi.

She ran her soft hand through my hair (generating some 3 x 10 statcoulombs) and asked, "What did you bring for me?" as she eyed the long object in my pants pocket. . . . "Oh," I said quickly, "that's not for you, that's my slide rule." I withdrew it dramatically and adeptly flicked the ash from her cigarette with the slide. "Are all engineers as strong, calm, and romantic as you are, Zerxes?" I was mentally computing the acceleration of my heartbeat to be 14.7 thumps per second. "Of course they are," I said, as I thought, Engineers—romantic——? Even I had learned in GE 711 that a woman is nothing but a slow-moving man with a lower specific center of gravity. . . . She might hypnotize some men with her curvilinear attractions, but not me—an ENGINEER!

I observed her coldly (114.7 degrees F.). She leaned over me and kissed me lightly—I glanced down at my lapel only to see a molten mass that had once been my Tau Beta pin. She watched in admiration as I casually put the lighted end of my cigarette in my mouth and blew the smoke from between my toes. . . . I rose with a masculine air of indifference and stalked from the room on my hands.

The Syracusan (Exchange Issue)

THE ENORMOUS PACKAGE

BY JOHN H. UPDIKE

Mrs. Breedle was sweeping shattered Christmas bulbs into the fireplace, and her daughter, Judith, was fluffing up the artificial snow on the tree when Mr. Rapport rapped on the window. Mr. Rapport, the mailman, had a large, red face with a yellowed mustache, and he always gave Mrs. Breedle a start. She opened the window. The breeze tumbled several more bulbs to the floor.

"Morn, Miss Breel," Mr. Rapport enunciated. "Got a thing for you."

"A thing?"

"Normous thing. Biggst ever devilvered." He smiled vacantly.

"Where is this, uh, thing, Mr. Rapport?"

"Put it on yer porch."

"*Our* porch?" Mrs. Breedle blurted in spite of herself.

"Dint put on somebody elses, thets for sure," the postman snapped. "Whood want a thing like that. It's ugly as blazes. Never misdevilvered anything in my life, not since I had this route."

"I'm sorry," Mrs. Breedle said. "I didn't mean . . ."

The mailman went on. "Next biggest thing ever I devilvered turned out to be a keg of spurts."

"Spurts?" Mrs. Breedle wondered why he didn't leave. His work was done.

"Spurts, I said. Spurts, sprites, spirruts. Don't matter how you say it; adds up to the same thing—*elkohol!*"

Mrs. Breedle slammed shut the window and raced through the house to the front porch. The package was immense. It towered over Mrs. Breedle, and she knew that she was a good-sized woman. It was roughly the shape of a coffin, but had several irregular protuberances. The entire thing was enveloped in red paper festooned with miniature representations of the Nativity and was tied with thin, green rope.

"Ugly, ain't it?" Mr. Rapport chirped as he romped around the side of the house.

"What am I going to do?" she said.

"Got me," he said. "I sure don't want it." He stamped off down the walk, his galoshes jingling, and Mrs. Breedle noticed with satisfaction that the neighbor's dog chased him for fully half a block.

"Mommy, I'm scared," Judith said.

Mrs. Breedle rested her hand on her daughter's head. "Don't worry, dear. Daddy will take care of this."

"What on God's awful earth is it?" Mr. Breedle bellowed. The package had nearly toppled on him when he came up the porch steps, and he was usually irritable before supper.

Mrs. Breedle was too tired even to rise from her chair. "Please, Frank, don't shout. The children will hear, and it's the day before Christmas. But what shall we do with it? Judith and I couldn't move it through the door."

"Have the kids haul it into the yard and build a snowman around it."

"Frank, please. Be reasonable."

"Well, where did it come from? We can figure this out."

"The postmark said 'Phoenix, Arizona'."

"Who do we know from Phoenix?"

"That's it. No one; that is, unless you count Elsie Getch. Her folks lived in Arizona."

"Getch, Getch? Oh, *Giggles* Getch! Your old roommate. How could I forget her. Buck teeth, glasses, always wore flannel." He laughed, and Mrs. Breedle felt reassured by his mirth.

"You know, Frank, she once had a kind of crush on you. She always thought I took you away from her. Ever since you took her out as a stunt for initiation into that frat. It's silly, but she was awful about it, and once spilled ink on my party dress the day before the formal. She was sure she'd win you back."

Mr. Breedle stood thoughtfully by the mantel, occasionally smiling, and eventually said "Let's open the damn thing now."

"We can't, Frank. It's specifically labeled, Do Not Open Until Christmas."

He was about to reply when Judith ran in, screaming, "Daddy! Come quick. A whole lot of bad boys are throwing snowballs at the thing on our porch."

Mr. Breedle cursed and disappeared through the door. Mrs. Breedle heard sounds of youthful laughter and violence. Once a snowball sailed through the open door and rolled to within inches of her feet.

After many minutes had plodded by, her husband returned, accompanied by Mr. Cuppy, a big man from down the street. "Jim helped me chase the little brats away," Mr. Breedle said. "We think the package had better be brought into the house. The carollers might get it tonight if we don't."

"Don't get up, Mrs. Breedle," Mr. Cuppy smiled, waving his hand. "My kids are outside and we're going to help Frank move the thing inside. It's better that way."

Mrs. Breedle smiled vaguely. She didn't alter that expression for the next hour, while the men tugged and yanked until, with a huge splintering, the package burst through the door aperture and crashed to the living room carpet.

"Somebody close the door," Mr. Breedle panted.

"Can't," one of Cuppy's boys replied. "Door came off its hinges."

"Well," Mr. Cuppy said. "The thing's safe inside. It's better that way. Better post somebody at the door tonight to see nobody steals it."

Mrs. Breedle kept watch until three in the morning, when her husband's shift began, then she went to bed. Her sleep was tormented by a nightmare of monsters and insects pouring from an enormous red package. At seven, she was wakened by a hubbub of voices downstairs.

"Let's go!"

"C'mon, open it up."

"My daughter hears things moving inside!"

"Give me a chance to see."

"Let's go, Mr. Breedle."

She put on a bathrobe and stumbled downstairs. Nearly fifty neighbors were milling about in the living room. Several children were playing King-of-the-Mountain on the porch, and one tot was tracing faces with his finger on the frosty panes. Frank was nearly frothing; she saw him slap a small woman who had begun to undo the ribbon.

Ignoring the advances of the Cuppy girls, Mrs. Breedle elbowed through the mob to her husband. "We had better open it now, Frank," she said. "It's Christmas."

The crowd became silent as the two of them stripped away the multiple layers of paper and cardboard that composed the bundle's outer shell. As they pulled off the excelsior, several crusts of bread and empty fruit juice cans tumbled out. A cheer went up. A flannel hat was revealed and, below that, a face. The heap moved and a trembling figure emerged. Someone in the crowd screamed, but the form held its ground, squinting at the light and baring its teeth at the crowd that pressed around it.

Mrs. Breedle made the first move. "Why Elsie Getch," she cried. "How sweet you are to come! And how have you been? Why it's been . . ."

Elsie, dazed but game, cut Mrs. Breedle short and looked her hard in the eye. "Where's Frank?" she said. *Harvard Lampoon*

TWENTY-FOUR, FORTY AND BUST

BY J. H. DOLE

Everyone, I suppose, is aware of the fact that men like to look at women. Perhaps far too few people are conscious, however, of the impressive scientific advances that have taken place in this field over the past few years. That this is so was brought home to me in striking fashion a weekend or so ago.

I was dining in one of the colleges with two acquaintances of mine, both engineer majors—Harvey Bloom, a sharp-eyed native of New York, and bald Stanley Hemp, Jr., of Little Creek, Virginia. Both men had impressed me in the past as being observant, yet of average intelligence. Certainly they had given no promise of the acuteness that was to be displayed that evening.

We were sitting near the kitchen, talking in desultory fashion and idly spooning the contents of our fruit compote, when a blonde girl in a grey suit swung by, bearing a tray before her.

"733," said Harvey Bloom.

"632," said Stanley Kemp, Jr. They both went on eating their fruit compote.

"I beg your pardon," I said. "Did you say something?"

"Why, yes," said Harvey, looking up. "I said '733,' and then Stanley said '632'." He saw by my expression that I did not understand. "Look, I'll explain it to you," he said. "It's our system. You noticed, of course, the young lady who just passed by?"

"Why," I replied, "I guess I remember her vaguely—strawberry blonde, about five feet four, hundred ten pounds, grey cotton tweed suit, nylon stockings, black patent leather pumps with—"

"Fine," interrupted Harvey. "Now, may I point out to you that your observations are at best superficial? It was precisely this need to strike to the core of the matter, to extract the essence of woman, that prompted Stanley and me to evolve our decimal system of female observation." He paused, and smiled proudly. Stanley took over.

"The first digit in the number evaluates the figure of the girl in question," he explained patiently. "Based, of course, on a perfection scale of ten. This rating takes into consideration proportion, grace of contour, and, shall we say, fluidity of motion."

"I think I'm beginning to see," I said. "Harvey gave that blonde a seven, but you only gave her a six because you didn't think she was stacked enough for a seven."

Harvey frowned. "The beauty of numbers lies in their purity," he said. "They are above common expressions which tend to be vulgar." Harvey is about the most serious engineer major I ever saw.

"The second digit refers to facial construction," said Stanley hastily. "Shape of lips, placement of eyes, tilt of nose, and so forth. All blended into an aggregate whole. Personal opinion naturally plays a large part here. It was quite unusual that Harvey and I should both assign a value of three to that girl."

"She was sort of a pig," I admitted. Harvey frowned again, and I apologized.

"The last digit," explained Harvey, "is what might be called the summation. Roughly, it comprises the total sex-appeal of the girl, the impression that she makes upon you.

"In other words," I remarked, "whether or not the kid rocks you."

Harvey ignored me, and went on to comment upon a few of the finer aspects of successful observation. "The selection of seats is of course important," he said. "By the law of frequency distribution the closer you sit to the kitchen exit, the better. For naturally if you sit at the further end of the dining hall the number of subjects who will come your way will be greatly diminished."

"Another point," said Stanley. "We consider it in bad taste to stare. A subtle examination while pretending to be absorbed in your food will eliminate the possibility of the subject's acting in a self-conscious manner."

Just then a soft-haired brunette in a pink sweater undulated her way past our table.

"989," said Harvey Bloom.

"999," said Stanley Kemp, Jr.

Harvey looked at me and shook his head. "I'm afraid that you've missed the entire point," he said. Well, maybe I had. I guess I don't have much of a mind for figures. The mathematical kind, that is.

Yale Record

IT PAYS TO KNOW A LOT OF REAL GOOD WORDS

BY WILSON HINCKLEY

Using long or obscure words is the easiest way to impress some people. This test will show you how little you really know about words.

If you want to be known as an intellectual but can't afford a beret, it will pay you to learn these peachy words.

1. BUT (butt)—A: *derrière.* B: except. C: nevertheless. D: the capital of Montana.
2. CRAPULOUS (crap' you lus)—A: full of beer. B: glib. C: mendacious. D: having thrown snake eyes.
3. ACRIMONY (ak' ri mo ni)—A: spaghetti with a hole in it. B: the high cost of living alone. C: the relationship existing between married persons. D: rent paid for the use of land.
4. ASCEND (ass end')—A: mount. B: soar. C: sore. D: but.
5. STEATOPYGOUS (stee a to py' gus)—A: morbidly sensitive to carillon bells. B: having eleven toes. C: having a large ascend. D: having eleven toes on each hand.
6. THE (the)—A: definite article. B: indefinite article. C: articulate defamy. D: warm tea in glasses.
7. BACCHUS (bahk' us)—A: wooden container. B: Greek god of wine. C: independent god of wine. D: in reverse order.
8. RED (red)—A: professor. B: student. C: government employee. D: a color.

ANSWERS

1. BUT—A: The capital of Montana is Helena.
2. CRAPULOUS—A: Full of beer, from the Latin *crapula,* intoxication. This word is not to be used in drinking with strangers.
3. ACRIMONY—B: From the Anglo-Saxon *aecer,* "acre," and the Old French *moneie,* "money." Thus, acres of money, or the sum paid to one's departing spouse.
4. ASCEND—A: to mount, from the Latin *ascendere.* The practice of ascending was so called because the Romans mounted their asses from that end, a trick they learned in Gaul.
5. STEATOPYGOUS—C: Especially in females.
6. THE—If you had to look at this answer you'll never pass the English achievement test and may as well quit school.
7. BACCHUS—D: Reversed, or hindside forward. Often seen in the form *bacchuswards.*
8. RED—D: It will surprise many people to learn that red is, in an archaic sense, an innocent sort of color, somewhere between orange and purple. *Flatiron (University of Colorado)*

MR. RUMPLE HAS ARRIVED

BY DIEBOLD

A young man appeared at the door.

"Rumple!"

"Professor Grisley. Not intruding, am I?"

"No, Rumple. Certainly not. Please come in," said Professor Grisley genuinely.

The young man, Mr. Rumple, came stiffly, quickly, uneasily into the study and the Professor rose to shake his hand.

"My, my, my, Rumple," he said, "it's good to see you. Very good. Let me look at you. Look good, good. Been abroad, eh? What're you doing now?"

"Good to see you too, sir," said Rumple. "I'm feeling well, thank you, sir. I've been to England, France—all over. I'm teaching now, sir."

"Teaching! Wonderful, Rumple, wonderful!" The Professor glowed a ruddy glow. "I knew you'd teach. Knew it. Where? Here?"

"Yes, sir," said Rumple, "teaching here."

"What, Rumple? What're you teaching?"

"Classics, sir. Ancient classics."

There was a long, silent moment.

Incredulously, the Professor breathed, "In *those?*"

Mr. Rumple was taken aback. "Pardon me, sir. Those what?"

"Oh come now, Rumple," said Professor Grisley, "those clothes, of course.

Mr. Rumple looked down his front and drew his hands over the neat, sergey lapels. "Is there anything the—?" he began.

"My boy, *I* taught the classics," the Professor said pedantically. "I know about these things."

"I haven't a great deal of money, sir." Mr. Rumple sighed a deep-down sigh. "I thought the clothes were very nice, if you'll pardon me, sir."

"Certainly they're nice. They're *too* nice," argued the Professor. "I can see, Rumple, that there are some things you must learn. Sit down, please."

Disconsolate, Mr. Rumple sat down. Professor Grisley stood squarely over him, looking down intently.

"For your own good, Rumple, and for the success of your first position here at the University, I cannot stress too much the fact that you must not only *be* a teacher of things ancient—you must *look* like a teacher of things ancient. To all appearances, Rumple, you might be a teacher of statics, or chemistry, or anything practical, for that matter."

Mr. Rumple shuddered.

"Yes," Professor Grisley continued, "you must impress upon your charges the fact that your knowledge of the past's treasures has been gleaned despite or, possibly, due to the loss of such contemporary things as Hart, Schaeffner, and Marx. They must know that you spent your rewarding formative years living simply and frugally, nourished in mind more than in body, Aeschylus your red meat, Euripides your heady wine, Aristophanes your frothy parfait."

"Actually, sir, if you'll pardon me," offered Mr. Rumple, "these past few years have been most pleasant. Especially abroad. You see, we have friends . . ."

"Possibly, possibly," granted the Professor, "but that is quite beside the point. As to the clothes, Rumple, you cannot afford to be radical even in these frenetic times."

"What do you suggest, sir," asked Mr. Rumple quite guilelessly, "a toga?"

"As a matter of fact," reminisced Professor Grisley, "I once knew a classics professor—elderly then, and a bit unsound—who came to class one day in a toga—really a light-toned kimono—and beach sandals. Witnesses laughed out loud."

"I would imagine," Mr. Rumple conceded.

"Don't make fun, though," warned the Professor. "Granted that the old gentleman carried things to the extreme a little, you will soon discover that a near-hidden snicker or derisive remark is as of much worth as thunderous applause. Little insults here and there will assure you that you have made your impression. But," the Professor pointed a finger, "you may be sure of your students' undeviating support only when you have earned a nickname."

"A nickname?" Mr. Rumple wondered.

"From my first appearance in class," revealed Professor Grisley, "I affected trousers whose bottoms were removed from my shoe-tops by quite a considerable distance, so that white stockings were very much in evidence. It was not long after that I became known as 'The White-Ankled Grisley.' "

"Ha, ha," laughed Mr. Rumple.

"I took later to wearing shirts of an off-maroon shade which, though belying my innate good taste, earned me the title 'Grisley of the Wine-Dark Bosom.' "

"Wonderful!" said Mr. Rumple.

"It was then evident that, to a man, I had the honest-to-goodness respect of the class."

"Yes," Mr. Rumple was sure.

"Have any tweeds, Rumple?"

Mr. Rumple brightened. "Why yes, sir. A lovely new suit. Really quite nice."

The Professor frowned a knitted frown. "Not good, not good."

"Not good, sir?"

"Well, we can fix it up, I imagine. When's your first class, Rumple?"

"Day after tomorrow, sir."

"Begin wearing the suit immediately," the Professor directed. "See to it that by day after tomorrow the trousers are as far out of shape as possible. Be good idea to suspend them between two tables at night with *The Complete Herodotus* in one knee, and *The Complete Xenophon* in the other. Try to fray up the coat's elbows a bit too, if you can. When occasion permits, lean back against a bookcase and rub them along the *Metaphysics.* Few spots or stains wouldn't hurt the coat, either. I've had a ketchup stain on my tuxedo for almost two years now. Drives Mrs. Grisley nearly mad, but we have to keep up appearances. Also keep your necktie fairly loose and just a wee bit awry. Think you can remember all this, Rumple?"

"I hope so, sir," said Mr. Rumple.

"When it's cold, my boy," added the Professor, "wear a coat as thin as the elements will permit. If you must carry a brief-case make it an old one, loose at the seams, you know. Might drop a hint that it belonged to A. E. Housman and is your most cherished possession. Build up a little legend. Got that?"

"Yes, sir."

"And for Olympia's sake, Rumple, don't walk so stiffly—*shamble!*"

"I'd find that a little difficult, sir," protested Mr. Rumple, "I was in the army you know."

The Professor shouted Stentor's shout. "I say *shamble!* If nothing else works, a good shamble will turn the trick."

"Yes, sir," agreed Mr. Rumple.

He rose, and the Professor clapped a hand to his shoulder. "And now *Vale,* Rumple, *Vale!* I know you'll do well."

* * * * *

Mr. Rumple paused on entering the old building to loosen his tie and jerk it just a bit awry. He tucked A. E. Housman's brief case under his frayed arm and shambled down the hall to his classroom.

"By Zeus," remarked a dapper instructor in Greek to his companion, "he looks like old Professor Grisley!"

Mr. Rumple smiled. *Yale Record*

THE MATRIMONIAL HANDICAP

BY BILL JURY

For the first year, married life is like a horse race. It's the Kentucky Derby and the Grand National rolled into one, with the right to wear the pants in the family as the ultimate bouquet of roses. And right from the start, the fillies are the favorites, 5 to 1.

When the minister smiles down on the soon-to-be-wed, it's like looking over a field of two, with Whirlaway and Old Dobbin the principal contenders. After the final "I do," the starting gate goes up and the filly comes in a winner by a furlong unless she's boxed in on the rail in the backstretch.

Many University men will go to the post this month and, unless they are forewarned, they'll wind up in the glue factory before they reach the first turn.

It's a dirty shame, but what can you expect? When the guys were playing Cops and Robbers at the age of six, Maw was showing the gals how she corraled your old man into being an obedient husband.

Today, girls are briefed on the art of tying apron strings around new husbands. College life is merely a continuation of their early training. While the male students are engrossed in finding the square root, the fillies are being versed in the fine points of the thoroughbred. They are told that a lady need only know how to arrange dashing bouquets and dry martinis. The drudgery, they learn, is delegated to the spouse.

It's always been that way, but it needn't be. Some husbands have beaten the odds on various occasions and have been awarded a spot in the winner's circle. A compilation of their systems is invaluable to the prospective bridegroom and I am happy to submit the following Matrimonial Dope Sheet. I am not responsible for last minute scratches.

Generally, the honeymoon is a period of bliss and not much need be said about it. However, this bliss is short-lived. The trouble begins when the wife discovers your honeymoon cottage is not the dream home she had anticipated. Watch out. This is the danger sign. She's felt the boot and she'll jump into the lead if you're not careful. Chances are she'll complain about the kitchen first. Usually the cupboards are too high. By no means agree with her. Don't be caught off guard. Tell her if she wasn't such a scrawny midget she could reach them, and whatta you want for fifty bucks a month? If she isn't a scrawny midget and stands about six feet four inches, you're on your own. Think up something for the occasion. You've got to move fast in this racket.

But the race isn't over. Not by a long shot. Nine times out of ten she'll switch to a new treatment. You'll notice it immediately if you are on your toes. The little woman's cooking begins to pick up. The beans no longer rattle around on the plate like BB shot and the gravy is almost palatable. But don't compliment her. If you do she will say thank you, and how about helping me with the dishes. You're trapped then and you've lost the race. Remember, the fillies have been groomed for this race ever since they were foaled and they're sharp. Tell her it's about time the chow was getting halfway decent, that you were about ready to move to a hobo jungle.

But she's desperate now. Chances are she'll reach into her bag of tricks and come up with the crying routine. This is followed by a feverish packing of baggage and an announcement that she is going home to mother. Tell her fine, now you can listen to the ball game in peace.

If you've maintained the lead thus far, you are an odds on favorite to come home a winner. Unless one of two things happens.

First, she realizes that you like to work in the yard in the warm weather. She also notices that the grass needs a manicure. She's no dummy so she suggests why not go out and dabble in the yard. Don't do it. In fifteen minutes you will be pushing the lawn mower for all you are worth. When that's finished it'll be weeding the garden and how about carrying up the ashes. Tell her she's put on twenty pounds of blubber since you were married and she needs the exercise.

Second, and far worse, she calls in reinforcements. One day you go to the door and find an intruder dressed in the colors of the other stable . . . it's the Old Battle Ax herself. Your mother-in-law. If she gets across the threshold it's the same as throwing a shoe or drawing up lame in the home stretch. You're out of it. Nice race, but you're no mudder and it just started raining cats and dogs.

You gotta move fast. Hand her a timetable, show her the road to the station and slam the door. Lock it. Move the baby grand in front of the door. Pull down the shades and board up the chimney.

If this subtle ruse works, you've won. You're under the wire ahead of the field. Take your place in the sun. You're Lord and Master and the world is yours. You've run your greatest race and you wear the pants in the family.

If it doesn't work, and you stumble and fall in this greatest steeple-chase of all, untie your apron, lay aside your dust mop for the moment. Take your place alongside the rest of us and reflect. The odds were against you from the start. *Columns*

MY SON JOHN

BY BEN PATT

I have a son, or rather a stepson. His name is John because that's what his mother named him. His father's name is also John. He is my husband and the man I married. My name will be anonymous in this story. If I have to have a name, call me Jane. It's easy to remember. Well, back to my son, John.

John is an average boy who enjoys people. He is a good student, too. He goes to college. He is a senior. When he isn't in college he comes home. Most boys his age come home and just use their parents. You know the kind I mean: comes home, has dinner, borrows money, takes the family car, drives it to a gas station where he can fill up the tank and charges it to his parents, and then isn't seen for days or weeks on end. Not John. He's my son, or rather my stepson, and he loves his home. John doesn't drink or smoke. John never goes out on dates. He never drives anywhere unless it's with me. His friends think that's very strange. They also think John is very strange. That's not true. John just loves his parents. And we love John.

John, Sr., that's John's father, doesn't love John as much as I do. He is a busy man and isn't home much when John is. John realizes that and tries to keep his mother company. That's me. He'll come home, take a coke out of the icebox, and then turn to me and say, "Jane (he's too old to call me Mother), let's stay home and do something together." I always tell him to go out and have a good time with his friends but he never does. He'd much rather sit down with his coke and talk to me. We understand each other because John is like his father, John. John is a year younger than I am. Maybe that's why we understand each other. I love my son, John, and John loves me. We're a happy family. I'm a lucky girl. How many women do you know that have two Johns at their disposal. *Colgate Banter*

MISDIRECTIONS

FOR THOSE WHO WANT TO WRITE
BUT HAVEN'T LEARNED HOW TO READ YET
BY KIDNEY SOX

I: *Nobody Can Tell You How to Write*

Absolutely nobody. That's why if you've got an ounce of sense in your head, you'll heave this little tome in the incinerator and go to the movies.

II: *What Drives a Man to Write?*

Is it an urge, something that knocks the cardiac about in the thoracic cavity like a punching bag? Is it a love and understanding of humanity which drives one to pour out one's soul on a piece of paper? Or is it the caustic welling of resentment in the pit of the stomach, the itching to distill this bitterness into something all men can see and understand?

No.

It's money.

Next question.

III: *Let's Start on a Modest Scale*

The world is a big place.

You are a little man.

Don't try to conquer the world in a day. Don't expect to write the Great American Novel in twenty-four hours. Don't attempt to dash off an epic between sunset and sunset. . . . Take a week or two. . . .

IV: *Poetry Is Truth Told Sideways*

Poetry is truth told sideways. Let's examine this concept more closely. Poetry is truth told sideways.

Hummmm.

Let's put it this way.

Poetry doesn't have to have meter to be poetry. Poetry doesn't have to have poetic language or poetic form or poetic imagery to be poetry.

What does poetry have to have then?

It's gotta rhyme.

Damn it, it's just gotta rhyme. Who ever heard of a poem that didn't rhyme?

V: *Why Don't You Write a Novel?*

Novels are divided into three classes: English, French, and Russian.

If you are going to write an English novel, you must write in English. As William Makepeace Thackeray once told me, "Make a bloody mess of the English novel if it were written in Sanskrit, wouldn't it?"

If you are going to write a French novel, *bonjour.*

If you are going to write a Russian novel, you'd better start when you're three and hope your grandson is able to finish the thing for you.

Of course you might try something really different and write a truly *American* novel.

Sooner or later, somebody has to.

VI: *Just a Word About Plagiarism*

It's not so much what you steal as it is who you steal from.

The best-selling author Benjamin J. Sash once told me how he came to write his trilogy *Sanctuary, Obituary and Son O'Bituary.* "There was an obscure young writer in Mississippi named Charlotte Brontë," he explained. "One night I serenaded her, and when her face was turned aside to hide a blush, I belted her one with the guitar.

"I stole all her manuscripts. At home I took each page, tacked it on the wall, and fired a charge of buckshot at it. Then I retyped each page, leaving out words that had been demolished by the shot.

"They sold like wildfire.

"I do that with all my writing now."

VII: *What's In It For Me?*

Plenty, bud, if you play the angles.

The field's wide open, and more people are reading than ever before.

Just don't go literary. They'll hate you for it.

Write about something robust and fiery and earthy.

And we all know what that is, don't we? *Jackolantern*

PART TWO

HISTORY REWRITTEN

The human pageant, as it never happened

*The garbling of history has always been a favorite campus game. It is a fine source of innocent merriment, and any number can play. All you do is take some dates, places, names, and events; shake well; and scatter them out like a box full of dice. Like this, for example:**

Today we take up the history of astronomy, from the Greek words *astro* meaning "sore" and *nomy* meaning "back." Sore backs were the occupational disease of the early Greek astronomers, and no wonder! They used to spend every blessed night lying on the damp ground and looking up at the sky, and if there's a better way to get a sore back, I'd like to hear about it. Especially in the moist Mediterranean area, where Greece is generally considered to be.

Lumbago and related disorders kept astronomy from becoming very popular until Galileo, a disbarred flenser of Perth, fashioned a home-made telescope in 1924 out of three Social Security cards and an ordinary ice cube. What schoolboy does not know that stirring story—how Galileo stepped up to his telescope, how he looked heavenward, how his face filled with wonder, how he stepped back and whispered the words heard round the world: *"L'état, c'est moi!"*

Well, sir, you can imagine what happened then! William Jennings Bryan snatched Nell Gwynne from the shadow of the guillotine at Oslo; Chancellor Bismarck brought in four gushers in a single afternoon; Hal Newhouser was signed by the Hanseatic League; Crete was declared off limits to Wellington's entire army; and William Faulkner won the Davis Cup for his immortal *Penrod and Sam.*

But after a while things calmed down, and astronomers began the staggering task of naming all the heavenly bodies. First man to name a star was Sigafoos of Mt. Wilson, and the name he chose was Betelgeuse, after his wife Betelgeuse Sigafoos, prom queen at Oregon State University from 1919 to 1931.

Not to be outdone, Formfig of Yerkes Observatory named a whole constellation after *his* wife, Big Dipper Formfig, the famed dirt-track racer. This started the custom of astronomers naming constellations after their wives—Capricorn, Cygnus, Orion, Ursa Major, Canis Major,

* This piece was originally in *On Campus with Max Shulman,* a weekly column I write for Philip Morris Cigarettes, and is reprinted by permission.

and so forth. (The Major girls, Ursa and Canis, both married astronomers, though Canis subsequently ran off with a dry-dock broker named Thwaite Daphnis.)

After naming all the heavenly bodies, the astronomers had a good long rest. Then, refreshed and brown as berries, they undertook the gigantic project of charting the heavens. Space is so vast that it is measured in units called "light-years." These are different from ordinary years in that they weigh a good deal less. This, of course, is only relative, since space is curved. As Einstein laughingly said, "$E = mc^2$."

A DEMOCRATIC HISTORY OF PENNSYLVANIA

BY P. C. REIST AND C. A. MC GREW

Editor's Note—The facts expressed in this article are not necessarily those of the History Department of The Pennsylvania State University.

CHAPTER I: *The Holy Experiment*

The first name in Pennsylvania history was the Crown, who owed a large amount of money to Admirable Penn, of the R.N. However, Admirable Penn died at an opportune moment and the debt passed on to William Penn (not to be confused with *William Penn*). This was in the days when Massachusetts was top state due to the Pilgrims' Progress, etc.

CHAPTER II: *William Penn, an Important Governor*

The change in debtors gave the Crown an opportunity to unload some property in payment of the debt, and Penn, realizing that he had been the victim of an elementary gambit of kingmanship, appointed himself governor to prevent the inhabitants of the land from laughing at him for his misjudgment. However, the grant was a *good thing* because Indians were the only inhabitants at that time, and they never laugh.

The Elm Treaty, a Good Thing

About this time Penn met with the Indians, led by Chief Tammany, and they sat around drinking firewater, smoking peace pipes, and discussing the coming Thanksgiving. Penn said that he owned the land, but he gave the Indians many concessions including the right to move their villages toward the Pacific Ocean, the right to bury the hatchet, etc.

The Walking Purchase, a Bad Thing

Following this democratic meeting, the Pennsylvanians decided they needed land because the population had increased quite rapidly. This was due to:

1. Male English Immigrants.
2. Female English Immigrants.

The settlers therefore decided to have another democratic meeting with the Indians so that they could swindle them. The red men readily agreed to this, thinking that the white men would follow Benjamin Franklin's old saying, "Walk slowly, the life you save may be your own."

But the wily Quakers hired two ringers, Mason and Dixon, who literally walked circles around the Indians. Unfortunately, this angered the Indians and they ravaged the countryside, scalping all in sight. The purchase, however, was *really* a good thing because it:

1. Created Bucks County, Claude Rains, Bucks County playhouse, *et al.*
2. Created graveyards.
3. Reduced the settler population.
4. Gave more land to the settlers, which they would have gotten, *in the end.*

CHAPTER III: *The French and Indian War*

Contrary to popular belief, the French were not at war with the Indians. In reality, the English, who were badly defeated, invented the name to mislead future historians. The most democratic battle of the campaign occurred in Western Pennsylvania near Fort Pitt, and her sister fort, Fort Neuweiler. General Lucien C. Braddock, advancing on the fort *with heavy odds,* met a small force of Indians, lurking behind a sapling. Braddock rallied his troops and gave the democratic order, "Pass in Review," which was executed, along with the rest of his force (with the possible exception of George Washington, who said as he left the scene, "I have but one life to give for my country").

This defeat, coupled with Lord Halifax's historic advance upon the cliffs of Montreal, defeated the English and left France top nation in America (with the possible exception of the Indians who were ravaging the country with fire, and, perhaps, the knife).

The Revolution, a Justifiable War

At this time a group of straight-laced Puritans threw a *tea* party in Boston harbor but did not invite the English (a very definite *faux pas* at that time) and the Revolution ensued. The first battles were all fought in Massachusetts, which the Americans, fighting at heavy odds, lost. This was most hard on little Massachusetts so the war was moved to Pennsylvania, making it top state.

All winter long, the Yankees had a spree staying at historic old Valley Forge. On one occasion, General of the Army George Washington crossed the Delaware River to retrieve a silver dollar he had thrown across earlier in the afternoon. This was very memorable because it marked the first time a man had crossed the Delaware *standing up* to retrieve a silver dollar. After this the colonists were always successful in their battles (while the English lost most of theirs) and so won the war. This was very correct since it established the Declaration of Independence, the Constitution, George Washington, the United States of America, infiltration, etc.

Following the war Wittington was elected president and the Capitol was moved to Maryland, establishing New York as top state. Pennsylvania unfortunately tried to fight back by becoming Republican which brought democratic history to an end. *Froth*

TENNIS: A HISTORY

When you hit a tennis ball, do you know what you are doing? Have you ever stopped to think how many thousands of others have done the very same thing before you? Or, in my case, how many thousands of others have done the same thing to the same ball before me? Neither had I. But now that we have a moment, let's just look and see what has happened to tennis, and how.

An excellent and informative new pamphlet on the history of tennis is rolling off the presses at this very moment. As soon as they can keep it on the presses we will be able to consult it. Until that date we will have to be satisfied with the following slightly abridged edition of the development of modern tennis.

The name of the game comes from the old Latin *tensa*—a car on which the images of the gods were carried at the Circensian games. Later it appeared as the Spanish *tendedor*—one who stretches clothes out to dry, and still later in the French *tenture*—colored wallpaper. So it is that the present English version of the name has the meaning "a circus car on which the gods stretched colored wallpaper out to dry."

The sport of tennis is an ancient one. It originated, along with mushrooms, in a dark prehistoric cave, as a means of nighttime communication between young lovers whose sleeping apartments were separated by strong nets (didn't know that, did you?). Over this net the young couple elevated the art of keeping the ball rolling. Soon the imperialistic tendencies of the mushrooms caused the nets to be weighed down and broken and the fledgling sport of tennis came to a sorry end.

It is difficult to trace the progress of tennis through the succeeding centuries. A few mosaics of the Minoan period were popularly supposed to depict a tennis match, but it was later discovered that the objects being brandished above the heads of the players were deer clubs, the woven appearance of which was due to the absence of many stones from the pattern.

It was not until 1789 that the game again took the stage. On the estate of the Marquis de Tennis, a revolting peasant fired a cannon ball at the noble, who was fiddling away while his chateau burned. The ingenious marquis beat the missile with his fiddle and so enjoyed the experience that he took up the game seriously. Stringing up a wooden frame with strips of cat tongue (the idea that cat gut is used is entirely erroneous and stems from a confusion in the wording of the popular expression "Cat gut your tongue?"), the marquis used a lighter ball and organized a game. His favorite opponent was the neighboring Marquis de Sweat. The names of the two players have been immortalized in the terminology of the costume in the game, "Tennis" shoes and "Sweat" socks. It was the latter of the two men who, after a hard-fought and disappointing game, uttered the famous Oath of the Tennis Court.

The popularity of the game spread rapidly among the Monarchists, Clerics, pro-Bourbon and Conservative Anarchist factions. When a Spanish delegation visited the court of Napoleon looking for interesting objects to be displayed in the grammar school Progress Day exhibition of the Indians of South America, the Emperor of the French shrewdly decided to get rid of a few tennis rackets. He saw clearly that the workers and the bourgeoisie might be kept busy and satisfied stringing rackets, and that the sports-minded aristocrats would be better for a little privation. Napoleon levied a tribute on tennis rackets and dispatched them to the New World.

When the Spaniards arrived at their destination and began to unload, they discovered to their horror that the dampness of the sea air had caused the racket strings to stretch and loosen. The resourceful Balboa, still smarting from the cavalier treatment accorded him by

Keats, stormed, "Faugh, stout Cortez!" and distributed the equipment to the native players whom he taught, taking advantage of the slack rackets, to play lacrosse.

Tennis appeared in the United States about the date May 3, 1849. Mrs. Bixby mentions the game in the following excerpt from her extensive correspondence:

"Mr. E., the unworthy bounder, has been drinking again and returned home in a frightful temper. He interrupted the tea party and we ladies were all so shocked that the young Misses Y, O, and Mac B. fainted on the spot. The remainder of us determined to leave at once and calling the dog cart, we made our exit.

"As we hurried along beneath the luxuriant maples for which the E.'s fine old home is famous (and my dear, you should see the porte-cochere!), we looked back over our shoulders to see Mr. E. beating the terrified Mrs. E. with what appeared to be either a lawn tennis racket or a butterfly net. (I had mislaid my eyeglasses in the rush and could not be sure.)"

So it would appear that Mrs. Bixby witnessed either the advent of tennis or the last stand of butterfly catching in the United States. Later Boston banned the playing of the game on Sunday on account of the racket.

Of course the Russians claimed the invention of tennis and surely no one else plays by the pseudo-Marxian rules they use today. In the Russian game both sides of the court are filled with players, all of whom participate using the same racket which is passed from hand to hand. While their forehand play is not exceptional, they are great on passing the buck.

Tennis is played in courts of either grass or clay. The difference in surface texture is compensated for by the use of the rough side of the racket on clay and the smooth side on grass.

Important in the evolution of the game has been the costume of women players. From the flowing skirts and feathered hats of the past we have come to the era of the pigtail and abbreviated leopard-skin shorts. The future of the tennis costume remains unpredictable, but the ingenuity of the American woman is a source of amazement to all.

Tennis has had a long and noble history in which most of the difficulties of the game have been smoothed out, but still one dispute remains unsolved. Is it more sporting to play one person at singles, or face three rivals at doubles? Then, too, badminton is nice when the wind is right. *Campus Cat*

SHORT HISTORY OF MIZZOU

BY JOE GOLD

The oldest state university west of the Seine, the University of Missouri was established by the Missouri Compromise in 1623. The national government took Boone County away from the Indians, who were quite pleased about this turn of events. The government turned the land over to settlers who lasted 15 days at which time they attempted to return it to the Indians. However, the Indians proved too smart and held the White Man to his bargain and took Oklahoma instead.

The Geyser Act established a state university, but it required federal troops sent in by President Pierce to shoe Missouri youths and carry them forcibly to the institution. The school officially opened in 1839, and the first class graduated in 1860. This individual later became Callaway County Coroner, and education had proven it could succeed even in the swamps and bogs of the Louisiana Perches.

During the Civil War the University became engaged in "Top Secret" activities for both sides. Boone County mosquitos were crossed with Boone County hams. This produced a super-mosquito whose bite was a fatal case of heartburn.

When Columbians discovered in 1900 that the proposed Panama Canal would not connect Boone County with the Mississippi, students, in protest, burned Academic Hall. This cut the faculty in half, since students had forgotten to notify the administration of the fire. However, insurance receipts from the fire enabled the university to construct a number of fine edifices around the campus, whose use was shortly outmoded with the invention of indoor plumbing by Samuel F. B. Morse. Columbians viewing this wasteful tragedy often quoted Morse's "What hath God wrought?"

The University and the county contributed their share to the United States' burden in the First World War. The first ROTC unit in the world was begun in Columbia in 1917, much to the dismay of Kaiser Wilhelm who surrendered promptly after viewing captured films of the marchers. With the war over, University officials received a communique from President Wilson asking them to disband the unit as a public safety measure. They complied and the five ROTC students transferred to West Point, where they later achieved fame as Generals Patton, DeGaulle, Rommel, Marshall, and Washington. Still visible effects of that war may be seen beside the Memorial Tower in a huge bomb crater that scared hell out of the town when students held an Armistice Day celebration and three cases of warm beer exploded.

It was at this time at the beginning of the Roaring Twenties that Dean Mott invented Journalism and chose Missouri as the place to start mass-producing journalists. When Forrest Smith, the man who was governor at that time, heard about the new J school, he coined the now classic remark, "Boys will be boys!"

Also during the Twenties, flagpole sitting was all the rage. However, since Columbia ordinances forbade any structure more than twenty-five feet high, all flagpole sitting had to be done with the pole in a prone position. At this time the Memorial Tower was constructed at an original height of twenty-four feet nine inches and an original cost of thirty-eight dollars and three hundred Wheaties box tops. Columbians used to mount the stairs to the top of the Tower and roost. Each year the height limitations were relaxed, and each year the University added a granite block to the top of the Tower. This piecemeal edifice soon came to be known as the "Finest Piece of Gothic Architecture in North America and the Virgin Islands". (Capital letters belong to the University; quotation marks to this magazine.)

When the second World War caught universities all over the country unprepared for the increased enrollment at the cessation of hostilities, the University of Missouri met the challenge. Fourteen hundred "temporary" barracks, shacks, and mousetraps were built all over campus. The veterans beat a path to the admissions office. This was one of the most turbulent periods in Mizzou's long, glorious history. The hardened veterans, meeting for the first time with Rah Rah Collegians, launched many a battle royal on the steps of Jesse Hall. Fraternities suffered the greatest losses, many of their members being found floating face downward in the Hinkson, their feet encased in solid blocks of Glukestite.

School spirit rose to a new peak during the GI Bill days. Snake dances through class rooms, The Battle of the Stable, the Henry Wallace tomato barrage—all were in keeping with the New Spirit. However, when the former president of the University was abducted, tossed into a vat of nitric acid, and melted down and sold as bars of soap, it was time to call a halt.

When the halt was called, the Curators decided to give students a place where they could relax, shoot pool, and play the pari-mutuels. To get the students off the streets, and to give the University some of the loot that town merchants were getting, they built a huge casino beside the Tower. This magnificent structure, replete with roulette wheels, bunco, direct wires to all leading tracks, and an indoor gridiron for the Homecoming game and waffles, is known as the Student Union.

MU has come a long way from those dark beginnings in 1623. The Union has been built, and perhaps, it will only be another decade before the World War I bomb crater is turned into a swimming pool. *Showme (University of Missouri)*

CROSSING THE DELAWARE

I realize someone is going to catch hell for this article, but it so happens I don't much care. Of course, this is not the kind of attitude that will get you very far, but some things just have to be said. Now you take this business about Washington crossing the Delaware. Good stuff, you may say. Well, I have it on reputable authority that American youth are getting taken for a ride when it comes to this guy Washington. He had some good qualities, I'll admit, but on the night of December 25, 1776, he was registering very low on the old hero-meter. But don't take my word for it. Decide for yourself.

WASHINGTON: God damn it! Stop rocking the boat. My head is killing me.

GEN. GREENE: Well, get away from the bow and stop waving that flag. Every time you get fried you have to ham it up.

WASHINGTON: The people love me.

GEN. GREENE: All right, the people love you. Now sit down.

WASHINGTON: What river is this?

ADJUTANT: The Delaware, sir.

WASHINGTON: The Delaware! What are we doing on the Delaware? Who gave this order?

ADJUTANT: You did, sir.

WASHINGTON: Why did you let me do it? I'll have you drummed out of camp for this. You, there! Don't row so hard. Can't you see my head is splitting open? How did this happen, Greene?

GEN. GREENE: Don't you remember? We were having our Christmas party and the liquor ran out. Someone told you the Hessians were having a big blowout across the river and you got the bright idea to come over and join the party.

WASHINGTON: Oh, my God! . . . What are these other boats doing here?

GEN. GREENE: You invited the rest of the army along.

WASHINGTON: The whole army! Greene, we're dished!

LAFAYETTE: Ha, ha, ha. *C'est drôle.*

WASHINGTON: What did the brat say?

GEN. GREENE: He says the whole thing is good for laughs.

WASHINGTON: Oh, he did, did he? Well, you can tell him to take the first ship for France in the morning. He's done nothing but gum up the works ever since he's been over here. I can't figure what Martha sees in him.

GEN. GREENE: The Continental Congress is going to raise hell about this. We'd better think of something fast.

WASHINGTON: They've got a lot of nerve. Trying to palm off those phony bills on me.

LAFAYETTE: Ha, ha, ha. *C'est très comique.*

WASHINGTON: What did he say?

GEN GREENE: He says he thinks you're funny.

WASHINGTON: Everything's funny to him. That's all he says, "*Oui, oui,* ha, ha, ha. *C'est drôle. C'est comique.* Ha, ha, ha. *Oui, oui.*" What a bonehead!

ADJUTANT: Lights, sir! The Hessian camp!

WASHINGTON: Where?

ADJUTANT: Dead ahead, sir! Don't you see them?

WASHINGTON: Stop shouting. Now look what you've done. I've dropped my teeth. Everybody look for my teeth.

GEN. GREENE: Which ones?

WASHINGTON: Damn it! The mahogany ones.

LAFAYETTE: *Reportez-moi à la vielle Virginie. C'est où le—*"

WASHINGTON: For the last time shut up!

ADJUTANT: Sir, we are about to land. What shall we do?

WASHINGTON: Do? There's nothing we can do but surrender. But first find my teeth! They cost $150 and they're all I got in the world.

I know what you're saying. You're saying the whole thing is ridiculous. That we won a victory at Trenton. But just remember this. The Hessians were pretty tanked that night, too. Just how tanked you'll find in the history books. Ha, ha, ha. *C'est drôle, eh?*

Yale Record

DR. ETHEL SNAVELY

BY HARVEY GREENBERG

Dr. Ethel Snavely, inventor of the Solovox and lecturer of Anthropology at Columbia University, was one of the most brilliant women of our time. A graduate of Barnard College, Dr. Snavely taught during the years 1929–1950, and in that short time was instrumental in flunking 652 College men, 875 Grad students, and 12,749 members of the School of General Studies. For this reason alone, she commands our earnest attention. She was one of those rare individuals who possessed both scientific understanding and philosophic humility, combined with a sympathetic insight into the problems of humanity. She was a compassionate old crow.

During 1935, Dr. Snavely spent her sabbatical among the Quariuba Indians of the Northwest plains. When she returned to Columbia, she was a changed woman. Her first book, *The Diversity of Cultures and the Science of Custom,* was published in 1937 and was placed on the Index during spring of that year. *The Diversity of Custom and the Science of Cultures,* which appeared in 1938, was banned in Boston. Her final work, *Sexual Behavior in the American Female,* was printed in 1952 and Dr. Snavely died subsequently of a broken heart.

The following excerpts are taken from pages 19–25 of *Die protestantische Etheik und der Geist des Capitalismus,* translation by John Peter Guy, with obscene references omitted.

THE QUARIUBA INDIANS

About sixty millions years ago, a group of Indian tribes crossed the land bridge between Siberia and North America. This was very difficult, because there is no land bridge between Siberia and North America, and never has been. Most of these foolhardy Indians were, therefore, drowned in the Bering Straits. About five hundred did make it across to the American shore, and they stood there whooping and hollering at the others who couldn't swim. Then they propitiated the Rain God who wasn't listening, because he has other things to do far more important than paying attention to a lot of crazy Indians. Believe me, I know. But the Indians kept screaming and stomping and whooping and hollering until the Rain God really got good and sore and sent a flood down. This killed off all of the noisy Indians except two: a boy Indian and a girl Indian. These two, John and Rebecca, formed what was to be the basic family unit of the Quariuba culture.

The Quariubas (or Kwariuba) are a fruitful race who have been roaming the Northwest plains and generally raising hell for upwards of fifty million years now. Their language is extremely simple. It consists of ten letters; five vowels and five consonants, four of which are never sounded. Most of the words of the Quariuba tongue are four letters which is very significant if you know what I mean. The word *Quariuba* means "noisy," which figures.

They are just about the loudest people on God's green earth. They believe that in order to avert natural disasters the Gods, at all costs, must be kept awake so that the trains can run on time. It is of the greatest importance that the great ceremonial drum always be pounded. For this purpose, each tribe is divided into four-hour shifts. Day in, day out, the goddamn great ceremonial drum thuds on and on. Most Quariuba are stone deaf.

They have divided the year into 362 days, and I'll be damned if I know why. The last three days of the year have no names (not even four-letter ones) and are sacred. At the end of the year all the tribes come from miles around to the great Indian Pan-Athenaic festival. They spend the first two days hunting the great brown elephant. As everybody knows, there are no great brown elephants in the Northwest plains, which complicates things. On the third day a great sacrifice is held in honor of the Elephant God, which nobody attends. The Elephant God goes unpropitiated, but nobody seems to care. On the night of the last day, another great festival is held in the main dining hall, during which everyone sleeps with everyone else's wife. Just about everybody attends this festival, and who can blame them.

There is no word in the Quariuba tongue for "adultery," but they don't let that stop them. There are also no words for "drunkenness," "incest," "polygamy," and "catharsis." Everyone has a great old time, let me tell you.

In the good old days the main means of subsistence was licorice root. Then, one fine day around 1500 A.D., all of the licorice plantations were completely devastated by the Chinese rot. This presented a considerable problem to the folk of Quariuba, but they solved it with characteristic ingenuity. Most of their food supply is now gained almost exclusively from the hunting of the great brown elephant. The Quariuba are slowly but surely dying out.

They are ruled by a theocracy of holy men, who are under strict vows of purity, chastity, flavor, and abstention from bathing. The holiest and oldest of these venerables lives completely removed from the village, for obvious reasons. He is the big chief, but few people have courage enough to get within twenty yards of him, and he is rarely or never consulted on matters of state. Most of the Quariuba do what they damn well please.

There are very few quarrels or wars among the Quariuba. Any misunderstandings which do take place are usually over the women of the tribe, who like to live it up and don't much care where they park their moccasins for the night. A typical argument (or *Unglick*) usually runs like this:

The offended individual approaches the house of the offender, accompanied by his armed brothers. He knocks three times on the door, steps back, and shouts:

"Lo, I am great drum-beater, who spits in your mother's milk and beats his Ceremonial Drum at you. Honorless old sonovabee, if you don't come out I'm gonn' breaka you face!"

Whereupon the offender steps solemnly through the door and intones three times: *Klaatu barada nikto,* which means, "In yer hat, ya dumb bunny!"

The two warriors then embrace and call it a day.

Thus we see the calmness of this simple society, whose tranquility is so alien to the confusion and chaos of our own complicated culture. Our only hope is this: we must break the chains that bind us, and join the fast-disappearing Quariuba in a new struggle for happiness. It's a great life, if you don't mind those goddamn drums. *Columbia Jester*

HOW WILLIAM RANDOLPH HEARST CAME TO OWN HALF THE STATE OF CALIFORNIA

BY DEMIN

It was nearly four in the morning but the tables and wheels of Harry's Tarnished Tupence were busier than ever. There was more gold dust changing hands in the Tupence that night than there are funny hats at a Legion Convention.

In the back room, at the big round table reserved for big round gamblers six such gentlemen were playing a friendly game of Stop-Smiling-Lester-I-Have-Aces-Back-To-Back, a charming little game with 48 wild cards and 4 jokers. The protagonists were grim. The stakes were big and round. And Harry himself was dealing.

The players were dealt their five cards, bets on each, blind and up. The mound in the middle grew. Deeds, charters, cash, and credit made the table sag like Harry's prosperous paunch. It came to the last round. The heavy betting drove out all but W.R.H. and a Lad Called Lou. Harry needed a rake to take the house raking. Nobody was whistling Dixie. Dixie was serving the drinks. The drinks were on the house. The house was Harry's and he was a rake.

The Lad plopped down $25,000 and grinned. Harry grinned. W.R.H. doubled it. Harry doubled up. The Lad doubled that. W.R.H. threw in his anti-vivisection campaign. It cut the Lad to the quick. W.R.H. was down to his last penny, the Lad had $.98 left. It fell to the kitty. Kitty and Dixie couldn't believe their eyes.

W.R.H. couldn't back down. He was there and there to stick. He stripped down to his long-johns and dropped the pile on the table. The Lad matched him and laughed out, "Yer shy $.98, W.R.H." . . . the tension of the evening had broken formality between the two men of destiny. But this wasn't destiny, it was Sacramento and W.R.H. was still shy.

Even Harry gasped. He couldn't figure out how he could take his raking. W.R.H. smiled and rose to his feet. It was a fantastic feat. With grace and agility he sprang on the table. Dixie, Kitty, and Grace screamed with disbelief. As comfortable as a babe in a cradle he nestled himself on top of the pile of loot. The Lad had no choice but to accept the wager, W.R.H. was a plump chap.

"I see you," he announced from atop the pile.

"I see you," replied the Lad.

Dixie, Kitty, and Grace hid their eyes in their hands. W.R.H. cut a fearsome figure in his long-johns, Harry cut ten percent of W.R.H.

The cards were turned over. It was wild. The Lad spoke first, "five aces, nine high." W.R.H. answered, "five aces, nine high. "8." "8." "6." "6." "5." "5." "3." "3."

"Split pot," Harry announced. The Lad consented. W.R.H. swore, only over his dead body. The Lad consented.

The two men were at terrible odds. Harry finally brought them to agreement. "Evens," shouted W.R.H., "three takes it."

The rest is history. Ninety percent of California fell W.R.H.'s way, Harry sold his share out to M.G.M., and they lived happily ever after.

Columbia Jester

HOW THE WAGONS CAME TO GO WEST

BY JACK E. PETERSON

The winter of 1847 was colder than a Salem witch's tombstone in a hailstorm. Especially around Sacramento, and the coldness is one of the main reasons so much whisky was sold, although Californians usually don't give excuses for drinking.

One of the busiest bars in Sacramento was called the Witch's Mammary, and it was owned by a fellow named George Lecher. The main reason Lecher's bar did more business than all the rest was Nelly Nubile, and jeez, could she throw that stuff around. As one might expect, George was violently in love with her. As he used to tell his bartender, "I'm violently in love with her."

One evening before the bars closed for Hannukah, George asked Nelly to spend the holiday at a little spot called Sutter's Mill. Just the two of them, he said, a nice log fire, a bear rug and a few pleasant surprises. Including a little something from Tiffany's, he hinted. This clinched it for Nelly and they were off.

George had built a nice, cozy little cabin on the side of a hill at Sutter's Mill. Sutter didn't mind; he got all the absinthe frappes he could drink for free.

Everything was progressing nicely for George; they were lying on the bear rug in front of the fire discussing the economical aspects of the Thomasian Synthesis and everything was cozy. When they had exhausted all aspects of the above topic, George reached into his pocket and pulled out a small white box marked *Tiffany*. With a squeal of delight Nelly ripped open the box and pulled out a solid gold ring. "Is it really solid gold?" she asked George. "Of course," he replied, making a little move. "Let's see," she said, flipping the ring into the fire. In a matter of seconds the solid gold plate had melted off, revealing a brass interior.

"In yer chapeau," said Nelly, and stalked out.

George pulled the molten ring from the fire and let it cool. Might as well have it melted down and put together again, he thought.

As the night got colder and colder, George got lonelier and lonelier. Finally, at the nadir of his despondency, he picked up the ring, walked to the door, opened it and threw the ring as far as he could. Then he shot himself.

The rest is history. When Lecher didn't show up at the bar after the holidays his bartender investigated and found Lecher's body in the cabin. He rushed back to town, got an embalmer, a preacher and three more pall-bearers. They returned to the cabin, fixed George up, put him in a box and started the funeral procession.

The preacher led the procession, book in hand and eyes on the ground. The little parade was not three hundred feet from the cabin when the preacher dropped his book and screamed, "Gold!" The embalmer dropped a gallon jug of formaldehyde, the pall-bearers dropped the box, and the Gold Rush of '49 was on. *Columbia Jester*

PART THREE

VERSE

Songs nobody's mother ever taught him

As a pre-juvenile delinquent on Selby Avenue in St. Paul, Minnesota, I first heard a poem that went like this:

Of all the fishes in the sea
The funniest is the bass;
He climbs up into seaweed trees
And slides down on his hands and knees.

Imagine, then, my surprise and delight when I found this limpid quatrain over and over and over again in college magazines dating right up to the current issue.

Which brings us to another great truth about campus humor: there are certain basic poems and jokes that never disappear. Year upon year they circulate, durable little nuggets that age cannot wither nor custom stale.

Most of the verses in the following section are of this variety. There are, however, many brand-new poems. No doubt some of these in years to come will be passed from hand to hand until their origins are lost in antiquity. If this is a prospect that dismays their authors, let them take comfort in the knowledge that they are enriching the folk literature of the land.

AND THEN

I felt his soft touch on my cheek,
And the gentle touch of his hand;
His very presence near me
Seemed a breeze on desert land.

He deftly sought my lips,
My head he did enfold,
Then he broke the silence with:
"Want this filled with silver or gold?"

HAPPY ADAM

BY B. LOTAR

Whatever trouble Adam had,
   No man could make him sore,
By saying when he told a joke,
   "I've heard that thing before."

Columbia Jester

EVENTS PRIOR TO DEATH

BY JOAN MATHEWS

The letter comes, and it says quite simply
That though you are witty and pretty and dimply,

You weren't endowed by the gods above
With some other points a man can love.
But the thrust of thrusts by this heartless lancer
Comes at the end: "I imagine you'll answer."

Unwisely you do. You write him a letter
Which, though it is good, could still be better.
You understand; it's quite all right,
"And you, you darling, can fly a kite."
Then you crawl into bed, douse the light, and sigh,
Shed a tear, gnash your teeth, tear your hair, and die.

The Sector

MOODY POEM

BY R. S.

I stood on a pier in Seattle,
Just off a long wild spree.
While in the water below,
A million devils were beckoning up to me.

The wind like a daspid crazed harpy,
Was screaming in my ear.
The thing to do was end it all,
With a dive off the lonely pier.

I will end it all I whispered.
But before I go I'll write,
And my pen shall pay for my wasted life
With the warning I leave tonight.

And if I should save some sinner
From leading a life of pain,
And turn him away from the gutter,
Then I will not have died in vain.

I fumbled my pocket for a pencil
As I tottered there on the brink,
Found a four-bit piece that I'd overlooked,
And ran like hell for a drink. *Columns*

TELLTALES

Finals, finals everywhere,
With drops and drops of ink;
And never a prof who'll leave the room
And allow a guy to think.

LAMENTATIONS
OF THE TIMES AND CUSTOMS

On Monday he started to talk about what's coming up on the test:
Osmosis, hypnosis,
Psychosis, neurosis,
We're keenly awaiting the rest.

On Tuesday he mentioned a few salient facts that he thought we should know:
Machine-gun ballistics,
Insurance statistics,
And homework to do as we go.

By Wednesday we've wrestled with all forty questions and problems he gave:
Gyration, vibration,
Amelioration,
It sounds like he's starting to rave.

On Thursday, he covered a number of various figures and odd little facts:
The Belt of Orion,
The Nemean lion,
And India's property tax.

On Friday, he lectured on everything east of the Realm of Siam,
Convection corrections,
Ejection, dissections,
Now bring on your simple exam!

On Saturday what do you think the professor had asked on the quiz?
Osmosis, hypnosis,
Psychosis, neurosis,
Machine-gun ballistics
Or vital statistics?
Gyration, vibration,
Amelioration,
The Belt of Orion,
The Nemean lion?
Convection corrections,
Ejection, dissections?
He did not.
He quizzed about:
Hand-painted ceramics,
And thermodynamics,
Organic detectors,
Mechanical vectors,
Agenda, errata,
Addenda and data,
Transmuting, polluting,
Disputing, refuting,
Exponents of x's
And why are there sexes.

And any number of other topics not even remotely hinted at during the previous week. *Yellow Jacket (Georgia Tech)*

THE WOLF

If he parks his little flivver,
Down beside the moonlit river,
And you feel him all aquiver,
Baby—He's a Wolf.

If he says you're gorgeous-looking,
And your dark eyes set him cooking,
But your eyes ain't where he's looking,
Baby—He's a Wolf.

If he says that you're an eyeful,
But his hand begins to trifle,
And his heart pumps like a rifle,
Baby—He's a Wolf.

If by chance when you're akissin',
You can feel his heart amissin',
And you talk but he won't listen,
Baby—He's a Wolf.

If his arms are strong as sinews,
And he stirs the gypsy in you,
And you want him close agin' you,
Baby—You're the Wolf. *Caveman (Wabash College)*

THE LITTLE BIRD

A little bird sits on a tree;
Now he flies away—
Life is like that.
Here today, gone tomorrow.
A little bird sits on a tree;
Now he scratches himself—
Life is like that.
Lousy.

The Crimson Bull (University of Indiana)

LEAVES FROM AN ASSIGNMENT BOOK

A TRIBUTE TO *Vassar Miscellany News*

Monday I've a paper due,
The subject very vital;
(But so far all I have is just
The paper and the title.)

Tuesday I must bring to class
A short but snappy theme

On dreams and their psychology.
(But all I've done is dream.)

Wednesday is the zero hour
My treatise to complete.
(But if I get it done before
Easter, 'twill be a feat.)

Thursday noon I must wind up
A long and boring thesis.
(By Friday I'll have time to go
Quietly to pieces.) *Campus Chat (Vassar College)*

I think that I shall never see
A girl who's good enough for me;
But that's all right; I've no complaint;
I much prefer the ones who ain't.

A Smith girl drinks to calm herself
Her steadiness to improve.
One night she got so steady
She couldn't even move. *Jackolantern*

"Im going to have a little one,"
Said the girl, gay and frisky,
But her boy friend up and fainted
Before he knew she meant whiskey.

There was a young lady from Trent,
Who said she knew what it meant.
  When men asked her to dine,
  Gave her cocktails and wine,
She knew what it meant—but she went.

There was a young lady named Ransom
Who loved three times in a hansom.
But when she asked for more
Came a weak voice from the floor
"My name is Simpson not Samson."

The horse and mule live thirty years
And never know of wines or beers.
The goat and sheep at twenty die
And never taste of scotch or rye.
The cow drinks water by the ton
And at eighteen is mostly done.
The dog at fifteen cashes in
Without the aid of rum or gin.
The cat in milk or water soaks,
Then at twelve it drops and croaks.
The modest, sober, bone-dry hen
Lays eggs for nogs, then dies at ten.
All animals are strictly dry,
They sinless live and sinless die.
But sinful, ginful, rum-soaked men
Survive for three-score years and ten.

ODE TO A ZO 3 PIG FOETUS

BY SIGMUND LOPHAUSER

Hail to thee, pink foetus!
Pig thou never wert.
Fourth-floor Silsby you greet us
On laboratory bench,
Wafting fumes of unprecedented stench.

Foetus, foetus, lying limply,
With your skin all-over dimply,
What eager hand with callous pride
Plunked you in formaldehyde?

From what lady pig or sow
Did they take you? Why and how?
Why must I, a harmless youth,
Cut you up? (It seems uncouth.)

Your mother's womb
Became your tomb.
Your world is now celestine,
But Zo 3 lab
To me is drab,
Dissecting your intestine.

They say your pharynx
Meets your larynx,
And while I wonder whither,
Your fibia
And tibia
Have got me in a dither.

O foetus, my foetus, the dreaded slits and slit.
I have severed every cell, your cerebrum is split.
My knife so keen has seen your spleen,
You're really, I confess,
(From my mauling
Overhauling)
A dank, ungodly mess.

Well, back to your formaldehyde,
Piglet, I will plunk thee,
Something tells me, here, inside,
That, foetus, you will flunk me. *Jackolantern*

Out of bed
And up the Hill
In the morning's
Cold, damp chill.

Looked to neither
Left nor right
Musing on
Last night's delight
"Blue-black eyes,
Vermilion lips,
Luscious girl
With slender hips.
Finally kissed her
In the bar,
Did the same thing
In the car."
Into class
In a daze,
"Why do all
These people gaze?
Look at me
As in disgrace,
God—I forgot
To wash my face!" *Rammer Jammer*

SONG OF EDUCATION

She learned to love
She learned to hate
She learned a Ford would carry eight
She learned to smoke
She learned to coax
She learned to tease
She learned new ways
Of cooking cheese
She learned to neck
And break a date
She's ready now
To graduate.

TWEEDLE DE DUM

A divinity student named Tweedle
Once wouldn't accept a degree.
"It's tough enough being Tweedle,
Without being Tweedle, D.D."

I walked into a barbershop,
The sign was very queer.
"During alterations,
We'll shave you in the rear."

The night was dark and dreary
And the air was full of sleet
The old man plodded through the storm
His shoes all full of feet.

His body shook with icy chill;
His limbs were wracked with pain.
He'd stagger, stop, and shiver there
And then move on again.

He had one match and that was all
No wood in any form.
What did he do? He lit his beard
And moved on snug and warm.

The Rebel (University of Mississippi)

MAIDEN'S PRAYER

Breathes there a man
Around this school
Sufficiently
Restrained and cool,
Enough to limit
His demands

And say "Good night,"
Just holding hands—
Who has the decency
To wait until at least
A second date
To reach a warm
Romantic state,
And give a girl
Some preparation
Before expecting
Osculation
At least an hour
In duration?
If such there be,
Go mark him well,
I'll date the guy
And make him tell
Me what the hell
He had for dinner, that makes him so sick.

Hullabaloo (Franklin and Marshall College)

The shades of night had glided down
Long since on the spires of Hadley town.

On the chapel steps, so the story ran,
Stood a Holyoke maid and a Dartmouth man.

In a voice that was husky and low, said he,
"Won't you walk around the lake with me?"

Quoth the Holyoke maid in a mournful tone,
"But I can't go without a chaperone."

The Dartmouth scholar raised his head,
"I'm sure you won't need one with me," he said.

"Then," quoth the maid, so sweet and low,
"Then," quoth she, "I don't want to go."

Holyoke Ravin' (Mt. Holyoke College)

When I'm wearing strapless things
Instead of buttons and bows,
I notice that my boy friends
Are always on their toes.

THIS

This is not very interesting
But if
You have read this far already
You will
Probably
Read as far as this:
And still
Not really accomplishing
Anything at all

You might
Even read on
Which brings you to
The line you are reading now
And after all that you are still
Probably dumb enough to keep
Right on making
A dope of yourself
By reading
As far down
The page as this. *Princeton Tiger*

Who comforts me in moments of despair?
Who runs fingers lightly through my hair?
Who cooks my meals and darns my hose?
Squeezes nose drops in my nose?
Who always has a word of praise?
Sets out my rubbers on rainy days?

Who scrubs my back when in a shower?
And wakes me up at the proper hour?
Who helps keep me on the beam?
And figures in my every dream?
I do. *Flatiron*

TEARS FROM ONE WHO DIDN'T REALIZE HOW GOOD HE HAD IT

BY GINIE BENNETT

Hail the benches 'neath the trees
And the passing birds and bees;

Hail to spring and hail to fall,
Hail the gals, we loved them all;

Hail the profs and past exams,
Likewise praise the cribs and crams;

Glory be the games and dances,
All the pinnings and romances,
Sleeping late and cutting classes,
And the countless brimming glasses;

Allah praise the morning after
And the headaches and the laughter;

Heaven bless the cigarettes
And the old still-unpaid debts—

Something I don't like at all
Tells me that the cruel world calls,
And my recommend for work
Praises an "accomplished Shirk";
College life was so carefree,
Oh what will now become of me?

So toast the good old campus feel—
Believe me, fellows, *it's been real! Old Line*

POEMS BY JOAN

BY JOAN LIFTIN

House mothers are a clan apart
They bear no traces of a heart.
They wait till you're a minute late,
Then gleefully they close the gate.
They seem in some way fiendish-bent
They chortle when they ask for rent.
Some day, to spite the damned old bears,
I think I'll bring a man upstairs. *Sundial*

If an apple a day
Keeps the doctor away,
They'll soon be condemned
By the A.M.A.

She's a pretty little wench
Sitting there upon the bench
Looking very coy and shy
At every passing college guy.
Ah, such eyes.
Concentric thighs.
It's too damned bad
She's bald.

I drink to your health when we're together,
I drink to your health when I'm alone,
I drink to your health so often
I've damned near ruined my own!

Rest is a surcease from worry and care,
Sleep is a blessing no one mocks;
Thinkers and statesmen agree on this fact,
I move we eliminate all eight o'clocks.

TREES: I

I think that I shall never see
  A girl refuse a meal that's free;
A girl whose hungry eyes aren't fixed
  Upon a drink that's being mixed.
A girl who won't forever wear
  A bunch of junk to match her hair;
A girl who looks at boys all day
  And figures ways to make them pay.
Girls are loved by jerks like me
  Cause who the hell wants to kiss a tree. *Penn Pix*

TREES: II

(If it had been written by a certain modern poet)

It often strikes me as being queer and unusual and really quite odd
that nobody in the whole world, with the definite exception of God,
can make a tree. Anybody can make pomes.
Anyone can make ash cans, automobiles, crêpes suzette, or homes,
but a tree is different; a horse of another color, something else again.
A tree that may, for all you or I know, or imagine, or care, be wearing
a nest of robins in its hair.
Who (meaning the tree) has a bosom on which snow has lain and
who has been kept by, or at least lived intimately with, the rain.
Now pomes, in brief, are made by fools like you, or more frequently, like me.
But I don't suppose you'll ever catch either one of us going around
dashing off a tree. *Covered Wagon* (*University of Oklahoma*)

TREES: III

I always hoped that I would see
A girl as lovely as a tree.
A girl that looks at me all day,
Whose lips to me all night would pray.
Upon whose bosom I could have lain,
Who would have necked with might and main,
Whose lips would meet with mine with zest,
Whose form would boast a lovely breast.
God alone creates a tree,
But, God, could I create with thee! *Jackolantern*

TREES: IV

I think that I shall never see,
Along the road, an unscarred tree,

A tree that looks at cars all day
And lifts her leafy arms to pray

That the next car whizzing by
Will not be driven by a "collich guy."

A tree that may in summer shade
A mass of tourists in the glade,

Tourists whose hungry mouths are pressed
Against Milwaukee's Bottled Best.

Cars are driven by fools like me,
But it takes a truck to wreck a tree. *Princeton Tiger*

CHAPEL HERO

They gave him twenty minutes
but he finished up in ten.
Oh, there's a prince of speakers
and servant unto men.

His diction wasn't such a much,
he hemmed and hawed a bit;
But still he spoke a lot of sense,
and after that—he quit.
At first we sat plumb paralyzed,
then cheered and cheered again;
For they gave him twenty minutes
and he finished up in ten. *The Skiff*

LIMERICKS FROM THE *PELICAN*

An earnest young teaching assistant
From the facts of the world was far distant
A girl in his section
Made an obscene suggestion
Which would have shocked him like hell if he'd listent.

There once was a model named Moyer
Who fled from her artist employer;
She said, "I will pose
In clothes in repose,
But I'm damned if I'll pose like for Goyer."

There once was an African Mau-Mau
Who got into a terrible Row-Row;
The cause of the friction
Was his practicing diction
Saying "How-How Now-Now Brown Cow-Cow."

A freshman from down in Laguna
Once fell in love with a tuna
The affair, although comic
Was so economic
He wished he had thought of it soona.

There once was a campus bohemian
Whose expression of face was so simian
The liberal folks
Made him butt of their jokes
And he never went out with no wimian.

A coed with eyes wide and starry
Missed lockout, which caused her no warry
She said, "That's allright,
I'm not sleepy tonight,
And the door will be open tomarry."

MEMOIRS

I knew a boy from Yale once
A Bulldog brave was he
But too much bull and too much dog
Estranged the lad from me.

And then there was a Dartmouth boy
Among the lads I knew
He grasped with a Beta grip
And broke my back in two.

I knew a boy from Amherst once
But that was way back when
I asked him who Lord Jeffrey was
He brought me home at ten.

My Princeton love was blithe and gay
The sweetest one of all
How sad, New Jersey College called
Him back to Nassau Hall.

A pre-med was my Harvard man
But how could you expect me
To madly love a monster who
One night tried to dissect me?

Où sont les neiges d'antan, I carry
Those past loves of our lives,
My only comment is: may God
Protect and guide their future wives. *Campus Cat*

The birds do it;
The bees do it;
The little bats do it.
Mama, why can't I take flying lessons?

The fog
Comes
On little cat feet
As you sit for a test
And sits
On silent haunches
Hovering over every desk
And then moves on—
Only sometimes it doesn't.

Spectator (University of Virginia)

LOOSE NUDE

"A nude man, loose on the corner of Linnaean and Walker streets, was reported to the Cambridge police last night . . ."—The Crimson

They tell there is something crude
About the antics of a nude;
They say the sight is quite obscene
And Radcliffe girls turn deathly green
When minus pants and checkered vest
The sprite appears and beats his chest.
I don't believe it.

They tell that one recent night
Five maidens took an awful fright.
While trudging their accustomed beat
They saw a nude on Walker Street
Who tipsily began to sing
And screamed he represented Spring.
I don't believe it.

It was a ghastly sight they say,
This lustful harbinger of May,
For there he stood without a stitch—
Adonis stolen from his niche—
No tie, no Oxford or gray flannels
(Unheard of in all college annals!)
I don't believe it.

But consider, if you please, Chief Randall,
(I don't accuse you of the scandal)
How colorless, how truly sad if
Nudes were to be banned from Radcliffe.
And after all, it's quite a trek
To trundle bare-skinned up from Tech.
And that I do believe. *Harvard Lampoon*

CALL HIM MISTER

BY JOHN H. UPDIKE

The man who dwells within the basement,
mending pipes, adjusting casement,
stoking furnace, burning trash,
and puttying the window sash,
is known to all as Mr. Smith;
he putters through existence with
no first name. He stands alone
among his fellows; all are known—
doctor, lawyer, Indian chief,
butler, gambler, fortuneteller,
people earthy, people stellar—
as more than surnames; not the man
who empties out the garbage can.
Had Percy Bysshe heaved coal, might well he
come to us as Mr. Shelley,

or GBS as Mr. Shaw.
Ere Elba, if Napoleon saw

a furnace, Mr. Bonaparte
would thrill the loyal Frenchman's heart,
and likewise, baseball-happy youth
might speak of Misters Cobb and Ruth.
For Latin scholars, high school teachers,
sacred saints or reverend preachers
cannot command respect like that
acknowledged him in grimy hat
who spins his web of pipe. He knows
the crannies where no other goes,
black bowels of buildings. Endless night
is his domain. He gives us light
and heat. His mistress, children, wife
have called him "mister" all his life.
And such the rigid, fearsome nature
of janitorial nomenclature,
upon the roll of Judgment Day,
among the names and records, may
this man be listed as no more
than Mr. Smith, the janitor. *Harvard Lampoon*

MODERN AMERICANS–I

BY JOHN H. UPDIKE

Mrs. Agnes Video
doesn't really care to know
how to be a useful wife;
she's content to spend her life
in a paralytic stare
at an idiotic square
of electrons on display;
subtle psychical decay,
spreading south, has sealed her lips,
stultified her finger tips,
then, from out her darkened womb
issue messengers of doom:
infants, born with bloodshot eyes,
–glassy, blank–shall modernize

this, our earth; the dusty world
will antennaed be, and Berled:
putrefaction of the mind
marks our Agnes's Mankind. *Harvard Lampoon*

SONG OF THE BOOZY SUSIE

But Mother, I tell you I really don't drink,
  I just bought that beer for shampoos.
That brandy is not for the purpose you think,
  I use it for seasoning, not booze.
That bottle of gin makes delightful cologne,
  And the bourbon is good for a chill.
That fifth of tequila's a friend's, not my own,
  She can drink it but I never will.
My temperance has earned me a wide reputation
  And won me attention galore.
I'm known far and wide as the new Carrie Nation,
  So help me up off of the floor. *Showme*

ENNUI OF AN ENGLISH MAJOR

BY LOIS JUDGE

You can take your Mr. Wordsworth,
And his yellow primrose, too,
And his friend old Mr. Coleridge
With his owl's "Tu whit, tu whoo."
You can take those nature poets
And do something awfully rash,
Even throw them in the ash can—
If you leave me Ogden Nash. *The Sector*

LITTLE WILLIE POEM

Little Willie wrote a book
Woman was the theme he took

Woman was his only text.
Ain't he cute? He's oversexed.

THE QUACKS AND THE QUIDNUNC

BY DR. BENJAMIN F. SLEDD

A doctor stood beside my bed,
I dreamed last night—and shook his head,
And in his wise slow way he said:
"Your system needs the vitameens
Of cabbage stalks and turnip greens
And Boston's slimy pork-and-beans."
And straight I bought a knife and fork
And went to sawing short my pork
And splitting fine each bean;

But daily grew more lank and lean.
And in another doctor came,
Unscrewed my bolts and pins,
And took apart my shacklin' frame
And sorted all my outs and ins.
"Your system needs the vitamins
Of rusty rails and tarnished tins."
And iron now is all my diet,
Till all my blood is in a riot;
And all my insides turned to metal,
With pot forever scolding kettle.

And in another doctor came,
And rapped my ribs
And knapped my nibs
And jammed my jibs.
(Reader, don't give a Boston bean,
If you don't know what these may mean
And where the same may be:
You're no more ignorant than he.)
But now he cried, "It is a shame!
"Your system needs the vitameens
That only grow upon the vines

And in the malted grain.
Bourbon or Scotch is what you need;
A gill or more at every feed,
And in between each table scene
A pint of beer or good red wines."

But here I woke; and, oh, the pain
To know that I have dreamed in vain!

The Student (Wake Forest College)

WILLIE'S GONE

We'll never more bail out our brat,
No more we'll pay his fines,
He hung himself with Pa's cravat,
Blest be the tie that binds.

Octopus (University of Wisconsin)

LINK BY LINK

I kissed her in the moonlight,
My head was in a whirl;
My mouth and eyes were full of hair—
My arms were full of girl. *Princeton Tiger*

I kissed her in the garden
And my brain was rather gladdish;
My coat lapel was powder white—
My lips and cheeks were reddish. *Pelican*

I kissed her in the vestibule,
I yearned for more and more;
I went to kiss her once again—
But kissed the closing door. *Notre Dame Juggler*

I kissed her in my dreams that night—
The kiss was wondrous sweet;
But I awoke, enraptured,
And found I'd kissed the sheet. *Bowdoin Bearskin*

I kissed her in her birch canoe,
But not so carefully;
And when I tried it once again,
I kissed the silver sea.

Panther (University of Pittsburgh)

Mary had a little lamb
The lamb had halitosis,
And every place that Mary went
The people held their nosis.

SIDE SHOW

Now, I'm all alone.
A minute ago
I was standing here
Watching the little monkeys
And a very pretty girl
Was standing in front of me
And just then one of the
Monkeys made a move
Towards her.
She suddenly screamed
And fell backwards
Right into my arms—
She hesitated for a moment there,
Then said,
"Oh, that little thing
Frightened me so,
I beg your pardon."

And then I said gallantly,
"Not at all. Let's go over
And watch the elephants"—
And now I'm all alone. *Lehigh Bachelor*

POME

BY D. R. TURGEON

While scanning o'er some poems one day
A thought occurred to me.
If Cummings had studied at ohms and volts
He'd be E. E. Cummings, E.E.

If Gertrude were a-sipping beer
And feeling rather fine,
Who'd run when e'er she slapped her hands
And fill up Gertrude's stein?

Returning from the wars at last
Would Conrad Aiken crack,
"Look, Ma, it's me. I'm home again.
It's me, your Aiken back!"

And finally, I ask myself,
While staring at the ground,
"If Ezra had a hammer, just
How hard would Ezra pound?" *Cornell Widow*

The men are very simple folk,
  I like 'em.
They take me out until they're broke,
  I like 'em.

I like them naughty, tall and lean,
And short and fat and good and green,
And many other kinds I've seen.
  I like 'em.

They take me to a formal hop,
  I like 'em.
They take me to the candy shop,
  I like 'em.

But when they show that they don't care,
And hug me roughly like a bear,
And crack my ribs and muss my hair,
    O Man, I love 'em. *Octopus*

THE SERENADER

BY JAEL (JOHN WOODS)

The moon was shining brightly in a cloudless sky of blue,
As I waited for her slim and graceful form to come in view;
And, having lost her once, I vow'd I'd let her go no more,
For the moon was shining brightly, as I think I said before.

Oh! her hair was black and silky on her bare and graceful head,
And she came across the garden with a slow and stately tread,
And her eyes were coals of fire with the joy of being free,
Close to Nature, and, although she didn't know it, close to me.

So I watched without a movemnt as she steadily drew near,
Tense with eager expectation for the sound I longed to hear;
For I'd sworn she should no longer spurn me, Fate's, not mine,
    the choice,
And I knew it would assist my aim if once I heard her voice.

Then her lips began to quiver as she gazed into the sky,
And I smiled, because I saw my opportunity was nigh;
Then she raised her song to heaven—so I rose from where I sat,
And next morning Mrs. Tompkins mourned her late-beloved cat.

T.C.D. (Trinity College, Dublin)

NEE JOANNE CONNELLEY

Tall, lissome Joanne Connelley was going to forego her debut and get married instead. The man of her choice was Robert Sweeney, thirty-seven, ex-amateur golf champion, ex-combat pilot. . . . To her practiced eye, the debutante party is a poor pitch. . . . Said Joanne: "I don't really like college boys. I know what they're going to say, and how they think. They're so silly, and don't know how to drink." **Time,** November 8, 1948.

Farewell to thee, Miss Connelley,
Farewell, and get thee hence–
You're getting in the big time now,
No more Pudding, no more Fence.

No more parties, they're the bunk.
No football weekends, they're too drunk.
No Elis, loaded with martinis,
Who can't hold them like the Sweeneys.
I know what they're always thinking,
Always saying "Let's get stinking!"
Dances are such bores, such pushes,
No more trips into the bushes.

No more weekends going down
To see the boys in Cap and Gown.
No more cocktail parties, lunches,
Watching clubmen throwing punches,
No more evenings spent at Mory's
Listening to those dirty stories.
No more watching Harvard lose,
No more dresses soaked with booze.

We'll sit back with many grins,
And stroke our adolescent chins.
Have a tall one in our frats
And leave you to your mewling brats,
Your cooking, sewing, pots and pans,
We'll settle for our night-club tans. *Harvard Lampoon*

END OF THE LINE

I have one admonition
To make in recognition
Of last spring's new addition
to the tree-lined River Drive.

It has to do with you and me and
modern trends and . . .
Mountainburgers,
Strangleburgers,
Better, Bigger Terrorburgers,
Roasted, Toasted Englishburgers,
Giant Bucking Broncoburgers,
Beefburgers, Mooseburgers,
Hellish Double Troubleburgers,
Eelburgers, Sealburgers,
Brand New Eagerbeaverburgers,
and Philly's Just Plain Scrappleburgers,
as well as Heavenly Soleburgers,
not to mention Granny's Welldone Route 128-burgers,
Even Peptobismoburgers,
Crab-And-Clam-Filled Cramburgers,
Mackerelburgers, Whaleburgers,
and . . . Justlikemother's Ownburgers,
Squeezeburgers, Grabbaburgers,
Grand and Glorious Twinburgers,
Whizzburgers, Bangburgers,
Impossible Jane Russellburgers.

You see, I must be growing old
to feel invaded by . . . a Flying Saucerburger,
Midwest Rabbitburger,
Pigeonburger,
Oysterburger,
Walrusburger,
Troutburger,
Owl or Jetburger . . .
but, even so, I sometimes sit and wonder what

the catsup-covered Hamburger is thinking of us now. *Harvard Lampoon*

NAUGHTY! NAUGHTY!

The sofa sagged in the center
The shades were pulled just so.
The family had retired,
The parlor light burned low.
There came a sound from the sofa
As the clock was striking two,
And the co-ed slammed her textbook
With a thankful "Well, I'm through."

Beanpot (Boston University)

ME MUDDER

"M" is for the million drinks she bought me.

Who makes a daily grind seem bearable?
Me Mudder

Who helps me over de bumps?
Me Mudder

When life's chorus
Makes me hoarse,
Who soothes me pantin' liddle t'roat?
Me Mudder

When all de woild's a stage
And I feel de coise of age,
Who raises me cane?
Me Mudder

When udder dames are frilly,
Who's me tiger lily?
Me Mudder

Life is just burlesque
And humoresque
But who's for real?

Me Mudder

When I'm bad,
Who's glad?

Me

Who's a cool Mudder?

Mudder

The Rivet

With inward chuckles
Of feminine glee,
You knew at last
You were rid of me.
With sentences caustic
And voice refined,
You charmingly gave me
A piece of your mind.
But the triumph's not yours
For if only you knew,
I've been trying for months
To get rid of you! *The Skiff*

The wonderful love of a beautiful maid,
The love of a staunch true man,
The love of a baby unafraid
Have existed since time began.
But the greatest love—the love of loves
Even greater than that of a mother—
Is the tender, passionate, infinite love
Of one drunken bum for another.

PARTY PARTY

People grasping
Cocktail glasses
Stand in gasping
Teeming masses.
People smoking,
People drinking,
Coughing, choking,
Getting stinking.
Some discreetly
Boiled or fried;
Some completely ossified.
Liquor spilling,
Trousers sopping,
Steady swilling,
Bodies dropping.
Glasses falling
On the floor;
People calling,
"Drop some more."
Bodies steaming,
Morals stretching,
Women screaming,
Some still fetching,
Heavy smoking,
Air gets thicker.
Someone croaking,
"No more liquor . . ."
What? What???
No
  more
    liquor . . .
People snicker,
Unbelieving,
No more liquor?
Let's be leaving,

No more drinking?
Groans and hisses!
What a stinking
Party this is.

Pine Needle (University of Maine)

MYSTERY

I think the Mormon prophet was
 A very funny man.
I wonder how his wives enjoyed
 His prophet-sharing plan.

There was a young flapper named Ruth
Who stepped out one night with a youth
 To a masquerade ball;
 She wore no dress at all.
When asked what she was, she said "Truth."

Columbia Jester

Last night I held a little hand
So dainty and so neat
I thought my heart would surely burst
So wildly did it beat.
No other hand e'er held so tight
Could greater gladness bring
Than the one I held last night
It was—
Four aces and a king.

Pointer (U. S. Military Academy)

A woman's whim is ever this—
To snare a man's reluctant kiss.
And snaring it, to make him pant
For things that nice girls never grant.

Rock-a-bye baby
On the treetop.
Don't you fall out
It's a helluva drop.

Once there was a man named Bound
While cutting his lawn, he drowned.
'Twas dark and he fell
Down the shaft of a well;
Couldn't tell his grass from a hole in the ground.

Little Miss Muffet decided to rough it
In a cabin quite old and medieval
A rounder espied her and plied her with cider
And now she's the forest's prime evil.

There was a little girl
And she had a little curl
Plastered on her forehead
And when she was good
She was very, very good
And when she was bad
She was marvelous. *Yale Record*

He was seated in the parlor
And he said unto the light
"Either you or I, old fellow,
Will be turned down tonight." *Yale Record*

A corpulent maiden named Croll
Had an idea exceedingly droll:
At a masquerade ball
Dressed in nothing at all
She backed in as a Parker House roll.

The Purple Cow

He came in through the window
As the innocent maid lay dreaming.
Her pretty arms beneath her head
Set his vicious eyes a-gleaming.
With a sudden spring he reached her;
She awoke with a violent shriek,
And smashed the darn mosquito
That bit her on the cheek. *The Purple Cow*

I never kiss
I never neck
I never say hell
I never say heck
I'm always good
I'm always nice
I don't play poker
I shake no dice
I never drink
I never flirt
I never gossip
Or spread the dirt
I have no line
Of funny tricks
But what the hell
I'm only six! *Froth*

I LIKE TO SING ALSO

JOHN H. UPDIKE

I like to sing in the same way that I like to cook, or to fish, or to watch a ball game, or go to our wonderful St. Louis zoo—or read an issue of LIFE magazine.

—Helen Traubel in *Life*, February 1

Traubel, Traubel, boil and bubble,
Gobble fish and cheer a double,
Warble nobly, ogle cages,
Wallow deep in Life's *dark pages.*

The throng at the Met was enormous;
It said, "We've been waiting too long.
Miss Traubel is scheduled to warm us,
To parboil our cockles in song.
Her absence implies she needs humbling—"
The curtain rolled back with a squeal:
There stood the stage manager mumbling,
"Miss Traubel is cooking a meal."

Traubel, Traubel, boil and bubble
Eye of newt and burdock stubble,
Stir it, burn it, serve with smile;
The Valkyries *can vait a vhile.*

The zoo was agog in St. Louis,
The cheetahs were bleating like sheep,
"Oh, why hasn't Traubel come to us
To gawk as we waddle and creep?"
Each tail from the cat's to the camel's,
Each in its own manner, went swish;
So the keeper explained to the mammals,
"Miss Traubel is catching a fish."

Traubel, Traubel, boil and bubble,
Cast and hook, no decent chub'll
Dare resist your tender trammels—
Other days you'll visit mammals.

A man was on first and on second,
The ball cleared the fence and was gone;
The manager sobbed, "I had reckoned
On Traubel to spur my men on.
Can Traubel be over the ocean?
Can Traubel be under the knife?"
The loudspeakers boomed with emotion,
"Miss Traubel is reading her Life."

Traubel, Traubel, boil and bubble
Over Life, *where mortal trouble*
Is engraved, arranged, admired.
Truly, Traubel, aren't you tired? *Harvard Lampoon*

PART FOUR

SATIRE AND BURLESQUE

Parodies of science, literature, and the arts

For me as an undergraduate writer, satire and burlesque were always the most fun. Even today, though my temples recede and my transmission needs oil, I still like to pick up a slapstick and belabor the arts, the sciences, and the humanities.

*Like this:**

Chemistry is the oldest of sciences, having been discovered by Ben Franklin in 55 B.C. when an apple fell on his head while he was shooting the breeze with Pythagoras one day outside the Acropolis. (The reason they were outside the Acropolis and not inside was that Pythagoras had been thrown out for drawing right triangles all over the walls. They had several meetings outside the Acropolis, but finally Franklin said, "Look, Pythagoras, this is nothing against you, see, but I'm no kid any more and if I keep laying around on this wet grass with you, I'm liable to get the breakbone fever. I'm going inside." Pythagoras, friendless now, moped around Athens for a while, then drifted off to Brussels where he married a girl named Harriet Sigafoos and went into the linseed-oil game. He would almost certainly be forgotten today had not Shakespeare written *Othello*.)

But I digress. We were beginning a discussion of chemistry, and the best way to begin is, of course, with fundamentals. Chemicals are divided into elements. There are four: air, earth, fire, and water. Any number of delightful combinations can be made from these elements, such as firewater, Dacron, and chef's salad.

Chemicals can be further divided into the classes of explosive and non-explosive. A wise chemist always touches a match to his chemicals before he begins an experiment.

A great variety of containers of different sizes and shapes are used in a chemistry lab. There are tubes, vials, beakers, flasks, pipettes, and retorts. (A retort is also a snappy comeback, such as "Oh yeah?" or "So's your old man!"

(Perhaps the most famous retort ever made was delivered by none other than Noah Webster himself. It seems that one day Mr. Webster's wife walked unexpectedly into Mr. Webster's office and found Mr. Webster's secretary sitting on Mr. Webster's knee. "Why, Mr. Webster!" cried Mr. Webster's wife. "I am surprised!"

* From *On Campus with Max Shulman*. Courtesy, Philip Morris Co.

("No, my dear," he replied. "*I* am surprised. *You* are astonished."

(Well sir, it must be admitted that old Mr. Webster got off a good one, but still one cannot help wishing he had spent less time trifling with his secretary and more time working on his dictionary. Many of his definitions show an appalling want of scholarship. Take, for instance, what happened to me not long ago. I went to the dictionary to look up "houghband" which is a band that you pass around the leg and neck of an animal. At the time I was planning to pass bands around the legs and necks of some animals, and I wanted to be sure I ordered the right thing.

(Well sir, thumbing through the H's in the dictionary, I happened to come across "horse." And this is how Mr. Webster defines "horse"—"a large, solid-hoofed, herbivorous mammal . . . used as a . . . draft animal."

(Now this, I submit, is just plain sloppiness. The most cursory investigation would have shown Mr. Webster that horses are not mammals. Mammals give milk. Horses do not give milk. It has to be taken from them under the most severe duress.

(Nor is the horse a draft animal, as Mr. Webster says. Man is a draft animal. Mr. Webster obviously had the cavalry in mind, but even in the cavalry it is men who are drafted. Horses volunteer.)

But I digress. We were discussing chemistry. I have told you the most important aspects, but there are many more—far too many to cover in the space remaining here. However, I am sure that there is a fine chemistry lab at your very own college. Why don't you go up some afternoon and poke around? Make a kind of fun day out of it. Bring ukuleles. Wear funny hats. Toast frankfurters on the Bunsen burners. Be gay, be merry, be loose, for chemistry is your friend!

MY ROD SPITS DEATH

BY PHOEBE ERICKSON AND LENNIE FEINBERG

I straightened the seams of my seamless nylons, opened the drawer of my desk, took out a bottle of Seagram's, and poured myself four fingers. It was so damn good I poured myself another four fingers. That was even better. Two hours later, I opened my eyes. I was lying on the floor, and a man was standing above me. With one swift glance I took in the empty Seagram's bottle on the desk, the empty Four Roses bottle on the floor, and the half-empty Dixie Belle bottle in the wastebasket.

"Hi, hon," I said, and dragged myself over to a chair. "Gimme a butt."

He took a deck of Fatimas out of his pocket, lighted one, and handed it to me. I propped open one eye and looked at him. He was the most beautiful man I had ever seen. A perfectly tailored gray flannel suit was draped over his magnificent six-foot-2-inch frame. The perfectly featured face was topped by a head of curly black hair. Only one thing marred his handsomeness. A jagged scar curved from the middle of his forehead to his right cheek, down around his chin, and up to his left cheek, ending under the ear lobe. I retched and ground out my cigarette against the chair leg.

"Listen, babe," he said, "I need your help. I need it bad."

"What's your problem, Big Boy?" I asked, and fished the bottle of Dixie Belle out of the wastebasket. I took a swig, undulated over to the washstand, and doused my face with cold water. "Damn that salesgirl," I muttered, "she told me this mascara was waterproof."

"Sweetheart," he said, "you gotta get me out of this. I been framed —framed!"

"Sure, babe, that's what they all say."

He lighted a butt, took a few drags, and threw it in my face. It burned a slight hole in my cheek. I undulated over to him, pulled out my rod from my thigh holster, and plugged him in the gut.

"I lose more damn customers that way," I said, and finished off the Dixie Belle.

After disposing of the body in an empty closet, I tore off the soiled suit I was wearing and pulled out of my wardrobe a new V-cut satin job with plenty of room around the thigh for my rod. I picked up my handbag and walked out of the building and across the street to the lousy joint a friend of mine was crazy enough to keep going.

As I sat there nursing my beer, a gorgeous hunk of the male species wandered over and sat down on the stool next to me. He inched over and stared down the front of my dress.

"How about a cigarette, babe?" he asked in a slow drawl.

"Sure, always glad to get one free," I replied, with a touch similar to his.

He peeled out a deck of Luckies and threw me one with a grubby mitt.

"Thanks, pal," I said. "Much obliged."

His eyes were still glued to the front of my dress.

"What are you looking for, buried treasure?"

He lifted his head and gave me the full voltage from a pair of deep brown eyes. The skin crawled up my back, but it slid back down again when I ordered another beer and heard his story.

"Listen, sweetheart," he said, "I'm in a tough spot. I heard you were the best private eye in the business, and I'm willing to pay plenty."

"I'll take the case," I replied. "There's something kinda nice about three squares a day. What's the story?"

"You've heard of Big Jim O'Flaherty, haven't ya? Well, I owe him fifty thousand dollars for a canasta game. I know damn well the cards were marked, but there was nothing I could do. I can afford to pay him, but I ain't gonna pay for anything he got by cheating."

"I like the man who sticks up for his rights," I said, and fished the deck of Luckies out of his pocket.

I slid off the stool, and I knew from the way he swiveled around to get one last look that he'd know where to get in touch with me. "Call me in a week, honey," I said, and ambled out the door.

Back in my apartment, I took a cold shower, put on my black silk robe, fixed a scotch and soda, and sat down to figure out my plan of action. A half hour later, I knew what I was going to do.

My first objective was Lou's Hawaiian Haven on the waterfront. I slid into a booth in the back and ordered a beer. A few minutes later, Lou was seated across from me. "What can I do for ya, honey," he asked, and lighted a butt.

"I'm looking for Big Jim O'Flaherty. You can tell me where to find him."

"Not so loud, Micki," he said, glancing around the joint. "You never can tell where one of Big Jim's crew is going to turn up. What do you want to know for?"

"You sling the beers and I'll ask the questions. Tell me where I can find him, and then scram."

"Okay, okay, honey, don't get sore. Just curious. Look for a guy named Gimpy at Joe's place on fifty-third. That's all I can tell ya."

I knew I could depend on Lou. We were buddies together at P.S. 159.

I walked into Joe's and bought a deck of butts. "Where can I find Gimpy?" I asked the pimply-faced kid behind the counter. He jerked a thumb toward the door in the back. "He's ina back room, gorgeous."

I kicked open the door of the back room and saw a man slumped over a table. There was a knife in his back, his throat was slit, and blood streamed from a gaping hole in his side. He was dead. I frisked him and found a book of matches with the name "The Utica Club" engraved on it in gold. I knew I had heard that name before. Then I remembered. Big Jim owned The Utica Club and used it as a front for his rackets.

As I walked past the kid at the counter, I gave him a slow wink. He leered back at me and dropped a carton of cigarettes he was stacking on the counter.

Outside, I climbed into the heap, and headed for my apartment for a shower and a quick change.

When I walked into Big Jim's night club, the headwaiter fell all over himself showing me a table. A few minutes later Big Jim himself was standing in front of me. He stared appreciatively at my green taffeta gown. He was short and pudgy, and his black hair was plastered down with half a jar of vaseline. His face had been pushed in by one fist too many. But with all of this, there was something attractive about him. Then I knew what it was. He was wearing the tie I had sent my father for Christmas.

Big Jim squeezed into the chair across from me and offered me a smoke from a platinum case.

"Thanks, Big Jim."

"Ya can call me Big, honey."

"Okay–Big."

"How come a beautiful doll like you comes in here alone?"

"Listen, Big," I snapped, "I didn't come in here to pass the time of day. I'm here on business. My name is Micki Slammer."

The blood drained out of his face, and the hand that held the cigarette started to shake. But a second later he regained his composure. Only now the smile was gone, and the watery eyes were hard.

"Follow me," he snapped.

I checked the rod in the holster through a slit in the gown and followed him through the plush club into his plushier office. Big Jim waddled over to a built-in bar and fixed himself a stiff one.

"What's the matter, Big?" I asked, "forget your manners?"

"You'll pay for anything you get in here, shamus," he growled.

I backhanded him across the mouth and knocked him against the desk. I slammed him a couple more times, slugged him in the gut, and gave him the knee. He lay slobbering on the floor, and I gave him a foot in the teeth with the special lead platforms I had built on my open-toed evening slippers. He stopped slobbering. I squirted him with the seltzer bottle until he opened his eyes. I yanked him to his feet and shoved him into a chair.

'Okay, Big," I said, "where's the I.O.U. for fifty grand that that stupid kid gave you?"

"I don't know what you're talking about, shamus."

"Maybe this will help you remember," I said, and chipped my nail polish on his ugly mug.

"Okay, okay," he gasped, "I'll get it for you." He staggered over to his desk and opened the drawer. Before he could put his hand on the rod he had hidden there, I had pumped four slugs into him. He slid to the floor, gurgled a minute, and lay still.

I rifled his desk and finally found the I.O.U. hidden under a copy of *My Gun Is Quick*. I tore it into pieces, burned them, and ground the ashes into the rug. I shoved the rod back into its holster, patted a stray hair into place, and left by Big Jim's private entrance.

Outside, the rain was a fine mist. As I climbed into my heap, shoved the key into the lock, and kicked the starter, I could feel the pleasant sensation of another evening well spent creep over me. I lighted up a butt, swung into a stream of traffic, and headed for my apartment and a good night's sleep. *Froth*

THE SUB-DEB

EDITED BY JAN WILD

So many sub-debs write me asking for information on what to wear, how to look, how to act and what to do on a first date that I thought I'd just sit down here at my rusty old typewriter and answer those questions right here and now. Before I get specific, let me give you innocents a few general words of wisdom.

Girls, good looks count. There is just no sense in denying that. Sure, boys are interested in your mental ability and your personality. But first (and may I say: foremost) they are interested in your physical attractiveness. And to be even more blunt: your body. There! Now I've said it. The fat's in the fire now. (If you'll pardon my pun.) If you are not a raving beauty play up your good points, like your Marlene Dietrich legs or your lovely chestnut hair. Take me for instance—and all the boys do, don't kid yourself on that score. Now I have an interesting chest; some say it's a deformity; I say it's a chest. Now, my chest (and forgive me, girls, if I am prone to boast, but being prone is one of my incurable weaknesses) is interesting, real dreamy, outstanding. I play that particular thing(s) up to advantage. And believe me the boys appreciate it. But, my dears, don't overdo the thing. For instance, you don't see me going around stripped to the waist. Not if you are a Sub-deb, you don't. So, like I say, play up your advantages. Think of your particular virtue like merchandise. Take a lesson from the shopkeeper: if he has a good piece of stuff he puts it on display, lays the goods on the line, so to speak. So be it with you. And then, sweets, that first date will be upon you, literally, before you know it. Or better: before you know it, literally. Or better . . . well, let's get on the question box.

HOW OLD SHOULD A GIRL BE BEFORE SHE DATES?

Before she dates what? Let's say men. Well, we feel that she should at least be in the fifth grade. By the fifth grade you've got something to talk about. You've studied algebra and geography and American History. After all, you can't talk spelling, can you now?

DO BOYS LIKE GIRLS TO WEAR MAKE-UP?

Boys like girls to wear nothing.

HOW CAN YOU LET A BOY KNOW THAT YOU'D LIKE HIM TO BE YOUR FIRST DATE WITHOUT APPEARING TO CHASE HIM?

Tell your best friend to hint subtly to the boy: "Sally's a sweet girl, have you had a chance to talk to her?" Or, "Why not take Sally out sometime? She's got her own apartment."

If you don't have a best friend to serve as Cupid, you can try a more direct approach. Look up the boy's schedule of classes and make it a point to be where he is. He's bound to catch on after seeing you around so much. Or if he works in the local drugstore, you could start getting your hypodermics there. But really, the best way is to find out those things that he likes and then casually ask him questions about them without letting him know you found out beforehand. Say, "Hi, Elmer. What's new with the ceramics of the Papauan element of the Southern Malayan Archipelago?"

WHAT SHOULD I DO WHEN MY FIRST DATE COMES TO PICK ME UP?

He's on time, and so are you. Boys are as shy as girls, especially when they've got to meet your parents. He'll appreciate your show of confidence when you calmly introduce him to the door and slam your parents. Here's an easy rule to remember on those introductions: the man is presented to the woman unless the woman happens to be your date in which case he would be a man and that would mean that you'd have to decide whether you should introduce to your mother or your father first. Say, "Mother, I'd like you to meet Dad." When you get around to introducing him to your sister say, "Nancy, this is Don." Yes, that's much better, except that this happens to be Elmer, remember?

Since this is your first date with Elmer, invite him into the living room. This gives your parents a chance to find out he's as nice as you say he is and it prevents him from trying to neck with you in the kitchen. To get the conversation rolling, throw Dad a line—"Elmer thinks winters are getting milder each year." Or "Elmer thinks Nick Kenny is the greatest living American poet." Watch that one rock Dad back on his heels! Or, rather than start a controversy, appeal to Dad's ego with "Elmer has been dying to meet you since you got your new glass eye." This starts a gabfest between the two men. But remember you are responsible for getting Elmer away and off on the date. So after ten minutes or so say, "Elmer, you'd better give Dad back his eye, it's getting late. The dance begins at eight-thirty."

WHAT CAN A GIRL DO IF SHE IS TALLER THAN HER DATE?

You may be a bit taller than your date because you are wearing high heels. If you continue to wear high heels your date will develop what is known in the trade as a "Shortie Complex" (or technically a Teenius Weenius Mentis-corpus psychos). Girls who are dating short boys definitely should not wear high heels. BUT, on further consideration, if the girl does NOT wear high heels perhaps the boy will think she is not wearing them because he is so short (and that's a fact) so he will develop as strong a shortie complex as if his date were wearing high heels. This leaves you up a tree, barefoot.

Of course if you, without shoes, are still taller than your date, then there is a more ticklish problem. You can send your date home and wait until the boy grows a little taller (boys mature later than girls) but this will take time. In the intervening years you can develop your mind. And there is nothing a boy likes better than a cultured girl. No siree.

If you are impatient you can slice off the lower part of your feet, but this, we warn you, is messy. And, anyway, you'll look like hell in a bathing suit.

For the present? First concentrate on your posture, tall gals. If you walk around all slouched over with your hands trailing on the ground this will only *accentuate* your height. Then, too, try to dress smartly rather than prettily. Well-tailored, conservative, easy-to-get-off clothes. After all, you can't help it if you are a great big slob of a girl. STAND ERECT. Straight as an arrow, with your chin held high. Be *proud* you're eight feet tall. *Columbia Jester*

BE-BOP'S FABLES

THE CRAZY, MIXED-UP END

Synopsis: (Cindy and her pater have taken up residence with a gold-leaf widow and her three offspring. The three chicks are really gone and have left Cindy out in the cold when they take off to the Prince's session in town. Cindy has taken up residence in the kitchen for the night, when out of the blue, her crazy godmother appears to set her hep to the jive.)

"You mean you're going to set me straight to the tune so's I can dance the tune at the session tonight?" Cindy asked.

"Now the clouds are clearing, Doll," her godmother replied. "Now Cindy-gal, go out into the garage and swing in here with the mouse-trap."

The chick made the trip in a short chorus and returned on beat with the trap.

"Let one of the mice out, Doll," quoth the G.M.

Cindy obeyed forthwith, and as the rooty rodent hit the carpet, post haste, the G.M. jazzed him with her magic wand. In his place, after a fancy flash of light, sat the coolest Jag ever tossed together.

"G.M.," quoth Cindy, "it is the most, to say the least."

"Take five, girl," sang the old doll, "and grab me a pumkin from the garden."

Cindy had picked up the rhythm by now and made a frantic dash to the cabbage patch. Back she came in ten with the pumpkin. The old doll hit it a crazy paradiddle with her stick. The flash came in for a short solo and left a cool pile of jewels staring up at Cindy.

"Mamma, it's crazy, but momentous," cooed Cindy.

"'Tain't nothing, Dearie, try this." So saying G.M. whacked Cindy on her golden blonde. Again the flash came by as advertised leaving Cindy garbed in the latest rags from Paris, complete with glass slippers.

"That's it, Doll," said her crazy godmother. "The union only lets us work three miracles within twenty-four. But before I go, I gotta tell you to be in by midnight. Yeah, it's crazy; but closing is closing."

"Check, G.M." Cindy purred. Forthwith, she grabbed the jewels, tossed them on her person, leaped gently into the Jag, and left in a cloud of leopard skin dust and chewed up whitewalls.

Arriving at the session, Cindy hocked a sapphire necklace and grabbed a box seat ticket. The combo was going mean and wild when she walked in; but switched to a fast chorus of "I Cover the Waterfront" as she gyrated down the aisle. The prince turned to his straight man and said, "Daddy, you and I have just seen heaven."

From then on the gang got hot. The group with the reeds and imagination really tore up the ozone.

However, as all of the most must, it soon became the least. Time was hanging heavy. Just as one of the musical madmen hit the last note, the clock struck the witching hour.

"Cripes," yelled Cindy.

Her dress turned back to rags in a wink, her jewels rolled back up into a pumpkin, and Cindy left the hall like daddy for a lodge meeting.

At the curb she found her waiting mouse and raced him home in record time for the four-forty.

Now all this time, the prince has been lapping up Cindy's looks, brains, and social poise. When he realizes that he has muffed his chance to pick her up for a night on the town.

He rushed down to the curb and found nothing but mouse tracks and a glass slipper. Picking it up he said, "This is the opening, now to find the finale."

The next day he grabbed the slipper and started checking all the feminine feet in the kingdom.

Finally, after an all-day search, he chimed it at Cindy's place. He knocked.

"Sorry, Charlie," one of the sisters called, "it's after closing."

"Don't feed me that jazz," he replied, "this is the prince."

The broad did a double take and opened the door.

"Well, Dad, come right in."

"Cut the gab," said the monarch, "and give me your foot."

"Frantic," replied the sis.

She offered her gunboat for investigation, and the prince said no thanks.

"Wait a second, Charlie," she yelled. "If you're really trying to dump that thing, I've got two sisters who will be glad to try and help."

The two other debs came in and tried the game.

"Sorry," said the prince. "You gals just aren't dancing the tune the shoe wants to hear. Anybody else of the feminine persuasion around?"

"Only Cindy," one replied. "She's a square from nowhere."

"Bring her on," quoth the prince. "I'll try anything once."

In came Cindy; and the prince took a long look.

"Plant your toes in this, Sis," he said.

Cindy planted her little ones into the slipper perfectly.

"You're it," said the prince.

"O.K." Cindy said, "you hide, I'll count ten."

"Naw," replied Harry. "You're not digging me. You're the gal for me. Let's play house."

"O.K. Jack," Cindy answered. "If you got the money, I got the time."

He grabbed her immediately, stuck her in the suicide seat of his Le Mans, and together they drove to the castle to catch the midnight disk jockey. *Hoot (De Pauw University)*

THE GIFT OF THE MANGOES

BY EDWARD PASTOR

The parts of Della and Sam Mango should be played by a man and a woman, preferably in that order. The lighting should be done by electricity, luminiscent paint producing a very unfavorable effect. All musical background can be amply provided by either a contra-bassoon or an E-flat cymbal.

ACT I

(Opening scene: The Mango apartment on the lower east side of the Lower East Side of New York. The effect of abject poverty is easily created by covering one entire wall with overdue shoe repair bills and the simple construction of papier-mâché *dung cakes by the stove. At down left sits Della, nonchalantly chipping small icicles from her elbow. Her skin has a strong blue hue, and she is stark naked. Sam enters from orchestra pit, accenting their inability to afford a door in the apartment.)*

DELLA: *(throwing her arms about him and laughing huskily)* Darling, how long it's been since breakfast. And how I love you! And how about wiping that oatmeal off your chin?

SAM: *(throwing his arms about the refrigerator)* Bare again I see.

Ah, but what care we! Do you want to dine at the Essex with the Giltbottoms, my dear?

DELLA: (*gaily*) I thought we might spend the weekend on Ceylon with the Duke.

SAM: (*throwing a dish rag over her shoulders*) All right then. Here's your ermine wrap, and we'll be off!

DELLA: Sam, it's smudged. (*She rises with inflection.*)

SAM: Why didn't you mention it before? How you must have suffered! I'll . . . (*Suddenly he stops and bites huge pieces from his lip to signify emotion.*) Oh, why go on like this!

DELLA: Sam, you mean?

SAM: Yes, Della, we're both flatbusted. Broke.

DELLA: Damn.

(*Curtain falls morosely*)

ACT II. *Soonly thereafter*

(*Same scene. Bills on wall are thicker, Della's backside is thinner.*)

DELLA: Woe is me. How to buy Sam a platinum rocking horse for only eighteen cents? What a hell of a Christmas this is gonna be. (*Suddenly she looks in mirror and smiles.*) I know! I'll sell my calvesfoot preserves. Of course, Sam has always loved them so. How he delighted running barefoot through them of a winter's eve. But it can't be helped. (*She rushes off in a flurry—a tight, ill-fitting flurry with torn pockets.*)

(*Curtain falls, but the price of platinum rocking horses stands fixed.*)

ACT III. *Christmas Day*

(*Same scene. Entire auditorium is ten degrees colder for effect.*)

SAM: (*Painting a Christmas tree on the floor.*) Well, Della, this is Christmas. (*Suddenly he wheels about, facing the prompter who is dozing quietly in the wing.*) Della, what's that strange smell that I no longer?

DELLA: I've sold my calvesfoot preserves to buy you this wonderful platinum rocking horse.

SAM: (*Putting his arm around her, speaking softly*) You shouldn't have, you know.

DELLA: I know.

SAM: You're wonderful, Della. That's why it's so hard to tell you.

DELLA: What is it, Sam?

SAM: I hope you won't be too hurt, but . . .

DELLA: Yes? Yes?

SAM: I've sold *you,* dearest, to buy a present for my mother. My Oedipus complex, you know.

DELLA: (*As she is carried into orchestra pit by several workmen*) I understand, dear. And a merry, merry Christmas. (*The gentle odor of frankincense, myrrh, and calvesfoot preserves fills the auditorium as—*)

THE CURTAIN DESCENDS

Sundial

AND THAT OLD WOMAN . . .

How graphic can the proper words be! It was June of 1902, and a sportswriter on the "Cleveland Dispatch" was driving along in a taxicab toward the theater. On the way, he conversed randomly with the cabbie, learned something about his family, became chummy. Just as the cab pulled up for a red light on the outskirts of the town, a small girl rushed headlong into the front fender and was knocked down. She lay screaming and wailing as the cabbie and the sportswriter rushed to her aid. Soon a small crowd had gathered, including three young exchange students, an elderly doctor, and two shopgirls, all of whom offered to help in any way they could.

Finally, an ambulance arrived, bearing an interne, a nurse and a stretcher bearer. An old grizzled fellow was driving. Just as they were about to take up the little girl, she burst out laughing and cried, "April Fool," and a host of heavy hearts suddenly became happy.

And that girl was Anna Rosenberg. And that sportswriter was Dante Alighieri. And that cabbie was Neville Chamberlain, of Munich fame. And those three exchange students, Pandit Nehru, of India, King Farouk, of Egypt, and Georgi Malenkov, of the Soviet Union. And that elderly doctor was Louis Pasteur. And those two girls were Charlotte and Emily Brontë. The interne was Doctor Vannevar Bush. And his nurse was Olivia de Haviland. And the stretcher bearer was Bronko Nagurski. And the old grizzled fellow who was driving was none other than Orville Wright. And that ambulance was the Santa Maria. And that taxicab was Bill Stern. *Columbia Jester*

THE RELUCTANT WEED

BY LEO HIEDE

From somewhere in the distance a horse neighed nervously. The raw, acrid odor of hot dust and baked sage filled the ever-lengthening shadows of approaching evening.

A magnificent figure of a man swung easily down from a spirited horse. Every muscle in his supple body rippled rhythmically as he carefully tethered the beautiful animal to the lone scrub tree in the canyon. His sturdy frame reflected breeding, courage, and a firm belief in the final triumph of virtue, purity and clean living. He paused before a flat boulder and breathed deeply several times. In the half-light, the strong angular lines of his tanned face gave him an almost spiritual look.

Nearby a horse neighed nervously.

Placing his tobacco pouch carefully on the rock, he grasped a cigarette paper between his strong fingers and raised it to his mouth where he delicately wet the edges. Taking the pouch in one of his lean hands, he sprinkled tobacco into the paper. A sudden transient gust of wind swept tobacco and paper to the ground.

Obviously unmoved, he reached for a second square of paper as nearby a horse neighed nervously. With his back to the faint breeze, he silently wet the paper and raised the tobacco pouch. The silhouette of his magnificent body cut a sharp design against the darkening sky. The tobacco poured in abundance, spilling lavishly on the ground. Somewhat irritated, he tightened the strings on the pouch, thus making the hole smaller. By this time, the paper was dry. Crumbling it into a tiny wad, he threw it with some feeling to the ground.

Grasping another paper, he wet it across his lips. In short, quick movements he shook the pouch over the paper. The hole was too small. Dropping the paper, he seized the pouch with trembling hands and jerked the hole open with thumb and forefinger.

Suddenly his beautiful body straightened as a flash of intuition hit him. Every nerve quivered in anticipation of a surprise. With one sweeping movement to his hip and back, he sneezed profusely into a large, red handkerchief. And again the tiny cigarette paper lay on the sandy floor of the canyon.

Behind him, a horse neighed nervously.

Grabbing the bag, he dropped to his knees. Laying a paper on the sand, he sprinkled tobacco carefully and accurately up and down the paper. Slowly raising the makings, he folded the paper into a smooth cylindrical shape. A satisfied gleam appeared on his strong face. Fairly quivering in his excitement, he lifted it to his mouth. Paper and tobacco fell from his mouth to the ground. He had forgotten to wet the edge. Fiercely, he seized the bag and paper and fell to the ground where he spat over the whole paper. In one grand gesture, he emptied the contents of the bag over the paper until it was completely covered.

Searching gingerly for the edges of the paper, every movement was a symphony of expression from his tense body. In agonizingly slow movements, he carefully and accurately rounded the cigarette until it lay gleaming white on the canyon floor—a perfect job.

Settling back on his haunches with a sigh that was almost a sob, he surveyed the job. Faint flecks of saliva danced on his lips.

With a cry, he leaped on the cigarette and forced it greedily between his feverish lips. Nervously, he searched his pockets, the linings of his coat, his saddle bag.

His body jerked in agony as the terrible truth struck him. There were no matches.

As he rolled convulsively on the canyon floor, from somewhere in the distance a horse neighed nervously. *Octopus*

BECAUSE

BY WAYNE ARIHOOD

Never will I forget my first day at this great university. My classes, dormitory life, new acquaintances, all the adventures of college reached up and enveloped me in a rapturous cloud of, logically enough, rapture.

I sprang from my bed at the crack of dawn on the first day and tugged at my roommate.

"Arise," I cried. "Arise to the dawn of this glorious day filled to overflowing with the education of the ages. Come with me out into this great society in which thousands of knowledge thirsting scholars are vying for the wisdom of our cultural forefathers. Arise!"

"What the hell," my roommate gritted, "ails you?"

"Ails me indeed," I countered. "Would that more were of my mind. Would that more sought the pearls of wisdom for his very own. Would that—." Too late, I attempted to dodge the blunt object that struck me in the temple.

When I regained consciousness, I seized my notebook and my shiny new Parker "1" pen. As the fogginess cleared from my brain I examined my schedule for my first class. Sociology! My head reeled with happiness at the prospect of studying and mastering this science. Oh, to learn of man's advances in society; of his peculiarities and eccentricities; of men's inter-relations with one another. (I blushed at this.) I stepped jauntily through the window.

When I regained consciousness, I hesitated long enough to cast a baleful glance at my open window three stories above before racing blindly to my first class in sociology. When I arrived the class had just begun. Flinging the door of the lecture hall open, I cried, "I am here, Oh fellow students! Instruct me in the glorious path of Sociology I. Blushingly now, in my ignorance I shall bow my head in diligent study; hoping, yearning to absorb the pearls of knowledge that fall from the lips of the instructor."

"For God's sake," rasped the lecturer, "sit down. Here, down in front."

"Show me not favoritism," I continued. "Judge me not by my attitude, but rather by my capacity for learning." I sat down. "Instruct me, most almighty instructor."

A shocked silence filled the auditorium as many students cast admiring glances at me. The lecture was continued without event as lectures are wont to do and at the end I had a very precious set of notes. "In other words," "To clarify my point," "As it were," and other gems of knowledge filled the first four pages of my notebook when I left sociology and made my way to geology.

As I walked down what I had fondly dubbed "the hill," I was confronted by a beauteous creature. It was a girl. She came toward me with lithe grace in her every stride. Timid, yet proud. A light of defiance glistening in her limpid red green eyes. A Christmas seal was stuck religiously in the center of her forehead.

"Gosh," I murmured, making an obscene gesture.

"My honor, sir," she shrieked disapprovingly at me, "is not to be bandied about by such an obviously nefarious minded creature as yourself. You despicable, despised, no-good, pitiable, down-trodden, —(She paused here, having exhausted Roget's pocket thesaurus of synonyms.) —Freshman!!!" she concluded, spitting at my feet.

I waved my Wisconsin pennant and stood, self consciously zipping and unzipping my fly as she retreated up the hill. How had she guessed I was a freshman? My cheeks smarted at this mild rebuke as I entered my geology class at Science Hall. Soon, however, I was swept up in the interesting happenings of the pre-Cambrian.

The lecturer shuttled to and fro, fro and to, down and up, up and down, interweaving fact upon fact into a colorful Persian rug of knowledge which illustrated plainly some of the greatest questions ever to confront mankind. Constantly shuttling fro and to, to and fro, weaving, interweaving. I fell to the floor in a fit of dizzyness.

Suddenly the lecturer spun around and screamed, "What is a rock?"

I leaped from the floor, the answer on my lips. Oh! the good fortune that had permitted me to come up with the answer to this question. I envisioned the beaming smile of my instructor as he patted me on the head, smoothing my tousled hair, and gave me an A for the day.

"Well, don't stand there with your fly open," the instructor snarled. "Say something."

"A Roc," I began with levity, "is a fabulous bird of Arabia, so huge that it bore off elephants to feed its young."

When I regained consciousness, I picked myself up gingerly from the boulder strewn aisle and contemplated the empty classroom. It must have been something I had said. But, what? What? I wept bitterly in my frustration.

"Oh," I sobbed.

"Oh," echoed the walls.

"Oh! walls who are my only companions in this hour of utmost grief," I cried. "What must I do? What will relieve the scourge, the plague, which has beset itself upon my hapless personage? What other than death will alter the tide of circumstances which has flung me into the depths of oblivion? Is there none?"

"None," echoed the walls.

"Alas, then it is true. The walls have confirmed my most dreaded thoughts. I have somehow bungled, somehow failed in my well meaning attempts to acquire those highly treasured pearls of wisdom."

I left the room, clutching spasmodically at my bosom.

As I approached the pier, I drew my shawl tightly around my frail shoulders and shivered at the cold night and my destiny. My feet thumped hollowly on the wooden pier as I raced the length of it and threw myself into eternity.

When I regained consciousness, I found myself lying on a cold slab of ice. Damn the fates for freezing the lake over and foiling my plans. Before I could muster courage for another attempt, however, I was tracing my steps home under the glistening light of the stars.

Steeped in misery, I entered my dormitory room and dodged the bottle heaved by my roommate. His attitude of antagonism lessened immediately at the sight of a tear on my lapel and he listened consolingly to my woeful tale.

"Don't fret, chum," he soothed, "tomorrow is another day."

This sudden inspirational statement immediately inspired me with its simplicity. "It is true," I yelped joyfully. "Oh, brother, fellow student, roommate, how can I thank you for your encouragement?" I licked his ear gratefully.

"With the rising of the morning sun a whole new vista appears. A chance to amend previous errors; a chance to make new and more profitable contacts; to absorb the precious treasured pearls of wisdom and culture offered at this great institution of learning. It is a chance to absorb the learning which is the symbol of America, of democracy, of motherhood, of all that is good and fine and just."

Tears of happiness welled up into my eyes and overflowed onto my pillow as I laid me down with a will. *Octopus*

THE CREEPING NOTHING

BY RON GOULART

Few alert readers of the National River Salvage Report for May 1925 failed to note the singular events occurring at the Kinsey Museum here in East Lust, Mass. I was curator of that museum during the entire period of weird happenings (1746–1923) and am writing now of them in order that some glimpse of the awesome terror may reach the outside world. I am writing this on the back of the 1926 calendar of the New Coolidge Granite Tombstone and Lifelike Birdbath Company and placing it in a bottle. I will throw the bottle in the Atlantic Ocean with the instructions that it is to be searched for only after my death. This may not be far off since I am now being followed by several heterogeneous mystical devotees, sinister Polynesians, and a man named Omar Sitlow, who claims I assaulted his wife. (Executor's note: *Prof. Horvarth was murdered at the Shanghai Pleasure Dance Palace six minutes after writing this terrible account. The only clue to his killer and/or killers was a note pinned to his left earlobe. It read: "Thus does Muhgo, the Serpent God, revenge himself on all those who defile the sacred temple of the Eight-toed god of the Flowering Punjab. Are you saved?" Dr. Murchlow, the museum taxidermist, was found a few days later stuffed with oyster dressing. And Prof. Shrewcraft was run over by a truck belonging to the Serpent God Moving Van & Storage Company.*)

Anyone who has read the forbidden *Cultes des Goules,* of which there are only six known copies (not including the Pocket Books edition), has some idea of the strange Elder Beings who once dwelled in the far reaches of the Pacific. We are all familiar with the eldritch statues on Easter Island and the weird carvings in the Smoking Room of the Seabreeze Hotel on Ponape. This whole affair began in the South Pacific when a huge cone-like rock was thrust up from the immortal sea. Capt. Thor Kurtiki of the whaler, the S.S. Edgar Rice Burroughs, spotted the island, and, having nothing better to do since he was three whales ahead that day, decided to investigate. On the island he found what appeared to be a rocket ship. Indeed, this was the case. For the strange writing on the craft's side, when held up to a mirror said: "I am Joey Rocketship. Who the Hell are you?"

Hearing of this I immediately wired (enclosing postage) for the ship to be sent (in a plain wrapper) to the museum. For that very morning Dr. Tree had said to me, "A rocket ship would sure as blazes pep up this damn rathole." Dr. Tree was known as the town Ralph Waldo Emerson. Emerson, who also lived here, was known as the town Dr. Tree.

No one paid much attention to the ship since our museum was a quiet and orderly one and did not admit people. But one morning Dr. Murchlow peered into the mysterious craft. He fainted on the spot. On further observation we found that a brown and white cocker spaniel of great age was frozen solid in a block of ice. We were never able to determine why the ice had not melted in all those eons although the Philco people tried to get us to make a positive statement. Before long the newspapers got hold of the story of the frozen cocker spaniel which they labeled, in a typical example of yellow journalism, "The Frozen Cocker Spaniel Story."

Curious town folk flocked from near and far. And with them came strange orientals. Soon twenty sinister orientals came daily to the museum, calling themselves Spade Managora and his Argentine Hawaiians. They played dixieland in the Guy Lombardo manner and every evening made a sacrifice of a newborn elephant to the ship.

More and more orientals came and lines two blocks long formed outside the museum. The police cracked down. But because of the size of East Lust the last 46 people in line were outside city limits and could not be arrested.

It was on the morning of June 5, 1933 that the weird events finally came to an end in an earth shaking manner. When Dr. Murchlow and I went to view the rocket ship we found no trace of it and in its place stood the twenty orientals, frozen solid in the various attitudes of playing "Muskrat Ramble."

But it is of no use to go further. We are doomed. For there are more things in Horatio than this world dreams of. From that day on whenever I walked the street cocker spaniels eyed me strangely. A few of them sniffed curiously.

Dr. Murchlow has left. I think that I will follow. He said he was going to the Sinister Oriental Saloon and get frozen. Perhaps he is right.

Pelican

RED BARGE OF GARBAGE

BY WALT ANDERSEN AND RON GOULART

(Ed note. We are happy to announce that the publishers of Tijuana Paperback Books have kindly consented to allow us to reprint in its entirety a truly great war novel. They even offered to ship us the authors in a small perforated container. Such generosity is truly great, and if anyone tries to tell us that our American culture isn't as good as all that Renaissance stuff, we'll tell them it takes one to know one.)

CHAPTER ONE

Bang.

CHAPTER TWO

Robert sat at a table in a small sidewalk cafe on the Via Flaminia and thought of how he had been hit during the first battle of the war. His left toe had been amputated shortly thereafter. It was a rotten way to be wounded.

It was not good to be without a left little toe. Some things they were good. Like the bulls at Seville. That was good. But this it was not. He sipped his ovaltine and thought. He was very lonely and the day was very hot. He looked up then and saw the girl coming toward him down the warm street. She was young and pretty. Pretty the way you can only be when you are young. He had been young once and had had all his toes and plenty of women. But things were different now. And he knew he was lonely.

The girl was a young native, with deeply tanned skin and an expression of barbaric intensity. She was carrying flowers.

"Unga, mistah? Costee one yankee quahtah. Goody one, too." Her voice was as soft as the velvet dirt of the Argentine pampas. Her quaint accent made her even more desirable to him. Youth.

Oh to be young again and have toes. But he had no left little toe. So he must not think of those things. To think of the bulls at Seville that was all right. But not of toes. Or of youth either. Except to think that this girl was young. And he wanted youth so much.

"You are very beautiful," he said.

"Can it," she said, dropping her eyelids.

"Will you go to bed with me?"

"I do not see how we can avoid it."

She was right. Some things you can avoid and some you can not. It would be good. He would make love and that too would be good. But he hoped she would not laugh at him when she saw he had no left little toe.

And always far off he heard the battle.

It was a damn lousy way to fight a war.

CHAPTER THREE

Bang. Bang.

CHAPTER FOUR

He was old now and going to hunt the ducks. He was old now and a long way off from the golden afternoon on the Via Flaminia. But he could remember. The girl. The bed. The flowers. And at Seville the bulls. The bulls at Seville were very good. He raised his gun and pointed it at the morning sky. *Pelican*

"YOU HAVE BETRAYED ME, JOHN DREW"

from the annals of Mayfair York

The lights blinked and twinkled, mimicking the stars that cast their effervescence downward from overhead. The lights were all around, but

I walked through them without even noticing. My head was down and my collar was up, and my spirits were down and my jig was up. "Damn," I cursed gently. Somewhere in this gigantic city of blinking, twinkling lights overlain at night by multitudinous stars and governed constantly by ruthless, cold-blooded, money grabbing ogres, was a killer. It was my job to find him. Me, John Dill of the maternity ward beat, insignificant, bungling me, supposed to find a killer. Tommyrot! I fell into an open manhole.

When I regained consciousness I was in a small subterranean room through which a stream of murky fluid trickled. I regurgitated aimlessly. Suddenly, a raft appeared around the bend and there she was. She was beautiful beyond belief and as she entered my chamber a million violins began to play. The noise was deafening. She raised her megaphone to her lips and spoke, "Are you—?" I nodded half blushingly and tore off my shirt. There emblazoned on my chest were the words, "Max Dill, Private." She was immediately overcome by the sight of my bare chest and prostrated herself at my feet babbling incoherently. There emblazoned on her boot-strap were the letters, "D.P."

As I lighted a cigarette for her, I questioned her, "What for is that there on you?"

"Aw geez," she murmured, "Whyd'ja have to ask me that?"

But before she could continue they were upon us. Hordes of them and all very beautiful in their busmodic lopsidity. Amazons! The thought struck me in a blinding flash.

When I regained consciousness I was alone on the raft in pitch blackness. The count was three and two. I picked up the bat. It was heavy. Then I realized that it was not the bat at all. It was my head. I replaced it and looked around. The sewer tunnel had enlarged into a beautiful lake. At the edge of the lake stood a doberman pinscher, ears alert, head erect. My mind returned to the grimmer business at hand. The killer; I really ought to find the killer. Then I knew. The girl, the raft, the dog, those letters, "D.P.", it all tied into a neat bundle. Neat and nice, ready to drop into the Chief's lap. I smiled at the vision of the Chief's pain distorted face and whipped my forty-five from my tunic. Then the doberman knew that he was going to die. But before I could shoot, the dog turned into a beautiful woman. I recognized her as the woman from the raft and I hesitated. She laughed wildly and pulled at a silver chain near her foot. Suddenly the water drained from the lake carrying me with it down toward the grinding jaws of the disposal. I cast a last futile glance upward only to see the girl standing there with a cork betweeen her clenched teeth, grinning triumphantly.

When I regained consciousness I was in a small subterranean room through which a stream of murky fluid trickled. I regurgitated aimlessly. Suddenly a raft appeared around the bend and there she was. I raised a gun to my head. *Octopus*

THINK AND GROW MONEY

BY DAVE DUGAS

Truly "money is something," and a powerful thing at that, when it is mixed with definiteness of purpose, persistence and a BURNING DESIRE for its translation into thinking. In 1937 a thoughtful man named Napoleon Hill produced a sort of book called "Think and Grow Rich." That all rights to the book were transferred to Rosa L. Beeland in 1941 is unimportant. That a new edition of the book appeared in 1945 and enjoyed some success is notable if not, considered in its proper context, particularly encouraging. The new edition was prompted rather by the fact that since 1937 there had developed several new ways of making money. That there had appeared no new THOUGHTS or ways in which to THINK them has prompted me to write this work.

Many notable men have become wealthy by thinking. Such men have been Henry Ford, Theodore Roosevelt, Arthur Brisbane, Napoleon Bonaparte and Napoleon Hill. It is discouraging to note that few men, already possessing wealth, have learned to think. I wish to propose what I call my THREE PRACTICAL STEPS TO THINKING. I am a simple man. The thoughts I think are simple. It is simple to learn these simple thoughts. Let us start simply.

THINKING, of itself, is not difficult if one avoids thinking about difficult (un-simple) things. Let us start with the SELF. All that is necessary for this simple lesson is a cerebral cortex and a ball-peen hammer. Here we go.

STEP ONE: Take the ball-peen hammer in your right (or left) hand. Place your left (or right) hand on a convenient table. Without giving further thought to the table, STRIKE your HAND with the HAMMER. IT HURTS! And without realizing it, you find yourself

THINKING ABOUT HOW IT HURTS. This is a simple thought to be sure, but you are on the way to better things.

STEP TWO: When the pain has subsided, take the hammer into your hand again. Spread the fingers on your other hand wide apart on the table. Without looking, cause the hammer to STRIKE ONLY ONE FINGER (any finger). Again you will be THINKING ABOUT HOW IT HURTS! But you have STRUCK ONLY ONE FINGER. Which one? Ah, that is for you to think about. It is easy to think that you have STRUCK YOUR THIRD FINGER. You can feel it, but more important, by THINKING HOW IT HURTS you can KNOW IT!

Let us review the progress we have made. First we have learned to THINK A SIMPLE THOUGHT. Secondly, we have learned to CHANNEL THAT THOUGHT IN A SPECIFIC DIRECTION. What a world of difference there is between thinking I HAVE HIT MY HAND WITH A HAMMER and I HAVE HIT THE THIRD FINGER ON MY LEFT (OR RIGHT) HAND WITH A HAMMER.

But we have confined our newly discovered thinking to SELF. Now we are ready to THINK about things OTHER THAN SELF. Let us begin to think about the OTHER THAN SELF or SOMEBODY ELSE! On to step three!

STEP THREE: Take the hammer in your right hand and STRIKE SOMEBODY ELSE! It does not matter at this point whom you strike. You will learn to THINK about that later. Once you have STRUCK THE OTHER THAN SELF or SOMEBODY ELSE, you will find that a whole new world of THOUGHTS voluntarily open themselves to you. The way in which you think them is unimportant. It is enough that you are THINKING. I suggest, however, that these particular THOUGHTS be given special attention. They are:

1. I STRUCK SOMEONE ELSE with a hammer!
2. Whom did I STRIKE?
3. Where?
4. With what part of the hammer did I strike him (with the ball or the peen)?
5. Does the OTHER THAN SELF FEEL THE HAMMER even as I FELT IT?
6. What about the HAMMER?

The importance of these last two questions cannot be overemphasized. For it is when we are able to THINK about THINGS and the

OTHER THAN SELF or SOMEBODY ELSE that we have really begun to THINK SOMETHING.

From thoughts of the HAMMER or THING, we may proceed to thoughts of OTHER THINGS. Lawn furniture! Orlon! The United Nations!

It is only a small step from the beginning we have made before we may begin to THINK about such OTHER PEOPLE as William Howard Taft! Alfred Kinsey! And Napoleon Hill! *Pelican*

RARE NEW PHOBIA DISCOVERED HERE

BY RALPH ESTLING

Berkeley, Oct. 8—The entire world of mental health was rocked back on its heels and forced to sit up and take notice today by a report submitted to the Gestalt Foundation for Psychiatric and Clinical Research on the Basic Neuro-Metabolo-Psycho-Somatical Redundancies to the Stimuli-Recall Mechanism of the Psychotic, Neurotic, and Nutty.

The report, submitted by Dr. Ludwig Fossly, professor of Abnormal Psychology at the University of California, was entitled *A Report on the Neuro-Psychical Basis of Doubleuphobia,* or fear of the letter *w.*

Doubleuphobia (or W-phobia), claims Dr. Fossly, its discoverer, is an extremely rare and somewhat trying condition of hypochondria brought on by an excessive exposure during childhood and early puberty to the letter *w.* The affliction may take on any of several forms.

In an advanced state, or Hypodoubleuphobia, the disease may assume new and interesting characteristics, such as a morbid fear, not only directed against the letter *w,* but also against all things and objects containing *w*'s—such as windows, watches, wooly teddy bears, Warren G. Harding, etc. The sight or even thought of a window washer, avers Dr. Fossly, is sufficient to send a hypodoubleuphobiac into hysteria or a sulk, depending upon his kinesthetic-neural makeup.

"I know of a most interesting case," writes Dr. Fossly. "We shall call the patient Mr. L, because that was his name, Philo R. L. L was a doubleuphobiac of my acquaintance. Up until the time about which I am writing, L was, barring his phobia, a perfectly normal human being. He exhibited no perceptible fear of windows, watches, or wooly teddy bears, and on several occasions I approached him on the subject of Warren G. Harding and found him conversant enough, although he would sometimes confuse Warren G. Harding with his (L's) uncle, Harding G. Warren. The mistake was a natural one since Mr. Warren always wore a celluloid collar, too, and was forever saying 'I do not choose to run.' When asked what he didn't choose to run *for,* he would only wink coyly and remark 'Walk softly and carry a big aardvark.' (See my article in the Saturday Evening Gestalt for May, 1949, entitled *A Report on Mr. L's Uncle.*)

"Mr. L worked in the advertising department of a large soap company. He was perfectly happy until one day he came to my office. I could see the hallmark of the hypodoubleuphobiac on his worried face.

"'It's getting worse,' he said. I nodded and asked why. He told me that his soap company had adopted a new slogan, 'Why be half safe?' I asked him what troubled him about that and he answered that the continual sight of 'Why' was breaking him down. After some confusion in which I though Mr. L was referring to the *letter y,* a letter which, up till now, had not bothered him, I came to see that it was the *W* in the *word* 'Why' that was preying on his mind. I told him to quit his advertising job with the soap company, but unfortunately he never did–until it was too late.

"A few months later I received a phone call from Mrs. L telling me to come right over. I found Mr. L in a state of semi-coma lying in a large crib. The bars of the crib were up so that he could not fall out. All the windows in the room had been smashed and there was not a wooly teddy bear in sight. One look told me that the doubleuphobia was now in an advanced condition.

"I approached him and said, 'Well, well, well, won't you wander over to the window with me where we will watch the window washers across the way.'

"He moaned as if in frightful agony.

"I was prepared for just such an emergency and from my coat pocket extracted a large plastic figure shaped like the letter *W*. 'Look,' I said, and showed it to Mr. L. He screamed and tried to hide under the blankets. I turned the *W* on its side.

"'Come out,' I coaxed Mr. L. 'See? the nasty old *W* has gone away. All we have here is the Greek letter *sigma.*'

"Mr. L peeked out from under the blankets and frowned at the *sigma.* He slowly emerged and reluctantly brought himself to touch the letter with one finger. 'See,' I said, 'it won't hurt you.'

"This reassured him a great deal and I decided to gamble. I gave the *sigma* a quick turn so that now it was the letter *M.* Mr. L was taken aback at first but gradually a smile broke out on his face. He wanted the letter to play with, but I realized that to allow such a thing might prove highly dangerous, inasmuch as it could, at any time, become a *W* again under Mr. L's inexperienced use. Convinced that I was on the right track, I treated him for eleven months, employing the Zweifel-Mitfer method.

"Mr. L is today a happy, normal person again."

This report caused quite a stir at the Gestalt Foundation and the board of directors voted Dr. Fossly a further $120,000 to continue his studies of *doubleuphobia*, with the hope that some day this dread disease, discovered by Dr. Fossly, may be cured.

Interestingly enough, it was observed that in Dr. Fossly's report the letter *x* did not appear once and, where needed, the letters *cks* were substituted, such as "ecksist" and "ecksample."

When phoned at his home, Dr. Fossly refused to state the reason for this and when pressed for an answer became irritable and hung up. *Pelican*

VARICOSE SOCIETY DANCE A REAL BLOODY SUCCESS

"The Red Drop Hop," sponsored by the Campus Varicose Society in connection with their annual blood-letting drive, was quite a success.

Great Hall was overflowing last night as couples danced to the liquid music of Les Anemic and his Pale Four. The dancers seemed to particularly enjoy "The Transfusion Tango" and "The Jugular Jump." Lovely redheaded Aorta, vocalist with the band, gave a thumping rendition of "Hemophiliac Blues" which raised everyone's blood pressure.

The decorations were certainly clever. Suspended from the ceiling was a huge heart which beat convincingly 70 times a minute. From the heart were suspended many red streamers which were supposed to represent arteries and capillaries. The effect was one of intense realism unless of course one has never danced in this vein.

Even the refreshments were connected with the theme of the dance. A corps of nurses served intravenously from the beautifully decorated tables arranged artistically around the floor. Blood flowed like water. Miss Leech, head nurse, poured.

Highlight of the evening was the entertaining mixer, "Find Your

Type." The game is a simple one, each person is supplied with a small knife or razor blade, and a vial. Into this vial the player bleeds, then runs around trying to find someone with the same kind of blood. Many lasting R.H. friendships were formed. One of the two survivors of the game was heard to remark, "This is lots more fun than Russian Roulette."

The Varicose Society extends heartfelt thanks to the Undertakers League for mopping up so thoroughly after the dance. *Octopus*

HOW ARE YOU FIXED FOR BLADES

BY RON GOULART

On October 7, 1917, occurred the first of a series of crimes that were destined to rock Willseyville, Kansas, and parts of Carnhoss County. It was raining slightly when Melissa Benchley left the 22nd Street-Egyptian Theatre and started for the one-room apartment she was never to reach. Melissa played piano at the theater. She would never have risen far in the field for she could play only the first half of the *Maple Leaf Rag,* which she had learned from her uncle, CowCow Benchley, a retired itinerant. The Egyptian Palace employed Miss Benchley only to play during Tom Mix pictures, although she had an understanding with Ernst Woodrow, the manager, that she might someday play during Hoot Gibson pictures. Possibly Miss Benchley thought of this prospect as she treaded the cold street that harsh night. At twelve minutes past eight she stopped at the fruit market of one Vern Pinkney and bought six lemons and a half of canteloupe. At 17 after 8 Officer Muldoon O'Shean found her decapitated body sprawled in front of Perth's Harness Shop. The only witness, Buddy Kingston, a three-year-old newsboy, said he had seen a tall man running from the scene of the crime carrying a guillotine and whistling "Didn't He Ramble." The Kingston boy later swore positively that the man had been Richard Dix, but the police refused to believe him. The boy was not bright for his age, and broke down under questioning. He always maintained the guillotine part of his story. Within a few short weeks he was to be proven all too right.

There was a newspaper war going on in Willseyville at the time between the *Times-Avenger* and the *Clarion-Sun*. The two papers immediately grabbed the story in all its frightening details. By the time the weekly editions of the papers hit the stands the editors had filled several inches with the crime story. Willseyville was afraid.

Exactly one week to the minute after the unfortunate girl's death officer Muldoon found the body of another young woman, again beheaded in a ghastly manner. The girl's name, oddly enough, was also Melissa Benchley. She was no relation to the first victim. A Mr. and Mrs. Orville Goggins said they saw a tall man leaving the scene of the crime carrying a guillotine and whistling "one of them jazz tunes."

By this time the law, egged on by the press, decided to investigate. Sheriff Oakum Pomfrey began a dogged investigation. Suspicion fell first on Paul Strachey, a man about town and part-time scissor grinder, since he was the only tall man in the town. Further, Strachey had been engaged to *both* Melissa Benchleys and had been eventually refused by both the girls. Strachey had alibis for both crimes. He had at both times been unconscious from overdrinking in the back of the Main Street trolley. When the next crime occurred exactly one week from the second and the girl was also named Melissa Benchley, Sheriff Pomfrey re-questioned Paul Strachey with a vengeance. It was found that Strachey had never been engaged to the girl and he was released. Years later Strachey committed suicide by throwing himself on his grindstone. Townspeople said it was because he had been the killer, but it was probably because he was wanted in Vermont for hit-and-run driving with a cultivator.

When the fourth and fifth crimes occurred on schedule the people of Willseyville grew angry. It was getting so "a body couldn't walk the streets at night," especially a body named Melissa Benchley. About this time Pomfrey began to sense some sort of pattern in the crimes. They had always taken place in front of Perth's Harness Shop at 8:15 of a Tuesday. The sheriff decided to station himself on the corner in question on the following Tuesday. However, it was his wife's birthday and he was unable to reach the corner until 8:16. Just in time to see a tall man running off with a guillotine on his shoulder. Stopping to see if he could aid the decapitated girl Pomfrey delayed in his pursuit and lost the trail of the slayer in front of Grenville's Hardware Store.

The press attacked Pomfrey and poked fun at his handling of the case, turning several Midwestern blasts of sarcasm on him. It was then that the canny Sheriff Pomfrey got the idea that almost solved the case. All the girls had been named Melissa Benchley. Were there any more girls with this name? He decided to look into it. He discovered two more Melissa Benchleys. He arrived at the home of the first at 8 o'clock on a Tuesday. After being admitted to the parlor by the landlady, a Mrs. Blanche LaVie, he was told to wait while the Benchley girl was summoned. Seconds later he heard a scream that chilled his bones. Running upstairs, he rushed by the trembling Mrs. LaVie and into the girl's room. Melissa Benchley had been saved from the slayer's blade. Someone had done her in with a hundred pounds of high explosives. Stopping only to ask Mrs. LaVie if she had heard anything suspicious the Sheriff rushed out to find the other Benchley girl and if possible save her from the slayer.

Here the strange story of the guillotine slayer must end. Sheriff Pomfrey was never seen again, nor was the Benchley girl. All that was ever heard from the remaining Melissa Benchley was a postcard from Chico, California, sent to Paul Strachey in 1923. The card, which I have seen, says only: "How's tricks?" It contains a picture of the Chico city hall on its face. So the dust of time settles over the sensational Willseyville slayer case, leaving countless questions unanswered. For instance, what *did* happen to Sheriff Pomfrey? How did it happen that there were eight girls named Melissa Benchley? Doesn't that stretch the laws of probability? Why wasn't Pierre LaSalle, a traveling guillotine salesman, ever questioned? Because he was only four feet, nine inches tall? Why wasn't his roommate, Fred Andren, a stilt salesman, brought in for questioning? Perhaps Paul Strachey knew the answers to these and other questions. But Paul Strachey is dead. *Pelican*

HERE'S A NUPTIAL FOR YOU

Yellow sweet peas and Spanish moss formed a colorful background this morning for the marriage of Miss Pearl Antilles, daughter of Mrs. Sadie Swinton and Mr. Anthony Antilles, of Grosse Point, Michigan, Punting-by-the-Sea, New Hampshire, Key Largo, Florida, Antwerp, Belgium, and 1069½ East Main, Toledo, Ohio, to Mr. Samson San Salvador, son of Mr. and Mrs. John San Salvador of San Diego, California.

Following the ceremony, a small reception for members of the immediate family and a few close friends was held in Madison Square Garden. Televising of the event kept the attendance down to 13,900.

Given in marriage by her father, the bride wore a close-fitting ivory satin tulle with pin-point lace and red piping, set off by a dazzling, finely-woven brocade, and a tiara of seedless pearls caught up at her wrists, the veil of which hung down to her knees. She carried a Bantam Book draped with eucharis lilies.

Miss Faith Farewell was maid of honor, while the rest of the bridal attendants were made of flesh. These lovelies wore fitted bodices and each carried a bunch of flowers.

Fergus Fonts, a school chum of Mr. San Salvador, was the best man, or at least the best they could find. The ushers were Floyd Bodoni, Dwight R. Turco, and Rocko Marconi, all of Loew's Poli.

After the honeymoon in Peoria, the couple will make their home in Peoria, where Mr. San Salvador runs his barber shop (9 barbers 9).

The bride attended school, struggling through a year and a half at Vassar before flunking out. She made her debut in the 1947 season and is now a member of the National League.

On the side of her mother, the former Miss Sadie Sierra, granddaughter of Sierra Leone, who was the sister of Sierra Madre, and the cousin of Sierra Nevada, the bride is the paternal great-grandfather of the late Claude Seabourne, onetime president of Seabourne, Inc., of Peoria.

Mr. Antilles, who, if you'll remember, is the groom, is an alumnus of Harvard College, where he was a member of the Hominy Grits Club of 1812, and the Harvard Co-op. *Yale Record*

NOT WITH A BANG, BUT A WLSOOOPP

BY DAVID KESSEL

A new military menace confronts the world. Recently, weapons have become increasingly more powerful. The A-bomb was more powerful than the TNT bomb. The H-bomb was more powerful than the A-bomb. But now these are all trivial; the last word has come. We now have the super bomb, the V-bomb.

The secret of the V-bomb has finally leaked out, or leaked in, depending on how you look at it. It is a vacuum bomb. Instead of everything being blown apart, everything is sucked in. What could be worse than being sucked in?

And this bomb creates no puny, old-fashioned vacuum. This is a new, highly concentrated vacuum, developed through the years of research and development.

A huge, immense vacuum is squeezed down into a small space. When it is released the results are devastating. It has been estimated that a V-bomb of average size exploded (or imploded) five hundred feet above New York City would suck Manhattan Island into a space of one cubic millimeter within half a second. It is reported that a small test explosion milked a herd of cows five miles from the blast.

Greatest secrecy surrounds the development of this project. Surprisingly enough, Congressional opposition to the project developed when it was found that the project was spending huge sums of money to produce *nothing*. The whole story was revealed when a reporter accidentally heard a high government official say over the telephone: "Things over here are all sucked up."

Naturally the University of Michigan is playing a large part in this project. The most difficult problem is finding something to hold such a powerful vacuum. Many university professors have put their heads to this problem. However, the peacetime uses of the weapon are not being neglected; it has been noted that the principles of the bomb's operation could do much to alleviate the parking problem.

Whatever the relative merits of the V-bomb, it is here, its existence has created many new problems; problems which all intelligent citizens should think about before waking up in the morning. *Gargoyle*

ANOTHER BOW

The season's social whirl reached a new and breath-taking point last night with the sumptuous party Mr. and Mrs. Horace Mannerbee gave to introduce to society their charming daughter, Mable. One sensed the carnival spirit in approaching the gaily lit, chromium-trimmed house from the long drive. Liveried attendants met at the door and carried the guests from their cars into the house. Mrs. Mannerbee and her daughter received in the exquisitely appointed drawing room. Standing in front of the fireplace, which was tastefully banked with delphinium and bunches of money, the two women, for we can call Mable a woman now, made a charming picture. Mrs. Mannerbee wore an exciting gown of black tulle. As she received, she twirled a rope of diamonds in her left hand which gave a casual note to the setting and set one instantly at ease. "Fats," as Mable is affectionately known by the younger ranks of smartdom, wore a bouffant creation in mauve. Mrs. Mannerbee later confided that she had the dress made out of some old shopping bags, reflecting the ingenuity that is such an essential prerequisite for social arbitresses.

All of the town's elite danced the night away to the lilting rhythms of Bobbie Jacobs' orchestra, which was flown in at great expense from Trenton, New Jersey. *Yale Record*

I'M HOT FOR YOU, BABY

BY "SPARKS" SIEGEL

"I'm hot for you, baby!" he bellowed through smoky breath, seizing her roughly somewhere between the waist and chin and hurling her viciously to the bed. With a precise motion, he ripped her flimsy dress.

(*How do you like this story so far? Good, huh? Just as I figured. You know what I should do right now? I should stop. You know why? Because sometimes you make me sick. But don't worry, I won't. Not while I have you eating out of the palm of my hand. And I do, you know. How many people, after seeing the above title, and first paragraph, skipped this story? How many would dare? Show me one, and I'll show you a liar.*

(*You know, you're all good kids, but sometimes you make me so mad! Month after month we courageously attempt to sublimate our literary efforts. We try to foment the intelligent capacity of a supposedly high level of humanity. And what happens? We get letters—tear-smeared letters. Not enough sex. Give us more sex. SEX! SEX! Aaah, you make me sick!*)

"Bruno!" she shouted, dropping her shoes to the floor and making herself comfortable. "You don't have to treat me like this because I'm hot for you too!"

(*Getting better, now, isn't it? Here's a girl who—well, who might possibly flunk or get a very low C on her convent entrance examination. But a girl, nevertheless, who is a victim of environment. Underneath —if you want to dig—you'll probably find she's pure. Why, she could be your . . . sister. Well, she could! But do you care? Nah. You're just sitting there chewing this up, swallowing it, and crying for more. All you want to see is——Aaah, sometimes I get so fed up!*)

"Malvina!" he roared. "Malvina baby! Don't torture me like this when I'm so hot for you!"

"Who's torturing you?" she asked, leaning back and loosening—well, whatever she wanted to loosen.

(*Who's torturing you? Who's torturing you? Did you hear what that horrid girl said? That—that—— Did you hear what your sister said? But, no, you won't go home and tell your mother. Oh no, you're really beginning to enjoy this. Aaah!*

(*Do you know what I had originally planned to write? A brief account of merchandising before and after the Middle Ages. What are you twisting your face like that for? It would have done you some good.*)

Deftly Bruno divested himself of his shirt and revealed a hairy chest, which rose and fell in the accelerated tide of passion. Eagerly she helped him off with his shoes. "Baby," he said, "I'm so——"

"So stop talking already!" she shouted.

(*So stop talking already! So stop talking already! Listen to her moan. Your own flesh and blood. Would you help her? Do you care? Naah. You're just squirming because I'm delaying this.*

(*I suppose you think you know all there is to know about merchandising before and after the Middle Ages.*)

Gently Bruno took her into his hairy arms and crushed her to his heaving bosom.

"Oooh!" she squealed.

With his right hand he——

(*I'll bet you think it's easy to turn out a college humor magazine every month and please everybody. Sure, you say, and put plenty of sex into it. It's easy to say. Put sex into it. Of course, you forget that we writers are conscientious, clean-living people who are making an earnest attempt to lay the groundwork for future, sober endeavors.*

(*My God, we're just Americans like the rest of you. We like picnics, hay rides, Coney Island, and Bing Crosby. We hate to see that evening sun go down. We like to wrap sandwiches in old Chicago* Tribunes *and go fishing. Give us a break. How far can we get writing stuff like this?*)

With his right hand he seized her left shoulder, and with his left arm he seized her right shoulder. Only her quick, uneven breath, which started from her nose and came out from her mouth—except when it was vice versa—interrupted the stillness of the room. Suddenly something dropped to the floor.

(*In a recent poll conducted by Thomas Trot, George Gallop, and Eddie Canter, it was revealed that out of the three hundred branches of the W.C.T.U. which are located in the area between Des Moines and Dobbs Ferry, not one—I'll repeat—not one subscribes to* Shaft.

(And do you know why? Do I have to tell you? Not enough sex.

(Well, I tell you, I'm sick of it. I hate sex. I'll get it out of the homes. I'll take it off the campuses. On the blackboards of sex-hygiene classes I'll write, "It ain't fitten to talk about."

(We could have had fun, you and I. You know, merchandising before and after the Middle Ages isn't anywhere near merchandising DURING the Middle Ages.)

"What dropped to the floor, Bruno?" Malvina asked, disengaging herself from him.

A surge of crimson enveloped his face. "It was . . ." he stammered. "It was . . ."

(Look at her now! Look! Look! Look at Malvina! Hah, Malvina! I only call her that. She could be anybody. She could be . . . well, you know who she could be; I told you before. Look at her! Disgusting! Look how she's dressed! What would your father say? What do you say? Listen to her; she wants to know what dropped on the floor. That's all that's important to her right now. Nothing else on earth matters. Schools, studies, the future, Russia; they're unimportant. And what about you—a blood relation? What about you? You want to know what dropped on the floor, too. To tell you the truth so do I. But you can ask her when she comes home, I can't. That's one of the reasons I get so fed up. Sex. Baah!)

NEXT MONTH—DEFINITELY: A DISCUSSION ON MERCHANDISING BEFORE AND AFTER THE MIDDLE AGES; OR MAYBE—A LITTLE TALK ON WHAT DROPPED ON THE FLOOR. *Shaft (University of Illinois)*

UNDER THE TABLE

BY LARRY SIEGEL

Now it can be told. With deepest apologies to Walt Whitman's classic, *Song of Myself* from *Leaves of Grass,* I scour the inner recesses of my mind and bare my thoughts, my life, my aspirations. 'Partake of this godly liquid, O Waiting World, it is thine (this sentence is published with permission from the *Sears Roebuck Manual,* Fall Edition)."

Oh, Larry Siegel, cosmos of Brooklyn, dean of Flatbush Avenue;
Laughing, crying, fleshy, cadaverous, sensual, nonsensual;
Walking, hopping, strolling, meandering, galloping, galloping, galloping (whoaaa!)
Through the boulevards of time; brother of mankind, sister of womankind, animal of animalkind.
They are I! I are they; we are we (and why not?)
The wounded sparrow plaintively looks at me with soulful eyes.
I squash him with my hobnailed boot (he was a goner anyway).
But I love him, for aren't I he, and aren't he I (or something)?
The bellicose, unemployed locksmith stands bare-chested in my path,
His massive shoulders so shoulderlike.
I dab salve on his aching heart; I embrace him; I wish him good lock.
The hardened, softened burlesque queen is removing from her foot runway splinters.
I help her, abet her, I aid her (I was hungry), I gave her new hopes.
She offers me money, monetary recompense, pecuniary tokens, jewels.
I tell her I want nothing; I take her phone number; I grasp her hand firmly; I say "God dress you, child."
The refuse pails, the hydrants, the sewers, I love them all.
The cigarettes, living from hand to mouth, them too.
The world: it is I, I is it.
I enter the billiard parlor and walk through the cigarette smoke.
I hug the hustlers, the bankers, the cueballs.
I rack, I sweep, I clean spittoons.
I adore them; them adore I.
Out of the darkness into the semi-darkness comes Sammy Darkness, my bookmaker, my bookie, my taker of bets.
I kneel before him; I take off my straw hat; my being is numbed with awe; I can't feel my straw hat; it isn't felt.
He chews his unlighted cigar; he drops it; I snatch it and replace it gently between his yellow teeth.
I rise at his touch; I fall at his touch; I grovel at his feet; I clean his shoes.
He rolls his bloodshot eyes; he removes his pince-nez (what a spectacle!).
He wants nothing from me; he loves me; everything I possess is mine.
All he wants are pennies, and nickels and dimes and quarters and halves and all kinds of bills.
These I give happily, joyously; I clean my pockets, he cleans my pockets; we clean together; he takes me to the cleaners.

I stretch out my arms; I embrace him; I hug him; I draw his sweating body to mine.
Sammy, I say, my Sammy, my own beloved, sweating bookie.
And now I am through, for the day. Tomorrow, I go onward to love everybody, everything, all, every, each, *tout le monde, chaque homme, jedermann.*
Leaves of grass, leaves of grass on the ground, my ground, your ground, our ground, coffee ground, Polo Ground.
Leaves of grass on the field, your field, my field, Marshall Field.
And in the darkness one leaf says to another, "I want to be a lawn."

Shaft

LOW TIDE

BY RON GOULART

I stood at the wheel of The Seabreeze with a fresh sea breeze blowing in my tanned and ruggedly handsome face. The thrill of adventure made my skin tingle and even break out in places. I adjusted my skipper's cap at a jaunty angle so that I could not see and headed for Port Sitlow. The craft shot through the water like a sleek, new cocker spaniel.

We sailed into the harbor and up onto the beach, sliding to a stop in the lobby of the Seabreeze Hotel.

"Mino bi sim dillyfork," grinned Maligoko, my faithful Javanese.

"Leave it to you to say that," I said, pretending to understand what he had said.

A blonde girl came over to me. "I hear you might have a boat for hire."

I took off my hat so that I could see her. She was a girl all right.

"Maybe," I said, being subtle. "Let me buy you a drink."

We ordered two bottles of creme de gin. It was fairly dark at our table but I was pretty sure there was a man sitting in the center of the table next to the ash tray. I played it smart. "Who's this guy?"

"What guy?"

That took care of that. "What's the scoop?" I asked, proud of saying something clever.

She leaned forward until her cute turned up nose touched my left knee. "This is big. Sail up to Port Morissitlow and meet me tomorrow at half past six."

"What's there?"

"Clams."

"Oh," I said, knowingly. Then she was gone, leaving behind only the faint and delicate scent of mothballs.

I was ordering another blonde when a short, plump man came over and sat down. "Hi sigh, guv'ner, wot's hup 'ere, heh wot?"

"Javanese?"

"British."

"Oh," I said, pretending to know where that was. "What's the scoop?"

"Clems, me by, surenow a fartune in clems."

"Your accent changed."

"Oh, pardon me." Somewhere in the next room a girl screamed. I stood up. Six Hindus disguised as Arabs were kidnapping the red-headed girl I had just spoken to. I went into action.

Quickly I reached under the table for my shoes. It was then that I noted that the plump man was whistling the third movement of the Sigma Ambler Phi drinking song.

"Are you a member of Sigma Ambler Phi, the Honorary Spy Fraternity?"

He wheezed knowingly. "The handshake?"

I placed my left hand against his right temple. He placed his left hand against my right temple. Then we locked the first and third fingers of our right hands. I then placed my left hand in his right coat pocket. And he did likewise to me. We unlocked right hands and placed our extended right thumbs firmly against our upper lips with fingers facing upward toward Grover Cleveland. "By Jove," I said. "You're one of us. Let's get those scoundrels." A half hour had elapsed since we had begun the handshake so we got as far as the bar and gave up the search for the brunette. Still the smell of mothballs haunted me and I vowed my allegiance to that little lady I some day hoped to call "my broad."

That night we set sail with Maligoko at the oars. The girl was tied to the mast in case a storm came up. We had an interesting time saving the girl from the river pirates, but that's another story. (It really isn't another story, but we feel it is too stimulating to be presented to our readers).

"Look," the girl said, "I'll let you in on the deal if you promise not to tell."

"Sufferin' shad, I wouldn't snitch on you. Jimhickies, you're special."

"Okay, buster, now get this. When we get there we'll find all kinds of clams. And with them we'll make chowder which we'll sell to the Reds in Korea."

"Why, by gumminy, that's a foul, foul plot. Our boys are fighting to make the world safe for democracy, our boys are making sacrifices to preserve our rights! If anybody gets those clams . . . it'll be Sitlow's Fish Pier at 740 East Lobster Ave., San Francisco 8, Calif. 'Cause that's what America is. A lot of little things. The kids playing in the streets, rolling drunks. A backwoods senator throwing out the first hot dog at Yankee Stadium. I never met a man I didn't think took a heap of livin'. An' he ain't heavy, he's my grand, ol' flag. Put them all together they spell mother."

I looked at the girl. She was crying. Her wig fell lightly to the deck. "You'll catch cold if your hair gets wet. But, say, you're not a girl . . . you're . . ."

"That's right. Claude Rains. This is all a joke. We're really making a movie called 'The Bowery Boys Meet Tuttle of Tahiti'."

We both laughed heartily.

The next morning he was carried off by cannibals. *Pelican*

HOW TO WRITE AN OBITUARY NOTICE

BY IBEX (R. B. D. FRENCH)

The obituary notice . . . is usually thrust upon junior shoulders. All aspiring writers in this field must learn that the first essential is to master the art of concealment. . . . A number of formulas have been evolved in the course of many years by which, while preserving the harmonious and dignified style proper to a sorrow, he can convey his meaning to all discerning persons. . . . A brief list is given below with their equivalents:

READS	MEANS
. . . died recently	We have lost the clipping giving the date.
possessed a fund of genial anecdote.	Bored everybody with ancient and interminable jokes.

Not for him the easy way of retirement.	He held on to his job long after he became senile.
His magnum opus, although it caused some searching of heart among the orthodox, gained for him many disciples.	His book was thought absurd by all competent judges, but a few cranks were deceived by it.
He was a man of strong loyalties.	He was a man of strong prejudices.
. . . although not everyone had the good fortune to be admitted to the company of his intimate friends . . .	Nobody liked him much.
. . . devoted a long career to unostentatious service.	Everybody had forgotten he existed.
. . . veneration for those fountains of classic culture from which he himself had drunk so generously . . .	. . . spent his life imparting useless knowledge on the understanding that his pupils in turn would gain a livelihood by passing it on to unwilling schoolboys.
He retained the uncompromising blunt honesty of his Northern stock.	He had no manners.
His Donellan Lectures were marked by a reaction against the popular treatment accorded to the subject by superficial exponents.	Nobody could understand them.
. . . could not suffer fools gladly.	Was a boor and a bully.
Although a man of profound scholarship he was by no means oblivious to the more convivial arts of life.	He drank.

This is neither the time nor the place to speak of his many achievements . . .	This is both the time and the place, but what the hell?

T.C.D.

CINDERELLA

From time to time we are fortunate to acquire material submitted from other countries. Voo Doo *is pleased to present, directly from France, a work by the well-known teller of children's stories, Henri de la Desqui. Monsieur de la Desqui will relate the beloved fairy tale,* Cinderella.

Bonjour, mes enfants. Today we tell ze storee of Cinderella. Cinderella, she ees a young girl. Gorgeous! But she ees veree poor. She always wears rags. But veree form-feeting.

Cinderella, she have two stepsistaires. Zey are ugly, but not *too* bad. Ze one, she have a beeg nose weeth a wart on ze end, and ze othaire have long stringy hair and a scar ovaire her ear, but still, zey are *girls.*

Also, there ees ze stepmothaire. Not bad for an old woman. She's fat and she's nastee and she has a terrible tempeur. But sometimes zeese old ladies weeth hot tempeurs—I remembaire one time in Marseilles there was—there was——

Well, anyhow, one night there ees a beeg partee in the castle. Ze ugly stepsistaires and ze ugly stepmothaire zey go. But lovely Cinderella, she don't go. Imagine—beautiful girl ees home and ze partee ees full of ugly women. Aah, zese Breetish.

Anyhow, Cinderella ees home crying, when, all of a sudden, pouf. *Voilà,* there ees her fairee godmothaire. Gorgeous! She wave zee wand and, *sacrebleu,* Cinderella have beautiful dress and glass slippaires. Ze reason she geeves her glass slippaires—zey are not comfortable—but everybodee can see zat her feet are *clean.*

Ze fairee godmothaire, she send Cinderella to party. But she must be home by twelve o'clock. Twelve o'clock. These fairee godmothaires, zey mean well, but what do zey know about parties?

Anyway, Cinderella go to zee partee and right away she see ze handsome preence who ees ze ruleur of ze whole land. He ees Preence Sharming. He ees ze son of King Sharming. He ees ze brothaire of Joe Sharming. He ees gorgeous!

Ze preence, when he see Cinderella, he fall in love weeth her. But just them, ze clock strike twelve. Bong, bong, bong, and nine more.

Cinderella run and drop ze glass slippaire. She care *more* about being home on time that about ze *romance.* Aah, zeese Breetish.

Ze next day, Preence Sharming carry ze glass slippaire around ze town and ees looking for a girl who have ze foot een wheech ze slippaire of eet—ze foot weel feet een eet—ah, een eet. He will marry such a girl whose foot feet een eet. Oui, een eet. Ze foot. This foolish man, he fall in love with a *foot.* He do not care about ze othaire end. Aah, zeese Breetish.

Finally, he come to ze home of Cinderella. Cinderella, she put on glass slippaire and eet feet like a glove. Well, naturally, she put her hand een eet. But then she put her foot een eet, eet feet perfect—her foot—een—eet. Een eet.

So at ze end of ze storee, Preence Sharming, he ees veree hapee and he asks for Cinderella's foot in marriage. *Au revoir. Voo Doo* (*M.I.T.*)

SWAMPED

The quicksand oozed ominously in his boot, squishing and gurgling softly between his toes. It was an uncomfortable feeling.

"Hell!" he said.

A bird called—*weetoooteee—weetoooteee—weetoooteee.* It was an unnerving cry—that relentless *weetoooteee.*

"Damn!" he said.

The tropical wind whipped through the fan-like fingers of the palmetto leaves and played ragtime hymns on his spine.

"Hell!" he said.

The quicksand was up to his knees now. The flesh on the back of his legs began to ache. He wanted to sit down. He was tired.

"There's no sitting down here," he said to himself.

He looked down at the slimy muck inching up his legs. A large mosquito from the swarm that zzz-ed about his head bit him fiercely, fiendishly, sadistically. He'd almost forgotten about the mosquitoes.

"Damn!" he said, "I'd almost forgotten about the mosquitoes."

He remembered the time when he dropped the diploma at the high school graduation and everyone laughed. He had blushed and smiled sheepishly and sat down.

Then there was the time his brother—or was it his sister?—had asked him what he was going to do with his life and he had answered, "Oh, I don't know."

These things and many more came back to him like a poof from the past and became meaningful.

Bloodsuckers latched on to his flesh and went about their bloody business. Sweat beaded on his forehead and trickled down his slimy face.

"Hell!" he said.

Yes, meaningful. In an instant he knew that every event in his life, no matter how unimportant, was an integral part of his small play in the tapestry of time.

He was now wallowing up to his chin in the thick slime. It was useless to fight—besides he had forgotten to take his hands out of his pockets.

And what was time now when he would soon not even be a part of space? That was a good question.

He laughed at the sloppy cold muck tickling his bottom lip. He had always been ticklish.

He remembered how his mother used to tickle him after dinner and how the rest of the family all laughed as he ran to the bathroom with his hand over his mouth.

He felt sick now. He had always had a weak stomach. It had roots in his childhood—the sickness did. But there were bigger problems to face now.

How could he save himself! He would soon be ensconced in the quagmire.

Suddenly an idea came to him. He turned to the crowd standing on the shore and screamed—"Help!" *Jackolantern*

CONQUERING THE COSMOS

BY ZEMMD PUGH

Jack Brigade, skipper of RX-434, the United States of the World's speediest spaceship, stood at the helm of RX-434, the United States of the World's speediest spaceship, and looked valiantly out of the Plexi-flamo glass windshield at the impenetrable darkness of the universe.

"What's our speed, Bill?" his strong voice called down the Merco-radar Intercom.

"Seventy-seven billion kilometers, sir," came trusty Bill Jackson's reply.

"Well, step it up a bit, old man," said Jack's rich bass. "How's the wife?"

"Fine, Jack Brigade, sir."

Jack always exchanged these pleasantries with the men. It lent an informal air of easy fellowship and good will and was especially necessary on a trip as arduous and dangerous as this one they were now undertaking, Jack thought. "Undertaking, yes—we may all end up at the undertaker's, yes," he said to himself with a wry, bitter, sardonic grin at his grim humor. He switched on the intercom.

"We may all end up at the undertaker's, yes," he screamed into the mike, laughingly.

"Yes, Jack Brigade, sir," came Bill's sturdy reply.

Loyal to the last, Jack thought to himself. A magnificent crew.

There were four people aboard the RX-434, in this year 2009 A.D. Jack Brigade, captain . . . Bill Jackson, the navigator, a trusty, sturdy young lout . . . then there was Simon Degree, the cook, a shifty fellow with a green mustache, and not, Jack feared, to be trusted. And finally there was Lona Griswold, lovely Lona Griswold. And beneath Jack's great stone face, his heart beat wildly for her. She had volunteered for this dangerous mission, and when he had first looked into her cameo eyes, there was love. They had spoken but little since the beginning of the trip, but each word had held depths of meaning.

Their mission was important. Jack had been asked by the President of the World to examine and investigate Auralee, a galaxy of stars about 100,000,000 light-years away from Earth, to see if it would make a suitable base for launching spaceships into the unknown. For this hazardous task, Jack Brigade had been given RX-434, the impenetrable, irresistible, fantastic, tremendous new Gravito-Spaceship, with twin turbo-compresso guns, so huge and powerful that they could demolish the earth if they tried. But the trip had gone smoothly so far. Jack Brigade crossed his fingers.

Suddenly Lona was there, looking into his eyes.

"What are you doing up here in the Control-panel Compartment, Lona?" asked Jack huskily.

"I love you, Jack Brigade," she replied meaningfully.

"But we must accomplish our mission first. My heart is heavy, Griswold."

"It should be light, Brigade. We have so much to live for."

"Yes, yes," he breathed hoarsely. "I must take over the controls now." He shouted down the intercom. "Bill, switch the Roto-Gravure Steering Facilities up here and push the De-Thermotator on. The Plexi-flamo glass is melting."

Lona clung to Jack's strong right arm. "Jack Brigade, you're a handsome devil in your Nylon Air-Suit."

"And you in your Spun-Glass Oxygenator, Lona."

They clung to their course.

Then it happened. A half hour later, the compartment door was suddenly flung open, and there stood Bill Jackson and Simon Degree.

Bill saluted smartly and said, "Excuse me, sir, Jack Brigade, sir, but—"

Jack Brigade felt the need for a little discipline. He whipped out his Uranium-Detonator Gun from its holster and fired. Bill, trusty old Bill, rapidly distintegrated.

Poor Bill, Jack thought. Maybe I was a bit harsh. But he should have known better than to interrupt me. Yet he was loyal, loyal to the last.

Jack Brigade wrestled with his soul. Had he been morally right? Which was more important, his mission or the ionization of a human life? There was something strongly resembling tears glistening in Jack's tired eyes.

"Onward and upward," he sighed unsteadily. "For the sake of humanity. Science must be served. Let this be a lesson to you, Simon Degree."

Simon Degree's shifty face shifted. "But, sir, the ship is heading for—"

"Enow! Have no fear," commanded Jack, lapsing for dramatic effect, into Shakespearean quotations. "We will not change our course. We must reach Auralee!"

"But, sir—"

"Enow of this palaver!" Jack's powerful right hand reached for his trusty Disintegrato Gun, but it had disintegrated. Taking advantage of the situation, Simon Degree shifted around to Jack's back, and with a quick move, struck him a dastardly blow on the back on the nape of the neck. . . .

When Jack awoke, he was bound securely hand and foot on the

floor of the compartment. Lona was screaming, desperately trying to fend off Simon Degree's insane advances.

"Aha, me proud beauty," shouted Simon Degree, clutching her close. "I shall rule Auralee and you'll be my queen."

"But what of Jack?"

"His fate is sealed, my pet. I will remove his gravity belt, and drop him out into space, where he will float aimlessly about until the difference of pressures inside and outside his body either burst or crush him, ahahaheeheeha!"

"You—you unspeakable fiend!" Summoning all her strength, she pushed away from him and ran into the rear of the spaceship. Simon Degree, his green mustache twitching with envy, rushed after her.

Jack Brigade, left alone, was helpless. He struggled vainly against his bonds. What was happening to Lona? . . . What were Simon Degree's plans? . . . Loyal to the last? . . . Hah! Loyal to the lust! Jack smiled wryly, bitterly, sardonically, to himself. Where was the ship headed for at seventy-seven billion kilometers a second? He must get free! Free! FREE!

With a superhuman burst of strength, Jack broke the ropes that held him. Leaping around the Control-panel Compartment, he rapidly switched on the Telo-fission Receiver, in order to locate what part of RX-434 Simon and Lona were in. Suddenly it flashed on the screen—they were in the powder room! With a shocked scream, Jack dashed to the place at once, his atom pistol drawn. When he arrived at the powder room, a horrifying sight greeted him. Lona's plastic shoulder strap had slipped, and Simon Degree was kissing her all over the place.

Jack Brigade fired.

Simon Degree was reduced to an atom.

Jack said, "Oh, Lona!"

Lona said, "Oh, Jack!"

The RX-434, said "Barumphspftxzeemdpugh" and crashed into something.

Jack and Lona were jolted out of each other's arms.

"I think we've landed, Lona," said Jack.

"Yes, Jack Brigade, love. What shall we do?"

"Man the twin turbo-compresso guns, Lona."

"I am here, love."

"Demolish this place we have landed on. I see strange creatures running about in great haste. They may be planning to attack us! Destroy this nest of evil, Lona, now."

"Yes, Jack Brigade, love."

She put her shoulder strap back and pushed a button. A great roar was heard, so great that it shook the very universe, as the twin guns, the acme of all science's progress throughout the ages, fired. The evil planet burst into flames and was washed away into space and time.

"But, Jack Brigade, love, that was the Earth!" cried Lona with astute realization.

"Are you sure, Lona darling?"

"Positive, love. I saw some people!"

"Maybe that's what poor Bill and that villainous Simon were vainly trying to tell me before–before—"

Jack's hard, heroic composure broke at last. He brushed a luminous tear from his eye.

"Ah, well—" A great sigh escaped from his lips. "We love each other. That's all that matters, is it not? You and I, Lona, *we* will build a *new* world–a world where dreams may be fulfilled, and where democracy may reign ever triumphant! It was an error on my part, I admit, to fire those guns without looking more carefully. But someday you'll be glad and I'll be glad. And we will laugh. And live. And love."

He put his arm carefully about her waist, and together they looked out of the Plexi-flamo glass windshield into the Impenetrable Darkness, into the Great Void. *The Purple Cow*

UP THE CANYON A PIECE

BY TEX HINDLE

"Put down that thing, you ornery critter . . . it's liable to go off." Polly Concarne, queen of Sore Gut Junction, slapped the gun out of Raw Lips' snake-bitten, frost-bitten, arrow-pierced, double-jointed, blue-veined hands. She had given up Russian Roulette for Lent and wanted no part of his little game.

"But, Honey-Bee Girl, you promised!" said Raw Lips in a gruff, masculine-like voice.

"Don't 'bee-girl' me, you white-nosed varmint," she answered in a sensual, woman-like tone. "Last time we played spin-the-barrel you had all the chambers filled and wanted me to go first. You don't want to play; you want to knock me off. You're just after my assets. Well,

Raw Lips, when I go I'm not leavin' the Raptured Nugget, best saloon this side of Naked Tip River, to you! Everything I've got goes to Pancho Gasset y Ortega Garfslinger, the one with which I am truly in love with, which, whom, with—"

"But I kinda thought it was you and me, Honey-Bee Girl," he blubbered.

"One more 'bee-girl' out of you," she scowled in a scowling tone, "and you'll be picking up teeth. Now get out there in the gambling parlor and do the job I'm paying you for. Get those games moving. The tables are slow tonight." If there's one thing that irritated Polly it was a slow table.

Raw Lips went to the door of Polly's upstairs office saying, "Just as you want, Honey-Bee Girl." He then bent over and picked up a few scattered teeth of his on the floor, and plucked one or two from the toe of Polly's shoe. Mopping the blood away from his mouth, he managed to say, "Gymphtt lrwb kllegt," and stumbled out into the laughing crowds.

Polly went to the window and looked down on the main street of Sore Gut. A little girl was playing in the dusk in the dust with her puppy. Suddenly the crack of a whip was heard and the little girl withdrew a swollen stump of a hand. A pistol shot sounded and her puppy bit the dust. Pancho was in town! Polly's carefree, handsome, unbathed lover was back from the plains. She quickly adjusted her safety belt and prepared for the take-off . . . he would be with her at almost any moment.

Across town, in the sheriff's office, wearing the sheriff's badge, was the Sheriff Pacos, the most daring sheriff west of the John. Upon hearing of Pancho's arrival in Sore Gut (the little girl had run screaming to his office, showing her mutilated hand, exclaiming that she would never be able to play poker again). Sheriff Pacos checked his guns and jumped on his horse, then the horse jumped on him, then he hit the horse, then the horse bit his elbow. Then Sheriff Pacos walked toward the Raptured Nugget where he knew Pancho would be (hiding?).

Polly popped a stick of gum in her mouth and waited for Pancho's entrance. A second later the door flew off its hinges and in strode Pancho. They embraced and remained lip to quivering lip. It was plain to see they were stuck on each other.

"It's great to be back," said Pancho, scraping flecks of singed gum off his chin.

"It's great to be a woman," offered Polly, swallowing hard to release the pressure on her eardrums.

"It's great for me to be back *and* for you to be a woman," said Pancho, checking to see if his wallet were still there.

"It's great for you to want it that way, Big One . . . I mean for you to be back and me to be a woman," said Polly, handing his wallet back. "I ain't seen a woman in weeks. And you're a woman, and I'm back," said Pancho, taking back his empty wallet.

"What is it you're trying to say?" said Polly, tucking a wad of bills down the front of her sequined costume.

"Kiss me again, woman, and I'll tell you," said Pancho. They embraced and Pancho put the bills back in his wallet.

Just then the stage manager of the Raptured Nugget appeared in the doorless doorway. "Time for your number, Miss Polly. The boys'll riot if'n you don't undulate a bit for 'em."

"Wish me luck, Pancho babe," said Polly. "I'm trying out a new number tonight. It's dedicated just to you. Called 'When There's Moonlight on the Mattress, There's Springtime in Your Eyes'!" As Polly left the room, she blew a kiss to Pancho and her gum came out with it.

She vibrated to center stage, and a roar roared from the audience—her pet lion was on the loose again. "All it wants is a little bit," said Polly. "Will one of you boys toss. . .?" There was a scramble to comply. Then the music started, Polly sang, and there was another scramble. Tables were overturned, the lion was mutilated, and hundreds were reported lost in the action.

Arriving via Anaheim, Sheriff Pacos flung aside the swinging doors of the saloon. His gaze was met by a flying spittoon. Picking himself up, he fired three shots above the heads in the milling crowd. Two horned owls, a mallard duck, and six limp geese fell at his feet. "Fudge," he said, "there goes my quota for the season. All right, you yaller-livered, no-good, rotten"—the crowd suddenly quieted—"you pranksters, you. Hi, fellas!"

Polly stepped over a few of the bodies and rumbled her way to the sheriff. "Listen, you baboon. When I want your help, I'll give you a call . . . and that won't be for a long time yet 'cause the telephone ain't been invented. Now crawl out the same way you came in!" Her earrings swung as she talked . . . the ones made out of beer-bottle caps set in champagne corks.

"I come for Pancho, Polly, I ain't aleavin' until he comes along," said Sheriff Pacos, looking her straight in the blouse.

"When Pancho leaves here," said Polly, "it'll be without you and when he pleases."

"Over my dead body, ma'am."

"That can be arranged, Crud-Face."

Crud-Face (i.e. Sheriff Pacos) stepped around Polly and started for the stairs to her office, his spurs jangling. Cling, clung, cling, clung, cling . . . crrrrunch . . . cling, thump, cling, cling . . . His left boot got stuck in a knothole and he had to leave it behind.

"Come back, you hear?" shouted Polly. "Pancho! The sheriff's acomin'. *Prenda garde!*"

Pancho ran out on the balcony; all eyes were on him. *Oy gevay*, what a mess! "Come and get me, Sheriff," he cried.

"What does it look like I'm doin'—trollin' for bass?" With that, Sheriff Pacos opened up. The crowd booed and he buttoned his shirt again. "I'm countin' three, Pancho, then I'm acomin' afirin' afor ayou."

"Speak English, Chowder Cheeks," retorted Pancho.

This was all the sheriff could take. Slapping leather, he whipped out his seven-shooter (shaped like an Australian swagger stick) and fired point-blank at Pancho. It was a good shot . . . in the back, between the shoulder blades.

Pancho toppled over the stair railing and was impaled on the tip of the roulette wheel, his head striking against the iron safe. A little dazed, Pancho started to get up, but Sheriff Pacos fired at close range into his vitals until he ran out of ammunition.

"Oooo," said Pancho. "I'm agoin' . . . bring me my woman." Polly waded through the blood to his side.

"I'm here, Gutless." Her voice quivered. "What do you want?"

"I'm goin' fast, Polly, but afore I go, I got somethin' to say."

"What is it, Paling-Rapidly?"

"You're mighty purty, Polly gal."

"Cut the frills, Lifeless. Where's your money?"

Just then, Fort Bravissimo (can be seen without glasses) was being attacked by a band of wild Indians. Molten lava poured out of the mountain, Lazy Water Creek overflowed its flood level by thirty-four feet, wild buffaloes stampeded through town, the bank was robbed, the dynamite store caught fire, and the west end of town left its foundations.

Raw Lips picked up Polly and headed for the old mine shaft up the canyon a piece (in consideration of which this tale has been named). Sheriff Pacos was forced to marry the little girl, and the Eighty-Second Cavalry Division rode into town, trampling the pair underfoot as they left on their honeymoon.

Off in the distance, on No-Help-At-All-Ridge, a lone gray wolf raised its snout to the evening sky and howled. This meant only one thing. There was trouble ahead. *Stanford Chaparral*

REJOICE

A bumbly-man shuffle-limped down the snow-slushy walk searching for munch-morsels to calm his grumble-tummy. Wicked-gleeful children laughty-teased him as they lazy-loitered by corner-curbs. But the bumbly-man did not hear-heed the snooty-nosed-nasty-namers, for he was fam-fam-hungry.

The crispy-cold made him shiver-shake and he yummy-yearned for his hearthy-home. Tickley-moist trickle-tears oozd from the corners of his squint-blinky eyes.

While he me-murmured of people-pride, stingy-self, and other thing-thoughts, he suddle-bumped a wheel-wobbly ickle-bike. The bumbly-man stare-started, for on the peddle-pede was a dump-fubsy budha-boy-burgher.

"Charity-hope!" exclaimed the boy-burgher. "You look tummy-empty. Folly-trail me on my ickle-bike and I will treat-foot you to a supper-feast at my fun-granny's."

"You're very kindly-nice," sniffle-sighed the bumbly-man, "for I am fainty-weak from lack of filly-food."

"There, there, there, there," soothee-soled the boy-burgher. "You just steppy-trud after me."

The bumbly-man fumble-followed the boy-burgher. Soon they hover-reached a gothy-shackle cottage snuggle-cozied in the woods. The boy-burgher frisky-frolicked to the door and ring-rang the bell. A spindly-old lady grunt-opened the door. She giggle-gushed in a grate-wispy laugh at the see-sight of the boy-burgher.

"Oh, fun-granny," cried the boy-burgher, "here is a bumbly-man who nessy-must have vittle-hots."

The prim-lacy fun-granny wrinkle-smiled at the bumbly-man and pretty-purred:

"Scram!" *Jackolantern*

THE PERFECT SQUELCH

BY THOMAS TIMBERLAKE

Mrs. Snog-Woody was known throughout Virginia for her fabulous parties. Her Southern mansion was the scene of countless festivities, of which the gayest was the annual Washington's Birthday Ball.

Early each February preparations would begin, and invitations were sent to the select gentry of Blue Ridge society. This year on the eve of the occasion, workers were putting the final touches on the ballroom decorations.

Old Erasmus, who had been sent over from the neighboring farm to help with the work, was adjusting the height of the crystal chandelier by means of a rope and pulley system.

Mrs. Snog-Woody, whose treatment of the servants was unusually severe, had kept Erasmus raising and lowering the heavy apparatus for almost an hour and a half as she tried to locate "just the right height."

Erasmus had patiently endured the whole affair until the hostess was directly beneath the chandelier. He released the rope and the heavy glass crushed her skull into a bloody pulp. *Stanford Chaparral*

PRIMROSE O'MAHANEY

BY RALPH ESTLING

Primrose O'Mahaney was in a slough of despond. Whenever someone would ask her, "What's wrong, Primrose?" or "Primrose, why aren't you smiling?" Primrose would only shake her head slowly and murmur sadly, "I am in a slough of despond." And the inquirer would smile kindly or sometimes laugh out loud because when Primrose said "slough" she would pronounce the g. Primrose was like that. Anything for a laugh, whether despondent or not, and besides, Primrose didn't know how to pronounce "slough."

From her room on the third floor of the Dambda Phi Letcha house, Primrose watched the sun, which resembled nothing so much as a giant globe of flaming gas at a mean distance of about 92,000,000 miles from the earth, go down behind the roof of the Hearst Memorial Mining Building.

"If the sun is setting here," she thought, "it must be just about ready to rise over the Soviet Socialist Republic of Kirgiz." But somehow that thought failed to move her.

She turned from the darkling landscape of West Berkeley and gazed at the row of books that were neatly stacked along the baseboard of the room, a typical Dambda Phi selection—the Complete Works of Frances Parkinson Keyes, Faith Baldwin, Temple Bailey, and the Marquis de Sade. Listlessly she opened *Les Cent et Vingt Jours de Sodome* and idly thumbed through the pages. But she found no help there. The words conveyed little to her mind, mainly because they were in French and she could not find them listed in the glossary in the back of her textbook. She flung the volume away and burst into tears. She was so unhappy. Also, she was a little lecherous.

Primrose was not like the other girls of Dambda Phi. Instead of being born, she had been found by two illiterate steamfitters one day stuck in between a chest of drawers and a wall. By the time they had jimmied her out and called the fire department and the police and a man namd Simmons or Simmonds who could whistle *The Battle Hymn of the Republic* through his nose, they had grown so fond of Primrose that they decided to keep her. They named her Primrose after their favorite flower and O'Mahaney after the head of Local 297, Steamfitters, Plumbers, and Plumbers' Helpers, A. F. of L.

Funny little Primrose. She had a funny little way about her that stole their hearts. She would be standing perfectly still and then suddenly she would hurl herself, hind end foremost, to the floor. "Aw faw down 'n' go 'boom,'" she would laugh. And everyone else would laugh too. Actually, it wasn't so much a 'boom' as it was a kind of a 'glunk,' but Primrose was only four years old then.

And that was why Primrose was crying. While other girls had mothers and fathers, Primrose had only two illiterate steamfitters and a chest of bureau drawers made in Grand Rapids, Michigan, and the second drawer from the top always stuck. And now, this very day was Presents at Dambda Phi Letcha. All the girls' mothers and fathers and boy friends would be there and there was to be a party and dancing and singing and favors that opened up with a loud pop and had funny little notes in them, like, "Stone walls do not a prison make, nor brass rails a saloon." Well, no wonder she was upset!

She could hear the sounds of joy and laughter as the guests began to arrive. She wondered if Harold would be there. Harold! Gay, charming, bon-vivant Harold, who was head of the biggest fraternity on the campus, president of his class, a Phi Beta Kappa student, an accomplished violist, and who owned a tie that lit up at night and read, "Will you kiss me in the dark, Baby?" She remembered when they had parted. Harold had come from one of the first families of Klamath Falls and when he discovered that Primrose had been found behind a bureau, there was nothing left to do but to give her back her pin. He wept, but he could not associate himself with a girl who didn't even know who her father was. Harold knew who *his* father was, although, as a matter of fact, he was wrong.

The party swept on beneath her. Water flowed like water. Everything was reaching a wild, mad climax. Two Dambda Phis had been winked at. They had burst into tears. A fine arts major from Barrington Hall had told the story about the cat who drank a full bottle of castor oil. He was arrested. The party was going along great and here it was, only eight o'clock. An hour and a half to go!

But as the noise and shouts drifted up to her room, the old Primrose O'Mahaney was giving way to the new. There was a new look in her eyes. There was life and sparkle and verve. Her little hands clenched. Yes, she had been found behind a bureau and the second drawer from the top always stuck! Yes, her foster parents were illiterate A. F. of L. steamfitters! Yes, she had two impacted wisdom teeth in her lower jaw! No matter. She would fight! She would go on! To hell with them.

And up above her, to the left of the Methodist Students' Guidance Center, a bright white moon—looking exactly as if it were an airless rocky wasteland 2,160 miles in diameter and at a mean distance of 238,857 miles from the earth—shone down upon a new, a happier, and, let us hope, a more perfect Primrose O'Mahaney. *Pelican*

HAMLET

A COMEDY OF EROS

BY JANET WINN

Hamlet is a melancholy but great Dane, who wanders through the gloomy halls of Elsinore talking to himself. He is in love with his mother and therefore hates his uncle Claudius.

In order to annoy his uncle Claudius he walks around in his bare bodkins and feigns madness. Actually he is mad, but nobody knows this, not even Ophelia, who goes mad herself in the mad scene. One of the central themes of this play is Danish politics.

One night the ghost of Hamlet's father pays a visit to the castle and is noticed by the guards who report this to Hamlet.

Hamlet is skeptical. "Get thee to a nunnery," he says, but his curiosity gets the better of him and the next night, disguised as a rogue and peasant slave, he goes to see the ghost.

The ghost also hates Hamlet's uncle because he killed him. He wants Hamlet to do something about that. Hamlet, though, does nothing. He is unsure, afraid. "Who would fardels bear?" he wonders. Ophelia then enters and tells him she would gladly bear his fardels for him anytime, but Hamlet is not interested and, pushing Ophelia aside, mounts his horse and rides off into the sunset, crying, "How conscience doth make cowboys of us all!"

Meanwhile, back at the castle, Gertrude is making her incestuous bed. "What stuff these seams are made of!" she exclaims, frowning petulantly. At this point Polonius enters, disguised as a petty thief. He goes to Gertrude's closet and begins stealing her furs and dresses. Hamlet then walks in.

"Mother," he begins.

Gertrude, thinking Hamlet has come to murder her, begins to scream. "Help! Help!" she says.

"But mother——" Hamlet tries again.

Gertrude pays no heed and goes on screaming. This annoys Hamlet, who has merely come to request a raise in allowance, and to show his annoyance he fires his six-shooter in all directions. He kills Polonius who is Ophelia's father, and disguised as Henry IV Part II, he flees to England.

Some years pass. Hamlet decides to return to Elsinore so the play can go on. England has changed him. He has become an alcoholic. "There is nothing either good or bad," he says, "but drinking makes it so."

At the castle he is greeted by Ophelia disguised as Rosenkrantz. He asks her to rub his back. She obliges him but he complains bitterly that she has not found the right spot. He tells her to go a little higher, then just a wee bit lower and to the left. Finally, he is satisfied. "Aye," he exclaims. "There's the rub!"

This goes on for a while. Then Ophelia dies, after which Gertrude drinks the poison Hamlet was supposed to drink, but Hamlet gets killed in a fight so it doesn't matter. Claudius gets killed too and so does Laertes. *Gargoyle*

MMMM . . . . IT'S JUICY

I couldn't believe it! There she stood—Juicy Gargle—one of the greatest personalities ever to grace the screen with her inimitable presence—doing housework! Like a real person in the workaday world of reality, she peered out from her nylon mop and greeted me with a poignant "C'm on in." Casually adjusting her perfectly stunning mauve apron with pink denims to match, she brushed aside a stubborn curl, and lo and behold, an honest-to-goodness smudge streaked her lily-white cheek. Think of the drama, the magic pathos of the moment! Juicy was obviously no Hollywood phony: here was democracy in its finest hour!

Once inside, Juicy, who demurely prefers to be known as Mrs. Bilious Green, wife of the producer-screen writer for 19th-Century Hoax (and a really great personality in his own right), graciously insisted that I take off my hat and my photographers and stay awhile.

I found myself so captivated by her charming smile that I asked her for an autograph. She graciously obliged and even added a very personal touch when she stamped a heartfelt "warmest regards from" right on the photo. It meant so much to me.

We chatted informally awhile like old schoolmates, while the minutes seemed to fly by. Juicy was all sweetness and light, a real doll all the way, and when the time came for tea, she actually waved the maid away and—though you probably won't believe it—poured the tea HERSELF, which was certainly proof enough for all those doubting Thomases that Juicy is no pampered, aristocratic glamour girl. No, sir! She even took the tray back into the kitchen, and although she was modest and unassuming about the whole episode, I distinctly heard the sounds of water running and dishes being rinsed by hand, and for those of us who know Juicy, there was no question as to whose hands they were. On her return she blushingly brushed aside my unbounded admiration for this feat, as if this sort of thing were condoned in Filmland (which is a clever slang term meaning Hollywood and environs).

Since it was so late, Juicy graciously insisted that I stay to dine, or as they say in Hollywood, "eat dinner" with the family. Here was a golden opportunity—another of those fabulous Hollywood expressions—to meet, I mean really get to know, the Greens of Bilverly Hells. This would surely be an exciting revelation to a world gasping in anticipation for someone to shatter the web of mystery surrounding the private lives of Juicy and her family for so long.

"I have a frightfully jolly idea," cried the vivacious Juicy. "Let's you and I cook dinner!" And before I could wax ecstatic, she had impulsively dashed off to the kitchen and gleefully fired the cook.

Hardly had we opened the modest freezer and retrieved seven of Ciro's Frozen Pot-Luck Delights when the back door flew open and in strode Juicy's lovable, gregarious husband, "Bil" with the three children perched on one arm, and his youngish-looking mother, a great favorite with the sporting set after her hilarious antics at Santa Anita last spring, when she booted underdog Odds Bodkins under the wire to nose out Bang Away in the Futility Stakes. They all seemed overjoyed to see me, hugging and kissing me enthusiastically, Mr. Green (always the soul of conviviality and hospitality) leading the way. He then went over to his wife, bussed her wholesomely on the cheek and read off an extemporaneous announcement that "at last I have found true peace and contentment in you, my soul's own." She curtsied and threw him a lima bean.

"Yes," happily rejoined Juicy, shooting what was obviously a tender glance at her beloved, who was broodily picking his teeth in the corner, "Ours is the Perfect Marriage." They then went into a little novelty soft-shoe routine to the tune of "Only Fake Believe," finishing off nicely with a cordial, gracious embrace.

Dinner was a delightful experience, with a feeling of gay camaraderie and real *joie de vivre* pervading the fragrant Bilverly Hells air. Ciro's Pot-Luck Delight, which turned out to be mock steak smothered in simulated mushrooms, was truly a tribute to our culinary arts, and when the children had gone off to romp with "Grandma," as they affectionately called their grandmother, we sat back for an exhausting evening of cordial and gracious conversation. Juicy did the conversing.

"Believe me," she began, "life with us hasn't always ben a bed of roses." We all laughed heartily for some minutes at her keen display of wit, perhaps not realizing that another really great line had been born in Hollywood. Juicy smiled deprecatingly and murmured that it really wasn't that good, but I could tell that she was all atwitter at the success of her bon mot.

"To be serious, though," she continued, "ours was a hard, long, and bitter struggle to stardom. If it weren't for the fact that neither Bil nor I eat, drink, or smoke, we would never have been able to send the children to the very best kindergartens and reform schools available. I was a struggling young stenographer at the G-O-P studios, while Bil was an assistant yes man at *National Geographic*. We met on an all-day cruise of The Baffin Island Chowder and Marching Society. It was all very romantic."

"I guess you can call it love at first sight," Bil shrewdly remarked in his usual piercing manner, while jotting the phrase down in a notebook, and looking quite sage.

"Bil always gets his freshest and most scintillating ideas right here at home," Juicy said proudly. "Don't be surprised if you find that very phrase as the theme to his next epic."

We eagerly called for more of his ready wit, and believe me, we weren't disappointed. "Maybe I'll call it The Greatest Schmoe on Earth," cracked Bil and we all rolled around the floor in sheer hysteria, weak with laughter.

Whereupon Juicy giggled, "Oh, Bil, you're such a wag," and Bil retorted quick as a flash with "Tut, tut, woman," causing another gale of mirth. Isn't that man a panic?

The whole evening was full of such fun and frolic, and I shall treasure it forever and ever. *Penn Pix*

PROPAGANDA

BY J. S. STEVENSON

Glancing through some magazines last week-end, I was struck with the idea that Yale today in its traditional arch-conservatism is missing out on something really big going on in the world around it. Yale, like any University has certain aims for herself and for her students, yet she does not convey these aims with any degree of inducement, compared with modern living. It would seem extremely likely to me that Yale in the future, in order to survive, will have to do a far better job of selling its ideas. Yale will either learn that it pays to advertise, or cease to exist.

For example, Yale's first problem must always be to bring students to her halls. Fifty years hence will see the following poster in high schools and prep schools all over the country:

SENIORS!!!

FOR QUICK RELIEF FROM THE
DRUDGERY OF WORK OR
ARMED SERVICE
TRY
YALE
LARGE ROOMING FACILITIES
NIGHTLY ENTERTAINMENT
SUPERB CUISINE
APPROVED BY WOMAN'S HOME
COMPANION
WRITE FOR OUR FREE BOOKLET ON RIOTS

Once a man is in Yale, three of the largest questions that must be answered will be then, as now, concerning his problems in the academic, social, and athletic fields. The advertising possibilities for getting men to take certain courses are extremly fertile. The Old Campus and college bulletin boards will undoubtedly look something like the following:

IT'S NEW! ENCHANTINGLY LOVELY!
REVAMPED ECONOMICS 12
THEORIES OF ADAM SMITH,
RICARDO, KEYNES
PLUS
THE EXCITING IDEAS OF MALTHUS ON
SEX AND POPULATION INCREASE
PLUS
LATEST DISCOVERIES IN MONETARY
THEORY AND FISCAL POLICY
ENJOY THE THOROUGH GENTLE ACTION OF
THIS NEVER-BEFORE OFFERED COURSE
SEE YOUR ADVISOR DO IT TODAY

Or:

ASTRONOMY 49
RARE ANTIQUE IMPORTED TEXTS
& INSTRUCTORS
MORE STUDENTS THAN EVER BEFORE ARE
PASSING BECAUSE OF ASTRONOMY 49
89% AVERAGE GUARANTEED
NO OTHER COURSE CAN MAKE THAT
STATEMENT!!!

Or better still:

ENGLISH 21

BECAUSE . . .

In the field of social activities, the Yale Man's companionship will be competed for with a poster like this:

SMITH GIRLS

ROUNDER, FIRMER, MORE FULLY PACKED

OUT-PERFORM ALL OTHER BRANDS

1994 MODELS JUST OUT!

LIBERAL TRADE-IN ALLOWANCE

$2.00 DOWN—ALL YOUR LIFE TO PAY

NOW SHOWING IN THIRD DIMENSION

As far as athletics are concerned, football probably has the least problem, yet the Bowl is rarely filled. This clearly indicates that the pep rally as an advertising device has got to go. It will be replaced by ads of the following type:

BOTHERED BY POST-NASAL DRIP?

COME TO THE YALE BOWL AND SEE

J. OLIVAR AND HIS ELATING ELI ELEVEN

LISTEN TO THE MUSIC OF

K. WILSON AND HIS YALE BAND

CALL RAY TOMPKINS FOR RESERVATIONS

The Rugby team, on the other hand, has a real problem, one which will easily be solved, however, by use of the common jingle:

BE HAPPY, GO RUGBY
BE HAPPY, GO RUGBY TEAM
BE HAPPY, GO RUGBY
GO RUGBY TEAM TODAY!

Yale's best, though often most poorly attended spectator sport is chess. Their problem will be solved when they learn that the following can draw thousands:

TIRED? RUNDOWN? OVERWORKED?
IS YOUR ROOM TOO NOISY TO SLEEP IN?
COME OUT AND WATCH YALE CHESS
IN ACTION!

This is Yale of the future if there is to be any Yale at all. The change it will bring will be stupendous, colossal, terrific, magnificent, unequalled—different, anyway. *Yale Record*

THE TREE OF KNOWLEDGE: EAT THEREOF

Zoology

After inbreeding 666 generations of Rhode Island Reds, Dr. Paul Ehrlich of Columbia's Zoology laboratories has come up with what he considers the perfect "eating fowl." Dr. Ehrlich attributes his success to testasterone and carefully introducing a limited quantity of schmoo germ-plasm into the strain. The present bird, which somewhat resembles Dr. Ehrlich, tips the scales at 365 pounds, pure white meat (before cooking). In honor of its discoverer the bird is to be called "Dr. Ehrlich's Magic Pullet."

English Literature

A recently discovered 17th folio has partially uncovered some of the mysteries concerning Shakespeare's works. Evidence in this folio indicates that the heretofore unidentified "dark lady" of the sonnets is in fact an illegitimate daughter born to Othello and Desdemona prior to their marriage. Prof. Andrew Fellow, who made the discovery, states that at present there is no conclusive proof that Shakespeare is the *nom de plume* of William Faulkner but the theory is being further explored.

Psychology

Innumerable important advances have been made in the Columbia Psychological laboratories in the past few years. Prof. Fred Kelder and Prof. Ralph Waterline have recently published an immense tome proving that reinforcement theory holds water in the vegetable as well as in the animal kingdom. Kelder and Waterline gave a pellet of food to a Century Plant when it blossomed and the plant subsequently blossomed 26 times daily for a period four months before it just pooped out. Similarly, a Venus Fly Trap was made to salivate upon the ringing of a bell by means of classical Pavlovian conditioning. The Abnormal Professors of the department have nothing to report at present.

Physics

The amount of information that can be released from the research done by this department is limited because you can never tell when a pinko or someone like that may be looking over our reader's shoulders. Columbia Physicists have perfected a method for repairing broken atoms. All that is known of the specific process comes from Prof. W. Newhaven and Prof. Red Foley who state that it is done with "a whole mess of glue and a hell of a lot of heat." In a report to the Apocalyptic Society of Physicists, Prof. Manyfish Krutch revealed that there is enough hydrogen in the sweat of your brow to completely destroy the Universe. Further advancements in this field are expected.

Columbia Jester

THE SEXUAL BEHAVIOR OF OUR COUSIN ALICE

Science is a sacred cow and it deserves to be milked to the last drop. If we are to rid ourselves of the black veil of ignorance that overhangs us we must get to the cream of the matter, sex. Our morals, mores, customs, and laws are built on a basis of archaic beliefs concerning sex. The two previous reports, "The Sexual Behavior of Our Cousin Albert," and "Tulip Breeding for the Layman," have begun to blaze the path. Only now have we touched upon the equally important and vital other half of the sex business, Cousin Alice. It is our hope that when "Cousin Alice" is layed before the public some important facts will reveal themselves. First and foremost we are scientists but it is for the enlightenment of the general public that we have written this book. We hope everyone buys a copy.

Since this is the definitive text on female sexuality we believe that our interviewing techniques deserve mention. Initially, millions of American women were screened by us and our co-workers. Only one would give us the answers we wanted. She was Alice, our second cousin. Young, of average intelligence, medium build, this pleasing welterweight from Irvington, New Jersey has had limited schooling. She is now employed in an executive capacity at a local beer-garden and is an alumna of Barnard College. She is typical of all American women, young and old, intelligent and simple, rich and poor, in sickness and in health.

TABLE I—WAYS AND MEANS

Friends	3%
Foes	9%
Rams	11%
Christine (before)	1%
Alice	21%
Christine (after)	22%
Cousin Fritz	2%

Our methods of interview were thorough and exhausting. 5493 interviews were needed to furnish us with the conclusive data used in this report. On each occasion a different interviewer had a fact-finding session with Alice; on each occasion a different technique was employed in asking Alice the same questions. The results were varied and fruitful. For security purposes not only the results of the interviews but the interviews themselves were conducted in code. Not even our carefully trained experts knew what they were talking about. Only Alice and the public at large know the results.

Processing the facts and figures from the interviews was a disgustingly simple task. Three IBM machines and 2½¢ worth of electricity did the job. We have found this method of statistical analysis to be infallible. By these means we were able to approach the 10% level of confidence 3% of the time. Although we found the null hypothesis void on all occasions our application of the t-test verified our opinions concerning the skewing of the asymptotic growth curves indicating a high negative correlation proving that we were damn near perfect.

If it isn't in Table I Alice didn't do it. The kids on her block may say she did but science has proved that she didn't. Alice's sexual behavior breaks down into these seven basic categories which we have numbered from one to seven for intelligibility. There is a significant correlation between each of these seven categories and Alice's age. Accessibility of the "love object" manifests itself as an important factor in women. Shortly after her fourteenth birthday Alice moved to the city, and so abruptly ended her "post-public pastoral period." During the time of the interviews, a notable increase in the Cousin Fritz category was observed.

TABLE II—HOW COUSIN ALICE DISTRIBUTES THE GOODS

Pre-Marital	8%
Pre-Natal	43%
Prepaid (Sales Tax)	3%
Extra-Marital	1%
Extra-Curricular	1%
Extra-Sensory	1%
Extra-Special	10%
Cousin Walter	2%

In this early stage of the interviews, it was noticed that Alice was twiddling her thumbs in ever decreasing concentric circles. The symbolism is obvious. The American Woman is permeated with a feeling of guilt. She is insecure in sex, and sexually insecure; that is to say, security in the sexual sense is absent.

In order to have a national cross-section represented, the data for Table II was taken from questions posed to Alice while she toured the nation with an itinerant medicine show. Still unmarried, Alice showed a great reluctance in revealing any data concerning her extra-marital relations. The taboos concerning female sexuality again reared their ugly heads. What havoc hath the old wives' tail wrought!

The findings pertaining to Alice's secondary sexual behavior are extremely enlightening. 23.97% of her meals are consumed in public restaurants; she prefers movies to TV, 3-1; her slip shows 16.1% of the time; she likes cocktail dresses, dungarees, peddle-pushers, and peddlers, in that order. The American Woman is not spending as much time in the home as did her predecessors, your Nannie and mine.

TABLE III—BOX SCORE

	b.av	ab	r	h	e
Gilliam, 2b	.273	4	0	4	0
Reese, ss	.271	3	1	3	0
Snider, cf	.335	4	0	4	0
Robinson, lf	.339	3	2	3	0
Fritz, 4f	.856	0	13	9	13
Cox, 3b	.287	4	0	4	0
Walter, 6a	.857	9	9	9	9
Walker, c	.233	4	1	4	1
Alice, p	.999	31	26	31	23
Meyer, p*	.143	0	0	0	0

*relieved Alice when she pooped out.

Many seemingly insignificant factors were found to influence the sexual behavior of the American Female. Rain was better than snow and a mean temperature of 71.4 degrees was preferred by Alice. The amount of education was also highly significant. Prior to entering school Alice never indulged in petting. As her education increased her petting behavior displayed an adiabatic rise and reached an asymptote shortly before her graduation last June. Throughout, there was an interesting correlation between Alice's sex drive and the seven year locust cycle and this is certainly a matter deserving further investigation. Sex is an untamed frontier wanting only the stout-hearted pioneers to blaze a path of truth through the wilderness.

In Table IV our definitive analysis of Female Sexuality is completed. Comparing these statistics with those in "The Sexual Behavior of Our Cousin Albert" some interesting parallels can be drawn. Both sexes of oysters found Alice more stimulating than Albert particularly during the months with "R" in them. A 12% difference existed between the male and female reaction to romantic movies. The blue litmus paper test for the men and the pink litmus paper test for the women further substantiated this finding. Again scientific method has proved that common belief is not always valid. Near-sighted co-worker, John X's interview with Alice revealed the startling fact that all women prefer men with mild myopia.

TABLE IV—HOW THE BASIC STIMULANTS AFFECT ALICE

Oysters	5%
Snow	4%
Jockey Shorts	14%
Hot Books	2%
Sex	1%
Mennen Skin Bracer	40%
Fritz and/or Walter	3%

In concluding this encompassing report there are some important factors that deserve mention. Our sampling was, of course, somewhat limited but is fully applicable, nevertheless. In specific instances the statistics in our report do not fully reflect the existing conditions. In some remote inland regions poor refrigeration conditions made fresh oysters not readily available. We can make no assertions concerning the canned or dehydrated product. For similar reasons our report is not fully valid for frugal Moravian housewives who hold Doctor's degrees from I. C. S., for Alaskan war-brides from downtown Nome, for women taxi drivers from Sheboygan, and for the little Philips girl down the block.

Throughout, we have attempted to present you with the facts, plain and simple, as they were given to us by Alice. It is to her, to our 5493 co-workers, and to the thousands of bookdealers throughout the country that we are indebted. Yet it still remains that without your aid this book cannot be a success. The facts are yours to be studied, savored, and enjoyed. It is with the knowledge gained from this book that our actions in the future can be made more meaningful. Up to now "Alice" has been ours, now she is yours. We have done our best to present you with the complete sexual profile of the American Female. Remember, she's 99 & 44/100ths% pure. She floats. *Columbia Jester*

WHAT WOULD HAPPEN TO YOU IN CASE OF A HOTEL FIRE?

I was lying in bed . . . I smelled smoke . . . Thoughtfully I nudged Mary and muttered something about the hotel being on fire. We were panic-stricken . . . trapped on the twentieth floor and no exits . . . But there, beckoning toward an open window was Mr. Amicable, my amiable insurance man.

We three leaped thru the window into the nite.

As we passed the eighteenth floor, Mr. A. pointed out the value of my insurance policies, explaining that my wife and myself would recover at once our personal losses of wardrobe, money, etc.

"But——" Mary and I stammered . . .

Between floors twelve and six he reminded us that had we perished in those wicked flames we would have passed on secure in the knowledge that our offspring would be provided for by the terms of the life insurance I held. . . .

"But——" We again started . . .

He smiled reassuringly as we hit the pavement . . .

Upon regaining consciousness in the hospital I found myself in a bed adjoining Mary's, and, bending over me, Mr. Amicable.

"I have taken pains to notify your home and have explained all details of this unfortunate (but calculated) mishap. . . . Friends are on the way to see you.

"But—" and this time I finished astride my benefactor.

"I'm supposd to be in Chicago at a convention . . . MARY IS NOT MY WIFE!" *Penn Pix*

THE IMMORTAL BARD

NEWS ITEM—William Shakespeare today signed a ten-year contract to write copy for Hiram Huckster and Rubicam, New York advertising agency. A talent scout for the agency dug him up in a little town in England. He is allegedly the hottest copywriter they have ever seen. His first show, "Portia faces Shylock," will be heard tonight.

NEWS ITEM—The advertising world has been set on its ear in recent weeks by the prolific output of William Shakespeare, now with Battin, Barton, Battin and Barton. They lured him away from Hiram Huckster and Rubicam with reputedly the highest figure ever paid a copy man. Here are some samples of his best-selling commercials:

> To use Drene or not use Drene, that is the question:
> Whether 'tis nobler in the mind to suffer the slings and arrows that greet dull, stringy hair or to get that beautiful luster, that sheen, that will glorify your hair.

> 'Tis now the very witching time of night
> When churchyards yawn and hell itself breathes out
> Contagion to this world.
> Now could I drink hot Ovaltine and tune in to Little Orphan Annie tomorrow at this very same time.

> Tomorrow, and tomorrow, and tomorrow,
> Creeps in this petty pace from day to day,
> And all our GE sight-saving lamps have lighted fools
> Their way to better sight and greater light at lower costs.
> Out, out, brief candle! Life's but a walking shadow,
> Without the new GE two-way lamp.

> O how this too too solid flesh did melt
> And in only a fortnight, too.
> The Dubarry Success Course did it for me—
> Perchance it could happen to you.

Neither a borrower nor a lender be,
With this sole exception—on this depend
Household Finance has very low rates
'Tis better than borrowing from a friend.

This above all—pay the dough when it's due
Or they shall follow you as the night the day. *Shaft*

YOU GOT A WIFE?
THIS IS FOR YOU
WE GOT WIFE SITTERS

Five (5) highly trained operators with whom you can leave your wife safely.

Look, you got to go to those lousy classes all day long, don't you?
You got to go away on trips, don't you?
You got to go out nights, don't you?

AND YOU GOT TO LEAVE YOUR WIFE ALONE.

If it was a baby you would get a baby sitter. Why entrust your wife to the safekeeping of your dog, even if you got a dog?

PUT YOUR MIND AT EASE.

Here's what Ido Care has to say about our wife sitters: "I use wife sitters all the time. I like 'em. My wife seems to like 'em too."

He goes on to say, "I used to leave my wife home alone when I went away on business. Now I just call up the wife sitters and know that my wife will be taken care of. My wife used to be sullen and peeved when I came home. Now she's happy and has that pleased, pampered look. I like wife sitters."

Leave your wife in safe hands. Our operatives are carefully checked to see that they have safe hands.

All through the long night, rest assured that your wife has a wife sitter standing by to be of service.

Our operatives are strong, virile men who know how to handle women.

They are not frightened by burglars and understand all kinds of wives.

WIFE, DEMAND A WIFE SITTER WHEN YOUR HUSBAND HAS TO LEAVE YOU. Our men will fill in for your husband.

Sour Owl

FASHION TRASH
OUT AT THE SLEEVES

Paris was all agog over Jack Fat's spring showing this year. Accordion-pleated sneakers and gold lamé garter belts had to step to the rear to make way for his newest fashion note, blouseless sleeves. In suède, leather, chamois, or just plain mouton, these versatile backless sleeves, or sleeveless sleeves, will be the rage this year. Designed to show off your prettiest nylon undies, and to keep you cool in summer. At all better drugstores east of Juanita. *Froth*

ADVERTISEMENT

AT LAST!
A HANDY
SLUDGE
LOTION DISPENSER,
AND IT'S
FREE!

Yes, friends, it's free, free as lies from your advisor. Now, with every dollar bottle of SLUDGE, the new hand lotion that is so thorough that one of our workmen fell into a vat of it and softened to death, you get absolutely free this cunning dispenser.

Three perfectly good
reasons why you
want one

1. Becuz when harsh soaps, detergents, nippy winds, and handkissing foreigners drain natural oils out of your hands, Sludge leaves them all sticky and greasy again.

2. Becuz you are thrifty and you'll love the way this new dispenser resists your best efforts to squeeze out more than a drop or two at a sitting.

3. Becuz you can't resist a bargain, sucker, and this is Free! Free! Free!

MONEY BACK
GUARANTEE!

YES, A MONEY BACK GUARANTEE!

If you find yourself dissatisfied, send us the unused portion of your Sludge *and we will return to you the unused portion of your money.*

Flatiron

A SILENT NIGHT . . . A FATHER'S THOUGHTS

It's late—way past twelve. The house is so quiet. Only the gentle click of the thermostat.

A gay mad hatter of a Christmas. Little Judy had been radiant in her new skin graft. And the way Tommy had seared his initials into the pedigreed boxer had made it worth every cent we paid for it.

Grace and the kids. A swell family. And I'm a swell father. Give them everything they ask for. More even. A helluva lot more.

If only I could give them a peaceful world, where people can run in the sun, face life free and unafraid. With no "isms" to worry about.

Of course, we've got a lot to be thankful for. A bright clapboard home in the suburbs. A wonderful Christmas tree—lighted by twenty-four 15 watt bulbs. And the hot water heater. The automatic stoker. The new electric stove.

Yes, perhaps that's the real meaning of Christmas—freedom and plenty of good hot water. *Sundial*

THE PUP COAT

An exquisitely tailored creation with oblique closings and acute angles . . . not just a coat! . . . How often have you found yourself out in the cold, with no place to sleep? . . . Well, no more, we say . . . at least not if you own our magnificent, stunning outer garment that hides you almost completely . . . at night just unwind those little strings at the bottom that were so darling during the day and out come adorable little spikes . . . just drive the spikes into the ground, pull in your head, and you have a warm home, all for nothing—a cosy pup tent that can be set up any place. . . . Ask, too, about our graceful new SLEEPING BAG DRESS, for a complete ensemble. . . . By SACKS, FIFTH AVENUE—in five daring colors, gunny, potato, flour, coal, and sad—only $10.98. *Yale Record*

BEFORE FIVE AFTER FIVE

RIGHT AT FIVE

BIRDOG–GOODFELLOW

PRESENTS

THE "ANY–OLD–TIME DRESS"

To look your most captivating—alluring—simply scrumptious, day or night, a dress for all occasions. . . . Before five it is a simple charming party dress with full awning skirt and a hem in the back—complete with Venetian décolletage and rhinestones, made from genuine rhines. . . . After five, just pull the cord and *whoosh!* down comes the awning, open go the Venetian blinds—and there you stand—*devastating!* $76.25 —in twilight gray, candlelight beige, flashlight yellow, burgundy, organdy, and mahogany.

Come and See with Your Eyes—Come and Pay through Your Nose.

Yale Record

CHAIN LETTER

Dear Sir:

This chain letter started in Reno in the hope of bringing relief and happiness to tired newspapermen.

Unlike most chain letters, this does not cost any money. Simply send a copy to five equally tired male friends, then bundle up your wife and send her to the man at the top of the list.

When YOUR name comes to the top of the list, you will receive 16,178 women. Have faith! Do not break the chain! One man broke it, and he got his own wife back.

Sincerely,

Very Tired Newspaperman

The Crimson Bull

HOTELS AND RESORTS:

BERMUDA WANTS YOU!

Bermuda is calling. Can't you hear her? Hear those tinkling bells from each pagoda that lines the shore of the lush Caribbean. Hear the Cacchian song of tropic birds from the peculiar little streets. Hear a radio in every room (to say nothing of a bath). Hear Bob Hope, Jack Benny, *Walter Winchell.* Only Bermuda offers you a helluva scare under waving palms.

Of great charm Bermuda is. Of indisputable corruptibility Bermuda is certainly. Of unparalleled enrationalism Bermuda certainly is.

BERMUDA CALLS YOU

IT IS YOUR MORAL OBLIGATION TO ANSWER

THE FLEECEWOOD HOTEL

MIGHTY HIGH IN THE POCONOS

"Thousands Have Used It as a Last Resort."

Opening for The Summer Season Real Soon	*Swimming, dancing, mountain air, food, mountain lions, sailing, mountain climbing, insurance rates.*

Honeymoon on our sandy beach—make pals with our dog—scratch the back of our chambermaid—pay cash to our desk clerk.

THE ROACHES

(MORE THAN A HOTEL—A ZOO)

Lively time day and night—get away from the swarming city crowds —our swarms are rural!

RELAX! BYBERRY FARMS RELAX!

(MORE THAN A HOTEL—AN INSTITUTION)

Come here and just relax! Just close your eyes and forget all about the cruel, lousy world. Relax!

Limousine service—smartly uniformed, powerful attendants—private, closed-off rooms—interesting games with scissors and paper——

Send for our incomparable folder.

RELAX!

SWELTER IN STYLE

THE HOTEL QUINCY!

In the Heart of Manhattan, West of Broadway

For informal adults—observatory overlooking Whelan's Drug Store—restaurant overlooking food laws—hear somebody learn a musical instrument at any hour. Tickets to the Strand Theater at the Strand box office! Why freeze at the shore when you can get hot cheap?

Seats for all.

Latest appointments.

Charmingly indiscriminate clientele.

Modern cooling with simulated Chinese fans.

Billiards, shops, penny arcade, dancing with 50 gorgeous hostesses just across the street.

COME TO THE BIRCH-IN-THE-WILDWOOD

Fish for the cod with our trusty codpieces. Get to the bedrock of reality on our lush 14-hole golf course. Overlook the Hudson at leisure. Riotous fertility rites every Saturday night in the forest preserve.

ARCHERY

STOCK MARKET RETURNS

EAT LIKE A PIG

GET THE HELL DOWN TO VIRGINIA

Every possible type of fun! Shrines, graves, desert skulls! No matter what your dream, you can find some languorous form of death in Virginia. Take your pick. Take your shovel.

CHATEAU AU LIT D'AMOUR

Sing, dance, make a careless look with amazing abandon in historic Quebec. The girl of your dreams may be clearing away your dirty old dishes in our svelte dining room. Who knows?

500 Beds. *Yale Record*

PERSONALS

MODEL OF MAIDENLY modesty, yet not bluenosed when considered from over-all viewpoint, especially from the front, desires playmate of proper propriety, yet not reticent and retiring. Inquiries invited. Box 36-X.

YOUNG MAN wants young woman. Box 65.

YOUNG WOMAN wants young man. Box 66.

YOUNG LIMA Bean Heiress desires to make contact with corn magnate, any age. Object: Succotash. Box 47-R.

DISTRAUGHT degenerate damsel seeks coruscating correspondence from young god-like Croesus. Send stamps. Box 44.

HOW'S YOUR OLD STRAW HAT? I'd like to know. I'm interested in everything. You'll like me. I like everybody. Won't SOMEONE please write me? Box 729.

WANTED: The blood of a new-born babe, a St.-John's-wart, the hind leg of a pregnant frog, two locks of hair from a horse's tail, and three voluptuous maidens before the next full moon is at hand. Box 28-X.

LONESOME? All alone? Sitting in your room listening for noises? We make noises. We're rowdy. Box 94.

QUALITY WORK at moderate prices. Gladys and Irene. Room 8, 47 West 12th Street.

PROFESSIONAL GAL, mature, sincere, liberal, open-minded, loose, desires contacts with ditto male. Box 65-P.

MALE MIDGET would like to meet female midget and talk about little things. Write Box 1.

FAT UGLY OBJECTIONABLE youth with no education and a hearty dislike of all the arts and culture in general desires to establish illicit relationship with similar woman. Box 88-V. *Jackolantern*

BRAIN SURGERY
SELF-TAUGHT

CUT OUT NAGGING
HEADACHES!
DO YOU HAVE
ITCHING SCALP?
DO YOU HAVE A
DIRTY MIND?

All of these inconveniences can be done away with if you send immediately for this amazing new book!

This month only, we are offering, as an added inducement, a complete set of surgical equipment.

1 saw
4 multicolored spools of thread
1¼″ darning needle
1 chisel
1 McCormick Drill

SEND NOW!

This limited offer expires June 32, 1984

DON'T DELAY!

Name . . . .
Address . . . .
Beneficiary . . . .

Panther

I CAN LEARN YOU ENGLISH!
IN SIX MONTHS ALREADY

Confound Your Friends by Using Proper English!

READ THESE UNSOLICITED TESTIMONIALS

Mr. Snerdian Dialect writes, "By God, sir, I could have thrown a cocktail party for every Hollywood starlet who has a mink coat with the money I threw away on your course. I'm getting fed up (an idiom, see lesson 12) with saying, 'Thank you, miss,' and 'I assure you it was no trouble, sir,' and '*En garde,* you wastrel,' to my friends, many of whom find such interjections irrelevant to ordinary conversation. Please refund my money, as I wish to speak with a vernacular again."

Mrs. Erogenous Mophandle, somebody's mother, writes, "I used to call my kids all sorts of foul names when they came in with muddy shoes, dead cats, neighbor's wives, and etc., and etc. Now I can swear at the little rats in proper English, with synonyms."

Miss Electra Dalliance, holocaust, says, "My friends are confounded just like you said, you little old clairvoyant. They are also prejudiced. Now that I have learned to speak the king's English I have no one to speak it with. Kindly send king."

Alechiev Vladamirescu writes, "I am a fifth generation American what I cannot speak English until I took your course yet. Plain like the nose by your face, I am much gooder at it now, what you can easily tell how I been studying at you. Send me more courses, size 36-B." *Rammer Jammer*

LETTER TO THE SCIENCE-FICTION EDITOR

BY WILLIAM MAYO HINDLE

Kind Sirs:

I am 20 years old, with blond hair, blue eyes, and have an exceptionally well-developed figure. My dimensions are: height, 5′6″, weight, 120 lbs., bust 38″, waist 24″, hips 36″. My father is a millionaire, and I am very generous with his vast fortune. I am well educated, friendly, and very passionate. In spite of this, no one ever asks me out. I am terribly lonesome. Please print my letter in your column.

DESPERATE

P.S. Unfortunately, I live on the moon. *Stanford Chaparral*

BE THE FIRST TO KNOW

WHEN AN ATOM BOMB HITS YOUR NEIGHBORHOOD!

Radioactivity from an atom bomb exploding within fifty feet of this rugged little instrument will set off a loud alarm that will alert every member of your family.

MONEY BACK GUARANTEE!

Don't gamble with your family's safety. Send $4.95 to Bombwit Teller, Box 10, Squee, Mich. *Gargoyle*

RAISE AMOEBAE

FOR FUN AND PROFIT!

Children love to cuddle these furry little pets.

Amoeba ranchers have been unable to keep pace with the growing demand from scientific laboratories.

See these friendly little creatures reproduce under your very eyes.

By long division already!

AMAZING!

Send $2.35 today and get your amoeba with a year's supply of clothes ABSOLUTELY FREE!

Send to Ordway Amoeba and Sons, Inc., Praise, Ala. *Gargoyle*

AN OPEN LETTER TO PORFIRIO RUBIROSA

Dear Mr. Porfirio Rubirosa:

Honest to God, I've heard just about all I can stand about you. I mean these articles and stories in magazines and newspapers about how you're such a hot-shot lover. Maybe you think you're a boudoir bloodhound but listen Buster I'd like to see you try anything with me.

Sure, I know you married Doris Duke and Danielle Darrieux and Flor Trujillo and Barbara Hutton and a few more I can't think of at the moment. I know they got dough and looks–stocked and stacked as the tabloid jockeys say–but I know something else, too. And that is you don't have me. I'm a true-blue American and I don't go for that sort of stuff.

And another thing. All this dishwater about irresistible charm and magnetic masculinity just doesn't reach me, Mr. Professional Lover. A good-looking chick like me has got a right to make her own choice, and you don't shape up. No, my $2,150,000 in stocks and bonds, my Fiji copra plantation, my $800,000 in rare and precious jewels will just have to wait until the right man comes along.

So don't you come crawling to my door at 967 E. 47th Street, New

York 14, N. Y., you Dominican dandy. And if you've got any bright ideas about dialing WE 6-1212 and trying to reach me at my apartment, well, you just wipe *that* little idea off your slate because I wouldn't speak to you if you had a ten-year lease to Paradise. Maybe you can push those others around like they were sacks of potatoes, but you don't touch this kind. So put *that* in your pipe, Mr. Porfirio Rubirosa. I hope you choke on it.

Yours,

Bon-Bon DuPont

Yale Record

PART FIVE

SPORTS

Football and lesser mayhem

I never engaged much in sports myself, for I am a squat, spongy fellow with a morbid fear of spheres.

I am, however, an enthusiastic sports fan, and I have on occasion written a word or two about the subject.

Regard:

FOOTBALL THROUGH THE AGES*

The football frenzy is upon us. But let us, in the midst of this pandemonium, call time. Let us pause for a moment of tranquil reflection. What is this game called football? What is its history? Its origins? Its traditions? These are not idle questions, for when we have the answers we will appreciate even more fully, enjoy even more deeply, this great American game of football.

First of all, to call football an American game is somewhat misleading. True, the game is now played almost exclusively in America, but it comes to us from a land far away and a civilization long dead.

Football was first played in ancient Rome. Introduced by Julius Caesar, it became one of the most popular Roman sports by the time of Nero's reign. The eminent historian Sigafoos reports a crowd of MMCLDDXVIII people at the Colosseum one Saturday afternoon to see the Christians play the Lions.

With the decline of the Roman Empire, football fell into disuse. The barbaric Huns and Goths preferred canasta. However, by the twelfth century A.D. football had emerged from its twilight and risen to its rightful place in the firmament of European pastimes. The eminent historian Sigafoos reports that the whole continent was in the grip of wild excitement in the year 1192 when the Crusaders, under Freddie Barbarossa, journeyed all the way to Damascus to play the Saracens in the Fig Bowl game. The Crusaders squeaked through, 23 to 21, on a field goal by Dick Cour de Lion in the closing seconds of the game.

October 21, 1512, will ever remain a red letter day in the history of football. On that day Leonardo da Vinci, who has often been called "The Renaissance Man" because of his proficiency in a hundred arts and

* From *On Campus with Max Shulman.* Courtesy Philip Morris Co.

sciences, was painting a picture of a Florentine lady named Mona Lisa Schwartz. "Listen, Mona baby," he said, as she struck a pose for her portrait, "I keep telling you—don't smile. Just relax and look natural."

"But I'm *not* smiling," she replied.

"Well, what do *you* call it?" he said.

"Gee, I don't know," said Mrs. Schwartz. "It's just an expression, kind of."

"Well, cut it out," said The Renaissance Man.

"I'll try," she promised.

And try she did, but without success, for a moment later the artist was saying to her, "Look, Mona kid, I'm not gonna ask you again. Wipe that silly grin off your face."

"Honest to goodness, The Renaissance Man," said she to him, "it's no grin. It's just the way I look."

"Well, just stop it," said Leonardo testily, and turned away to mix his pigments.

When he turned back to Mona Lisa and saw the smile still on her face, he became so enraged that he seized the nearest object—a casaba melon, as it happened—and hurled it at her with all his strength. Showing great presence of mind, she caught the melon and ran with it from the studio until The Renaissance Man's temper should cool.

This was, of course, the first completed forward pass.

The end of football in Europe came with the notorious "Black Sox Scandal" of 1587, in which Ed Machiavelli, one of the Pisa mob, paid off the University of Heidelberg Sabres to throw the championship game to the Chartres A. and M. Gophers. It was a mortal blow to football on the continent.

But the game took hold in the American colonies and thrived as it had never thrived before. Which brings us to another date that remains evergreen in the hearts of football lovers: December 16, 1773.

On that date a British packet loaded with tea sailed into Boston harbor. The colonies had long been smarting under the English king's tax on tea. "Taxation without representation," they called it, and feelings ran high.

When on December 16, 1773, the British ship docked at Boston, a semi-pro football team called the Nonpareil Tigers, coached by Samuel (Swifty) Adams, was scrimmaging near the harbor. "Come, lads," cried Swifty, seeing the ship. "Let's dump the tea in the ocean!"

With many a laugh and cheer the Nonpareil Tigers followed Swifty aboard and proceeded to dump the cargo overboard in a wild, disorganized, and abandoned manner. "Here now!" called Swifty sharply. "That's no way to dump tea overboard. Let's get into some kind of formation."

And that, fans, is how the tea formation was born.

ME HONGRY–ATHLETE

BY JOE GOLD

Dodging body blocks and flying tackles we made our way through a broken field of yo-yos and bubble gum to find our hero–Me Hongry, Tiger star sacked out in his dormitory room. Two monstrous feet hung over the bottom of the bed, and a huge shaggy head hung over the other end. The middle was taken up with six feet five inches of brawn that weighed almost two hundred and twenty pounds according to the last football program.

Gently tapping the five letter man, quadruple-threat back, on the shoulder, we waited for signs of life. None came. We tapped, and we pulled, and we pounded, and we shouted. Nothing happened. Seeing a whistle on the dresser, we blew, and then all hell broke loose. Me Hongry leaped from his cot, took careful aim at our posterior, trotted five steps toward us, and planted a size eighteen foot right in the middle of our rear. We went sailing gracefully, end over end, toward the opposite wall. Evidently, the sight of our poor, mangled body brought Me Hongry around, for when we started to come around, the athlete was applying cold compresses to our splattered forehead.

"Gee, I'm sorry, buddy, but when I hear a whistle I kick off automatically."

"Well, that's all right," we said, on our feet, because we couldn't find a soft enough place to sit down. "The reason we're here is to give our readers the inside story on a football hero. They want to know what makes you tick."

"Gosh," he goshed, "I sure am honored." His yo-yo was frantically jumping up and down, so we knew that he was happy.

"When did you first become interested in attending this institution of higher education?"

"Huh?"

"When did you decide to come to Mizzou?"

"Oh. Well, I was working at the garage like I usually do on Saturdays, when this long-jawed guy drives up and tells me he's got a flat, and he has to be up in Columbia in a couple of hours for the football game. I didn't know what it was then, but he tried to explain it to me. Anyway, I lift up the car like I usually do to change a tire, and he jumps out with his eyes flashing on and off. I ain't too good at reading, but Ma said it spelled out 'Orange Bowl', when they flashed like that. He told me to call him Uncle Don, and he put me in the trunk, and we were off to the big city. I played that afternoon."

"Yes," we said, "you were a sensation in your first game. You tackled the goal posts on the first play, and they had to hold up the game for an hour."

"Yeah, then I got the hang of it, and I broke three legs and a collar bone." The bubble that he burst just then sounded like the cracking of bones, and we leaped on top of the dresser.

"Don't be skeered," Me Hongry said, "it's only gum."

"Er, yes. Me, we're sure all our readers know about your heroism on the gridiron, but suppose you tell them about your life behind the scenes. Did the university give you anything to play?"

Me Hongry was cracking his knuckles, and it sounded like an entire ten cent bag of popcorn. "No, they didn't give me nuthin. All I got was this room, a red MG, and a deep-freeze full of steaks."

"Did they supply your books?"

"Books? What's them?"

"Them's . . . er, *they* are what you study with."

"Oh, yeah, I almost forgot. They give me a broad to study with. She's my tu . . . too . . . tut. . . ."

"Tutor?"

"Don't you say nasty things about my girl!" His hands were on our lapel, and we were two feet off the ground, frantically trying to walk out of the room Finally, we managed to explain what a tutor was, and he calmed down.

We tried to get the conversation down to a less emotional level. "Tell us, Me, what do you plan to do when you get out of school."

"Uncle Don says, I don't never have to leave. I get a new name when my eligi . . . eligib. . . ."

"Eligibility?"

"Yeah, I get a new name when that runs out."

"But, surely you must have some dream you want to fulfill besides playing football."

"Well," Me Hongry bashfully grinned, "someday I want to get married up with some girl and go down in the Ozarks and raise mums to sell at the football games. I jest love mums."

Our thought that he could certainly use some was interrupted when some damn fool blew a whistle. Sailing high over the dorms, we were happy that we had added three more points to Me Hongry's scoring average. We were a field goal. *Showme*

STADIUM "T" PARTY

BY RED FALKENSTERN

It's Saturday afternoon and the essence of legal whiskey already hovers over Memorial stadium. Pouring into the stadium are students. Pouring into cokes is whiskey, in direct violation of Section 82, Chapter 242, Kansas Statutes of 1949, as printed on the reverse side of those green ID cards, which you damn well better have if you want to get into the game and drink with your buddies. The essence grows to an odor, and the odor to a smell, which means it's nearly kickoff time. We're ready to cheer like hell.

The team is up for this game, since they just got their checks, and the coach wants to hold the other team under fifty points so he can win on his parlay card.

Suddenly you are accosted by a broad-headed youth who is beating you over the head with what he says is a program, without which you cannot enjoy the scientific game of football. Having purchased this little jewel for a mere twenty-five cents, you turn to find a picture of the athletic director as he used to look when he was umpiring men's softball games. For a living.

Turning further, you find the autobiographies of eight of the coaches, inaccurate weights of the players, and other useless information concerning a man who runs a hotel downtown. But nothing is said of the infallible scoring system, called the "T" formation.

After sweating out two blazing seasons on the sun-drenched student side of the stadium, one of our researchers was able to jack-roll a drunken alumnus and obtain a ticket for a plush seat on the west side. And, sitting there among all the wealthy athletic supporters, he was able to see the playing field for the first time. Thus, by being able to watch the game, the intricate inner mechanisms of the mysterious

"T" were revealed to him. Through his observations we have been able to write the following explanation:

"T" is the twentieth letter of the English alphabet and is formed by the intersection of a horizontal line by a perpendicular near the midpoint of the former. It comes through Latin from Greek, tau, which the Greeks stole from the Hebrew, taw. The "T" formation looks like the letter "T" in that the quarterback is usually in the horizontal position, running into the fullback between the perpendicular halfbacks. . . .

Th quarterback gets the ball from center—then all hell breaks loose. The QB hands off to the fullback so the opposition won't tear his arm off, then the FB pitches out to the right halfback, who drops the ball.

The left end, who luckily had forgotten the play and had drifted into the backfield, scoops up the ball and runs like hell with the opposing line hot after him. In desperation he heaves the ball and is immediately stomped into the ground by the enemy sophomore tackle who hopes to impress his sponsor. The right end snatches the ball just before the opposing backfield converges on him to administer an atomic drop.

The left halfback doesn't do anything. He's a square. The linesmen don't do anything either. They think they're underpaid. But the play had gained five yards. No! Wait! There's a flag on the play. A horn. A whistle. A bell. A bronx cheer. A girl's scream in the press box. Both teams were offside. The play does not count. . . .

On the field, the marching band has formed a heart and is playing "Let Me Call You Sweetheart," while girls in white sweaters make an arrow through the heart. Just as soon as the governor and other dignitaries get off the field, a public wedding will take place on the fifty-yard line. Overhead, a baton twirler is riding a unicycle on a tightwire stretched from the press box and the flagpole. On the cinder track, the Aggies are leading in the thirty-two-lap midget-auto race.

Down under the stadium the scene is different. The coach realizes that he has lost his parlay bet. So the trainer is carrying a white flag, and now he is announcing that with the score eighty-six to six against them, the home team has decided to concede. A cloud passes over the sun and a loon cries over the campus lake. It begins to rain, so you go home. The cheerleaders stay behind to sing the alma mater.

Sour Owl

BITS OF GOLD

BY VIC GOLD

PORTRAIT BY BILL STERN

One fall day in South Bend, Indiana, when the Notre Dame football team was going through its daily scrimmage, a small, anemic-looking lad approached Coach Frank Leahy.

"Coach," the kid said, "I wanna play football for Notre Dame."

"G'wan, punk," the coach said. "You'd get broken in two. Beat it."

But the gritty young kid insisted. Day after day he reported to the field and registered his desire to play football for Notre Dame. Finally, out of sheer anger, Coach Leahy agreed.

"Report at the dressing room right before game time Saturday," Leahy said. "I'll give you a uniform."

That Saturday, the boy showed up promptly and waited for the coach. Leahy, upon arriving, was surprised to see the young, spindle-legged kid there.

"So you really want to play, eh kid?" Leahy said.

The kid's eyes dropped. He stammered, "Look, Mr. Leahy, I wasn't kiddin'. All I ever wanted to do since I was a kid was play football for Notre Dame."

The genial coach smiled.

"Well," he said, putting his hand on the boy's shoulder, "if you think you're going to play for one of my teams and screw up the works, you're nuts."

The freshman was crushed. But the coach, ever mindful of a youngster's feelings, explained his position.

"You're just not built for football, kid," Leahy explained paternally. "Why don't you go to China and get into politics instead?"

That young boy—turned down by the Notre Dame coach—followed that advice.

His name: Chiang Kai-shek. *The Skiff*

AN APPLICATION FOR AN ATHLETIC SCHOLARSHIP TO A UNIVERSITY

Name?

Name used in last school attended?

Age? (Application from anyone over fifty will not be considered seriously.)

Can you read and write? (If candidate is unable to read and write English, this application blank should be filled out by a Notary Public.)

What remuneration shall you expect each month?

What was your salary at the last school attended?

What have you been offered from other universities?

Shall you expect more than you received last year?

Less?

How often will you expect news pictures and feature stories of yourself?

Do you have your own press agent?

Do you photograph well? Are you camera shy?

Can you write your own autograph?

If not, can you secure the services of someone who can?

What is your favorite fraternity?

Will you accept pledgeship from this fraternity?

If you do not choose a fraternity, would you prefer the president's house?

Will you mention the name of the school in advertisements for soap, cigarettes, cereals, etc., that you may endorse from time to time?

What time will be convenient for you to go to school?

Shall we send a taxi for you every morning or would you prefer your own car?

Will you be in school after the football season? If not, where shall we send your weekly check? *The Skiff*

COLLEGE FOOTBALL—THE REASON WHY

Football makes better men. And better men are better Americans. That's the reason why.

Now look. I was tickled when the boys at the *Lampoon* asked me to write a few words for the 73rd Anniversary of the Harvard-Yale game. But I said they better not use my name. Here's the reason. My job is to keep one of the Universities in good order—I won't say which one—and I think that my name had better be kept out of the news. I'm not publicity-mad. I've had plenty of power in my life. Enough for any man. But I'm only too glad to discuss college football in a college magazine, because I think it needs discussion. And plenty of it.

Football builds citizens. There isn't a man on the field who isn't red-blooded and right-thinking. You must be, after playing football. Just one taste of a clean tackle, just one little touchdown is enough to wash away any thought of subversion or anything else that isn't clean and manly. Playing football makes a man a better football player, and hence a better American, and hence a better man.

It's too bad women can't play football. It's the reason there aren't more women in positions of power. They never play football, so they never developed the stuff needed to make better men.

Sure, I played football when I was young. I still attend football games. And I played football not because of the headlines or the fancy cars or the scholarship, but simply because I wanted to be a better person, and football seemed to be the way to make me a better person than I was. And it worked.

DECLINE OF THE IVY LEAGUE

They say that the Ivy League has declined. They say it, and I just nod and try to keep out of it. Because I have a nasty temper. So does any man, if he's worth a pinch of salt.

Now has the Ivy League declined? Or has everybody else gotten better? That's the way I look at it. The Midwest and the Pacific Coast are just building better men. These men aren't heavy "thinkers," or "fancy talkers," or "liberal-minded." But they can carry a ball and pivot away from a rush, and straight-arm when they have to, and they can throw and catch and kick a football.

Why? These men aren't thinking about "theories" and "axioms" and "foreign policy." They're thinking about how to play football and how to be better men, better Americans. And it's working. Last November we elected one of these men president, and he's doing a fine job, despite the "mess" of theories and axioms and policy the non-football players left behind. You can't tell me Dean Acheson ever played football.

INJURIES

A man whom I had always liked once said to me, "You can't tell me God intended two men to run as fast as they could right into each other. It's murder." Right then and there I decided to stop speaking to that man, but if I hadn't made that decision I would have said this to him.

Who are you to say what God meant? I bet one thing right now. If God wasn't for football, He would have stopped it long ago.

Sure, once in a great while a man gets a little kick in the shins. But it's all in the game. Life is like that. Life and football are a succession of hard knocks and do-or-die, and the quicker everybody faces up to it the better world we're going to have. What the world needs are men who know that if everybody looks out for himself, and isn't afraid to give the other fellow a tap on the chin when the other fellow has what he (the first fellow) wants, then everybody will get the best possible deal and we'll all be prosperous.

Furthermore, I would have asked that man if it really was a bad thing to get knocked down once in a while. It reminds you of how little you are. And when you're on your knees, you aren't thinking about what bully boys the Socialist philosophers were. You're praying.

And if there is a man who gets badly hurt, that man shouldn't have played football at all. He wasn't top-drawer material, and he was bound to fall by the wayside.

YALE AND HARVARD

There isn't enough football at Yale and Harvard. There's too much non-football, too much word-juggling and mind-warping and fact-twisting, and not enough real sport.

Basketball is all very well, but it isn't a real sport. It's a game with a ball and a hoop. Life isn't like that. Life is like football. It's getting down and looking the other man right in the face and saying to him, "Brother, it's either you or me."

What Yale and Harvard should do is make every young man who comes there go out for the varsity, and stick it out. That's the way to put the Ivy League back on top. That's the way to cut down on "thinkers" and "theorists."

That's the way to build better men. Football makes better men. And better men are better Americans. That's the reason why.

Harvard Lampoon

THE RECORD'S 1950 ALL-AMERICAN TEAM

Well, fans, this certainly has been an odd year on the old gridiron, hasn't it? Across the country went a wave of defeat with the end result that not a single team in the nation won a game, a combination of circumstances which hadn't occurred since 1891. As if it wasn't enough for us guys to pick an All-American team, now they gotta go and lose all the games. Enough to make sensible men cry and if there's one thing we've got it's our sensibleness. Just the other day I was talking to Roger Culpepper, brother of Dr. Pepper, and he said the same thing. Interesting thing about Roger Culpepper.

Well, fans, this certainly has been an odd year on the old gridiron, hasn't it? It's been a year full of thrills and chills, heart-breaking spills, plenty of the old razzle-dazzle, hobber-dobber, line bucks, long runs, incompleted passes, leaps over the lime into El Dorado, upsets, downsets, sunsets, and indoor pets. Yessir.

Well, fans, here's the poop. Our board of experts is composed. We've been sitting around jawing for quite a spell now and we've come up with some pretty fine men. Not the best maybe, but certainly the best. It all depends on where you're standing. You can see this is a ticklish and often confusing job.

Well, fans, here's the poop. This is your list of gridiron giants for 1950. First in line is Ludlow Fonts, a big strapping giant from Hardly Normal Tech. Ludlow is a senior this year, but he didn't let that stand in his way. Why should he? He's been a senior now for five years. Ludlow, combining intelligence and brawn in the quarterback slot, led the Big Ten League of Wauwatosa with 954 yards gained all on one play. How he did *that* we'll never know. Ludlow was elected unanimously by the board of experts with the exception of Roger Culpepper. Funny thing about Roger Culpepper.

Picking a fullback for this year's team was a mighty tough job. There were so many good fullbacks around, we just couldn't decide, so we picked a tackle instead. His name is Flirtin' Lewis and there's a story behind this boy. Born in a backwoods area, he was still a youth when his father and mother died, and he was cast out onto the mercy of the world. For years he read every book he could get his hands onto, straining his eyes by the light of an open fire. During the day he worked long hours in a rail-splitting camp, splitting rails, naturally. Eventually he got so he could split a rail at thirty paces. When this began to pall, he decided to go into law, and at last set up offices in Springfield, Illinois. When this began to pall he decided to become the president of the Yewnited States, which he did. Later on this began to pall, too. And that man was Abraham Lincoln. This is the story behind Flirtin' Lewis. He read it once when he was a youth and it failed to impress him, but what a story.

Skipping to the West Coast for a moment we pick up the trail of Lucious Baby, stalwart of the South of Southern California University backfield. Although sidelined for most of the season with athlete's foot up to his knees, Lucious managed to keep his team on top by walking barefoot through the visitor's locker room each week. Back in 1945 Lucious, just out of the army, led his childhood sweetheart to the altar. Lucious is a family man and likes string beans. Voting for him was unanimous except for Roger Culpepper.

Perhaps the most popular man on our squad is young Harry Hockmeyer, a sophomore at Jones Junior High, the best Junior High in Toledo. Though only six years old, Harry makes up for this deficiency with size. Weighing in at 234 pounds, Harry stands three feet high and moves like a bullet. However, he doesn't confine his activities to the football field alone. He is also president of his class, editor of the school paper, member of the Glee Club, Phi Beta Kappa, and married. Although sidelined most of the year with an injury, Harry managed to play in every game. He's all heart.

Last but least comes Desire Fleischaker, playing his last year on the Snaf U. eleven. Desire is only a freshman, but after the 1950 season it's going to be his last year. He carried the ball 167 times during the fall and was held for no gain each time, principally because freshmen are not allowed to play varsity ball. This may seem to be a contradiction and is. Early in the season Desire earned national recognition by running the length of the football field width-wise, a feat which is impossible. He *deserved* national recognition.

Well, fans, that does it. There's your All-American football team for 1950, selected by the board of experts. It may not be a large team, but it's slow. And what it lacks in speed, it makes up in stupidity. While we're at it though we'd like to throw a bouquet in the direction of Coach Weepy Spinoza and his team. Like all of the nation's teams, Weepy's charges didn't win a game this year, but it's the spirit that counts and Weepy's boys didn't have any. Working from his new split-P formation nothing happened and Weepy's boys took advantage of it. Hats off to you and the boys, Weepy.

Well, fans, that does it. You may not agree with our choices, but it's difference of opinion that makes horse races. All in all, it was a pretty lousy season and we're proud of it. The men who made the grade didn't miss by much and those that did probably shouldn't have. So long, fans. *Yale Record*

PART SIX

LACERATED LANGUAGES

Fractured French, Splintered Spanish,
Lacerated Latin, etc.

It was inevitable that the national pastimes of Fractured French, Garbled German, Splintered Spanish, Lacerated Latin, etc., should be clasped to the heaving young bosoms of campus America.

A sampling follows:

FRENCH?

Tête à tête—Tight brassière
La belle étoile—My date's in the bathroom
Eau de toilette—I haven't got a nickel
Chateaubriand—Your hat's on fire
La même chose—Mother is a strip-teaser
Fin de siècle—I'll give you five dollars for your bicycle
Chacun à son goût—That chicken is so good
Début—North end of a southbound mule
Froid—Psychoanalyst
Garçon—Greer's last name
Loin—What you came to college to do
Petit—What you should do to your dog
Peu—Garbage heap
Refaire—Doped cigarette
Votre—What you get from a well
Autre—Last name of famous cowboy, Gene
Barbare—Empty bar
Bois—What girls marry
Coup—What they keep chickens in
Cour—Where you find worms in an apple
Débarquer—A watchdog
Carte Blanche—Better take Blanche home
Pas de deux—Pass the duck
Port de Bras—Your left shoulder strap is slipping
Ooh la la!—Where is the la la?
Tant pis—Paging Dr. Kildare
Fille de chambre—A chambermaid's work is never done

En queue—You're welcome
C'est à dire—That's a honey
Pommes de terre frites—Kick Fritz in the pants
Chef du gare—Shift the gears
Au contraire—Away from the city
Eclair—What did you say, Claire?
Jeanne d'Arc—The light is out in the bathroom
Pas de tout—The horn doesn't work
Sabotage—How old is that boat?
J'y suis, J'y reste—I am Swiss and I'm taking it easy
La petite chose—You can see she's pregnant
Verre d'eau—Where's the money?
Moi aussi—I'm an Australian
Matin—Ouch, my sunburn
Bigamist—Foggy day in Italy

LATIN?

Advocatus diaboli—The hell you say
Caldarium—California cowherd
Lax no scripta—Too lazy to write
Habeas corpus—Built like an oak outhouse
Hic haec hoc—Who's been drinking?
Laud-abar!—Let's stop for a drink
Gallia est divisa en partes—My girl is wonderful at parties
Rogabo quis venerit—Roger necks with anyone
Ut tecum loquar?—Who's bringing the drinks?
Sic est ut dixi—I was sick down south
Victoria gaudet—Vicky has it
Este homo!—I don't have a date
Hoc te rogo—Roger runs a pawnshop
Pax vobiscum—Pass the biscuits

SPANISH?

Avagado—Sack of money
Ayudar—Are you there?

Castillo—Abbott's partner
Porqué—Pig's meat
Tres—What grow in Brooklyn
Mujeres! las de San Jose—Migawd, we lost to San Jose
Dice que se que no!—No, you can't shoot crap here
Me pregunta donde esta Pablo—My donkey, Pablo, is expecting
Sin embargo—The Mann Act
No salimos—Don't spit on the floor
A menudo—I lost my clothes
Digale que sobre—The girl is sober
Que lo haga Carlos—Carl's got a blind date
Digales que lo hagan—The girls weren't so pretty
Pedro aprende a leerlo—Pedro caught a peeping Tom
Coman, Tomás—Come on to my house
Dónde estara a Juan?—Which way is the men's room?

FOREIGN DICTIONARY

à bon droit . . . . A bone in the throat
alter ego . . . . Change my egg order
avoir du pois . . . . . . After you, Papa
anno Domini . . . . . . One lump of sugar
ante bellum . . . . . . My aunt has a big belly
ante meridian . . . . . . Aunty wants to know the correct time
apparatus belli . . . . . A girdle
aux nuits . . . . Aw nuts
auf Wiedersehen . . . . Off with the shirt
à votre santé . . . . . . A vote for Santy Claus
billet d'amour . . . . . . Dorothy's brother Billy
bona fides . . . . A bone for Fido
Bois de Boulogne . . . . No matter how you slice it, it's still baloney
crêpes suzette . . . . . . Susie is dead
coup de grace . . . . . . Mow the lawn
crème de menthe . . . . Crime of the month
cum laude . . . . Speak louder, please
caballero . . . . Hey, taxi!
distingué . . . . This stinks
entre nous . . . . New entrance

fine herbes	Herbert is fine
Gott mit uns	Have you any mittens?
hic jacet	Farmer's coat
hoi polloi	High prices
Honi soit qui mal y pense .	Suit with two pairs of pants
Helmut Dantine	Gum on your hat
je ne sais quoi	What Jenny said
liberté–égalité	Can't take liberties with that girl
maître d'hôtel	Meet her in a hotel
mise en scène	We missed the first act
modus operandi	The operator made us mad
Monsieur Beaucaire . . .	Be careful, mister
merci beaucoup	Cute nurse
Nescafé	Stop at the next bar
notre dame	That dame knows too much
omnibus	I'm taking the bus
pâté de foie gras	Keep off the grass
rue de la paix	Let Rudy pay
savoir faire	Save enough for fare
sic transit gloria mundi . .	Gloria takes the subways on Mondays
très chic	Three chickens

PART SEVEN

JOKES

Little dandies, old and new, sweet and blue

The exchange editor, a vital component of any college humor magazine, is a student with sharp scissors and a strong stomach. It is he every month who must go through a great pile of magazines received from colleges all over the country and clip the jokes that will be used to fill up short pages in his own magazine.

This section is composed of such jokes, all of them from the public domain. The problems of selecting them are well told in the following exchange editor's lament from the Stanford Chaparral:

EXCHANGE EDITOR'S LAMENT

Ah, pity the poor exchange editor,
The man with the scissors and paste;
Oh, think of the man who must read all the jokes
And think of the hours he wastes.
He sits at his desk until midnight,
How worried and pallid he looks,
As he scans through the college comics
And reads all the funny books.
This joke he can't clip—it's too dirty.
That story's no good—it's too clean.
This woman won't do—she's too shapely.
This chorus girl's out—it's obscene.
The jokes are the same: full of co-eds
And guys who get drunk on their dates,
Bathtubs and sewers and freshmen,
And stories of unlawful mates.
Jokes about profs and the readers,
Jokes about overdue bills,
Jokes about girls in their boudoirs,
And each one as old as the hills.
The cracks must have fire and sparkle,
Sprinkled with *damn, louse,* and *hell,*
The blurbs must be pure—and yet filthy
Or the manager swears it won't sell.
Oh, pity the man with the clipper,
He's only a pawn and a tool.
In trying to keep his jokes dirty and clean
He's usually kicked out of school.

LEAD ME TO HIM!

"I've a friend I'd like you girls to meet."

ATHLETIC GIRL—"What can he do?"
CHORUS GIRL—"How much has he?"
LITERARY GIRL—"What does he read?"
SOCIETY GIRL—"Who are his family?"
RELIGIOUS GIRL—"What church does he belong to?"
SORORITY GIRL—"Where is he?"

THE GREAT AMERICAN NOVEL

CHAPTER ONE

Three men were grouped about a small fire. The tiny flame sent flickering shadows dancing among the trees of the Kentucky forest. It was the winter of 1776, and there was a chill in the air which made the men huddle closer to their fire. To all appearances, they were three ordinary wayfarers. One stood by the fire, a gaunt, bronzed man who was filing the lock of his long rifle. Another, to the casual observer, was absorbed in nothing more than the fate of his bacon, which crackled in the pan. The third sat a little apart. He said nothing but looked out into the night with a vacant stare. He was no more exceptional in appearance than the others. No ordinary layman would have thought that this quiet group of men would play a part that was to affect the history of an entire nation.

As a matter of fact, he would have been right. The men were three squirrel hunters named Smith, Jones, and Harris who were never heard of again.

A LETTER FROM THE HEART

"I want you to understand, Miss Mush, that you are to write my letters as they are dictated and not as you think they should be," said Jasper T. Wurtzz, president of the Amalgamated Whirlwind Laundry Company.

Miss Mush did so. Here is the letter that Lorin P. Haphazard, president of the Elastic Soap Corporation, received in the next mail:
Mr. L. M. or something, look it up, Haphazard.
President of the Elastic Soap, fake stuff that, Company.
Detroit, Michigan, ain't it?
Dear Mr. Haphazard:

You're a h - - - of a businessman. No, start that over. He's a crook, but I can't insult him, or the bum'll sue me. The last shipment of soap you sent us was of inferior quality, and I'd like to soak him in the eye, and we are, no scratch out the soaking part. Unless you can furnish us with the regular soap, comma you needn't ship us, please pull down your skirt, Miss Mush, any more of your soap period.

Paragraph The soap you sent us wasn't fit to wash the dishes, no, make that dog with, let alone laundry, and we're sending it back, period. Guess that'll hit the stiff and close yours truly.

Now please read that over, no, never mind. We'll waste no more time on that egg. I'll look at the carbon tomorrow. Sign my name and let's take lunch out, eh.

MISCELLANEOUS JOKES

In Red Cross the instructor was quizzing her students on commonsense lifesaving techniques.

"What article of clothing," inquired the teacher, "would you remove last if you fell into the water with all your clothes on?" General perplexity; the girls looked hopelessly at one another, and finally at madame instructor. That worthy, distressed as they, finally tried to give the girls a little help.

"The blouse," she informed them; "the blouse, because air gets underneath and acts like a buoy." Class dismissed.

They were huddled close, the lights were low. He pressed his lips into her pink little ear and whispered, "What are you thinking about, darling?"

"The same thing you are, sweetheart," she shyly answered.

"Then I'll race you to the icebox!" he shouted gaily.

Ole Swenson was taken to a hospital with a broken leg. "How did it happen?" asked the nurse as she came to sit beside his bed to take the case history. "Well," he began, "It was twenty years ago, and—" "I don't want to know what happened twenty years ago," she said impatiently. "What happened now?" Each time, however, he began the same way and finally in desperation she had to let him have his way.

"I went to work for a farmer twenty years ago," he explained, "and the first night after I went to bed, the farmer's beautiful daughter came into my room and asked if I wanted anything. I said 'No!' The second night she came again, and this time she was clad in her nightgown. Again she asked if I wanted anything and again I told her 'No.' The third night when she came in she was almost entirely nude. I could see every curve plainly as the moonlight streamed in the window. 'Do you want anything?' she inquired warmly. 'No thanks,' I said. 'I have had a good supper, the bed is comfortable and I feel fine.'

"I wondered at the time what she thought I could possibly want? Then, yesterday, as I was shingling the roof, it came to me like a flash."

We were buying our beloved mother a birthday present in one of the stores on Palmer Square the other day and happened to overhear a saleslady tell a young lovely from Miss Fine's School that there was a special sale of sachet that week.

"Sachet?" said the young lady. "Just what is that?"

"Well," explained the saleslady, "it's a sort of a little bag of perfume. You put it in your drawers to make them smell sweet."

"I understand what you mean," returned the girl, "but isn't it awfully uncomfortable?"

An efficiency expert walked into an office and asked the first clerk he met, "What do you do here?"

"Nothing," answered the clerk.

The efficiency expert nodded, made a note, then asked a second clerk, "And you; what's your job here?"

"I don't do a thing either."

"H-m-m," said the efficiency expert, "duplication."

Then there was the woman with varicose veins who went to the masquerade party as a road map.

I hear Jake quit school for a job.
Yeah. Ain't it awful what some folks will do for money?

The best way for a girl to keep her youth is not to introduce him to anybody.

The unwed mother was in the hospital next to her illegitimate child. The doctor entered on his tour of the patients.

"Your hair is red," he said to her. "But the child's is brown. What was the color of the father's hair?"

"I don't know," was the innocent reply. "He didn't take off his hat."

There are a lot of couples who don't neck in parked cars. The woods are full of them.

MAID: "I can't come to work tomorrow, ma'am. My little boy is sick."
MA'AM: "Why, I thought you said you were an old maid?"
MAID: "I am, but I'm not one of the fussy kind."

Ali and Kubla were riding their camels out on a desert that was really deserted—no trees, no water holes, not even a cactus; just miles of sand. As they rode they noticed a dark spot far to their left, and although it was miles out of their way they decided to investigate.

What they found was a man lying there with a huge stake driven into his chest, dried, sticky blood spattered on his clothes. They got off their camels and discovered the poor fellow was still alive. Ali, in a pitying voice, asked him what had happened.

"Robbers—robbers—they rode in and ruined me—burned all my buildings—drove all my stock away—took my life savings—killed my wife and children—dragged me out here and drove a stake in my chest—nothing to eat—nothing to drink—two or three days."

"Well, buddy," Ali said, "we've got some water and a little food here, but that stake in your chest—doesn't it hurt?"

"Only when I laugh," was the reply.

Notre Dame was playing an innocent little college that accidentally happened to get the Fighting Irish on its schedule. The score had gone into three figures for Notre Dame, but the Irish were still tackling hard and blocking without quarter.

The coach of the other team finally called the referee—a timid runt—and asked him to do something about the roughness of the game.

"Look at my quarterback," the coach said. "That Notre Dame tackle just took a bite out of his leg. What are you going to do about it?"

"Well," said the referee, "we c-could ch-change the game to Friday."

The farm had been mortgaged to give the daughter a college education. Father drove the Model T to the station to pick her up after graduation exercises were over. She crawled in beside honest Pa, in his clean, worn overalls. She snuggled beside him in a confidential mood. "I have a confession to make, Pa," she whispered. "I ain't a virgin any more." The old man wrung his hands and his head dropped low as he said with remorse, "After all the sacrifices Ma and I made to give you a good education, and you still say 'ain't.'"

"I have a report here that says coke, soda, and whiskey were found in your room. What do you make of that?"

"Highballs, sir."

PROF: "I will not begin today's lecture until the room settles down."
VOICE FROM THE REAR: "Go home and sleep it off."

And then there was the man who was so accustomed to having things done for him that he went out and married a widow with three children.

PROF: "If I saw a man beating a donkey and stopped him from doing so, what virtue would I be showing?"
VOICE IN THE BACK: "Brotherly love."

A young co-ed brought charges against an elderly professor and had him sentenced to jail for a long term. As he was led away, a friend approached him.

"I know you're innocent," said the friend. "Why did you plead guilty?"

"Well," he admitted, "the complaint was so flattering I just couldn't resist."

Then there was the janitor who worked in the girl's dorm and was entrusted with a pass-key to every room in the building.

The following week the dean ran across him and asked, "Why didn't you come around Friday for your pay, John?"

"What! Do I get wages, too?"

A logic professor really wanted to give his class a difficult question. "The United States is bounded on the north by Canada, is bounded on the south by Mexico, on the east by the Atlantic Ocean and on the west by the Pacific. How old am I?"

Student: "You're forty-four."

"Right, but how did you reason it out so quickly?"

"I have a cousin at home who is twenty-two, and he's only half crazy."

A college professor was calling roll in one of his classes.

"Robinson."

"Here."

"Rosenthal."

"Here."

"Mary Smith."

"Here."

"Wanamaker."

Chorus—"Yes."

A fraternity had sent its window curtains to the cleaners, and there was some delay in having them returned. One morning a note arrived for the president from a sorority across the street.

"Dear Sir:" it read, "May we suggest that you procure curtains for your windows. We do not care for a course in anatomy."

The president replied promptly with the following answer: "Dear girls: This course is not compulsory."

The freshman's father paid his son a surprise visit. Arriving at 1 A.M. he banged on the fraternity-house door. A voice from the second floor yelled, "Whatdya want?" The father answered, "Does Joe Jones live here?" The voice answered, "Yeah, bring him in."

The father of a pretty co-ed asked her boy friend to see the basketball game over the television set. When the boy arrived, he brought a jug that obviously contained a mixture containing alcohol, and during the game he took a nip now and then. At last the father could stand it no longer.

"Young man," he said, "I'm forty-seven years old, and never in my life have I touched liquor."

"Well, don't get any ideas, Pop," the student snarled. "You ain't gettin' any of this."

Ivan Pophissnootoff liked to know all about the employees who toiled in his vast business. One day he came upon a new young man who was dexterously counting out a large wad of the firm's cash.

"Where did you get your financial training, young man?" he asked.

"Yale," the young man answered.

"Good," he said. "And what's your name?"

"Yackson."

"I shall now illustrate what I have on my mind," said the professor as he erased the blackboard.

"You've heard the story of the lawyer who stayed up all night trying to break a widow's will.

SALESMAN: "Yes, sir, that's the smartest hat in the store."
FRESHMAN: "It doesn't need to be smart—I'll put the brain in it."

HEIGHT OF CONFUSION: The guy who shouts, "Thank God I'm an atheist."

You must know of the goose that got peopled.

RADAR: An ingenious product that will never succeed because advertisers can't spell it backward.

DIFFERENCE BETWEEN A SOUTHERN GAL AND A NORTHERN GAL: The Northern gal says, "You may." The Southern gal says, "You all may."

"Say when, darling," he said as he poured a glass of beer.

"Okay," she replied, "right after the next drink."

And then there was the sophomore who sowed his wild oats on Saturday night and went to church Sunday to pray for a crop failure.

ADOLESCENCE: The age when a girl's voice changes—from "no" to "yes."

DEAN: "Are you writing to a man?"

CO-ED: "It's to a former roommate."

DEAN: "Answer the question."

PROF: "Who split the atom?"

No answer.

PROF: "Who split the atom?"

STUD: "Don't jump on me. I ain't touched the damn thing."

ECCENTRIC PROF: "Why didn't you answer my questions?"

BEWILDERED STUDENT: "I did, sir, I shook my head."

E. P.: "Do you expect me to hear it rattle way up here?"

Once upon a time there were three Co-eds, a great big Co-ed, a medium-sized Co-ed, and a little Co-ed, who went for a walk in the woods. When they came back they were very tired and wished to go to bed. So they went to their rooms.

Suddenly:

"Somebody's been sleeping in my bed," said the great big Co-ed in a great big voice.

"Somebody's been sleeping in my bed," said the medium-sized Co-ed in a medium-sized voice.

"Good night, girls," said the little Co-ed in a little bit of a voice.

It happened recently when a man, complaining of severe pain, visited a psychiatrist.

"Where is your pain, my good man?" asked the doctor.

"In my navel, Doctor," the victim replied.

"Well, what does it feel like?" the doctor asked.

"Like I had a big screw in my navel, Doc," he replied.

"Why don't you get a screwdriver and remove the screw?" the doctor suggested. The patient brightened visibly. "A great idea, Doc," he said; "I'll try that."

The next day the doctor's phone rang and the caller turned out to be the man with the navel. "Doc," he said, "I did what you told me. I bought a screwdriver and removed the big screw that was in my navel."

"Fine," said the doctor. "Now how do you feel?"

"I feel okay," the patient replied, "but the damndest thing happened. When I took the screw out my legs fell off."

Knock, knock.

ST. PETER: "Who's there?"

VOICE OUTSIDE THE GATES: "It is I."

ST. PETER: "Go to hell. We have enough English teachers in here now."

A political-science professor was struggling with a drowsy class on a warm spring afternoon. They were discussing the constitution.

Spotting a particularly sleepy fellow in the back row, the professor snapped, "Sir, if the President of the United States died, who would get the job?"

The student puzzled a moment, then replied, "A Republican undertaker."

The author of a famous book on economics received a phone call from a stranger recently. "I question your statistics on the high cost of living today," said the stranger. "My wife and I eat everything our hearts desire and we get it for exactly sixty-eight cents a week."

"Sixty-eight cents a week!" echoed the economist. "I can't believe it! Won't you tell me how: and to make sure I get the story straight, please speak louder."

"I can't speak louder," said the stranger. "I'm a goldfish."

A happily married couple—a jealous wife and a husband who believed in reincarnation. Finally, the husband died. Keeping a pact they had had for years, the wife communicated with him in the spirit world twelve months after his untimely demise.

"Are you happy there?" she asked.

"Happier than I ever was before," he replied. "The pastures here are greener, and it's indeed a beautiful world. And the weaker sex are the most gorgeous creatures you ever saw. Wistful eyes that speak of love; sleek bodies and beautiful rounded forms."

"Oh dear!" she expostulated. "With so much temptation about you, I'm afraid you'll do something you'll be ashamed of. I do hope I can soon join you in Heaven."

"Heaven?" boomed back the reply. "Who said I was in Heaven? I'm a bull in Montana."

"No," said the centipede, crossing her legs, "a hundred times No!"

"Who's that?"

"Girl I used to sleep with."

"Shocking! Where?"

"Physics lecture."

Then there's the one about the sweet young thing who bought herself a bicycle so she could peddle it out in the country.

PROF: "This liquid turns blue if your unknown is basic, and it turns red if unknown is acid."

CH. E.: "Sorry, but I'm color blind. Have you anything with a bell on it?"

Trying to rest after an exceedingly hard day at the office, poor father was being bedeviled by a stream of unanswerable questions from little Willie.

"What do you do down at the office?" the youngster finally asked.

"Nothing!" shouted the father.

After a thoughtful pause, Willie inquired, "Pop, how do you know when you're through?"

Then there's the indignant co-ed who exclaimed: "I'll give you just forty-five minutes to get your hand off my knee."

FRESHMAN (*slightly stewed*): "Ish thish the way to go to professor hic's lecture?"

SENIOR: "That's the only way to go to his lecture."

MOTHER: "What made you so late? Did you have a flat tire?"

DAUGHTER (*dreamily*): "No, I'd hardly call him that."

FOUND: Roll of five-dollar bills. Will the owner please form a line at the north entrance to administration building.

The bride was very much concerned upon finding twin beds in the hotel room. When asked what was the matter she replied: "I certainly thought we would get a room to ourselves."

"So you desire to be my son-in-law?"

"No, sir, but if I marry your daughter I don't see how I can avoid it."

The wolf was too poor to buy etchings, so he asked the girl friend to come up and see the handwriting on the wall.

Two little girls were busy discussing their families.

"Why does your grandmother read the Bible so much?" asked one.

"I think," said the other little girl, "that she's cramming for her finals."

JOE: "I just brought home a skunk."

ROOMMATE: "Where you gonna keep him?"

JOE: "I'm gonna tie him under the bed."

ROOMMATE: "How about the smell?"

JOE: "He'll have to get used to it like I did."

DEAN: "Young man, I have just been informed that you were drunk last night and were pushing a wheelbarrow around the campus. Is that true?"

STUDENT: "Yes, sir."

DEAN: "And where was I during this time?"

STUDENT: "In the wheelbarrow, sir."

Washing windows bored a sweet young housewife and she forgot she was hanging out an open window. She lost her balance, fell one floor, and lit in a garbage can. She just sat there, disgustedly. A Chinese student passed by and saw her.

"American velly wasteful," he reflected. "That woman good for ten, twenty years yet."

Joe College decided to reform. He cut out smoking the first week. The second week he cut out drinking. He cut out women the third. The fourth week he cut out paper dolls.

An elderly man approached the little boy and asked, "Tell me, young man, do you have a fairy godmother?"

"No," replied the little boy, "but I have an uncle we're a little suspicious of."

Confucius say, "Wash face in morning. Neck at night."

A student and a professor were sharing a seat on a train. Tiring of conversation, the professor suggested a game of riddles to pass the time.

"A riddle you can't guess, you give me a dollar and vice versa."

"O. K.," agreed the student, "but you are better educated. I'll only give you fifty cents."

"All right," consented the professor. "You go first."

"Well, what has four legs swimming and two legs flying?"

"I don't know. Here's a dollar. What's the answer?"

"I don't know either. Here's your fifty cents," responded the student.

The sorority girl had just received an engagement ring and wore it down to breakfast next morning. To her exasperation, no one noticed the ring. Finally, after fuming and squirming throughout the meal, a lull came in the conversation, and she exclaimed loudly, "My goodness, it's hot in here. I think I'll take off my ring."

PROF: "Will you men stop exchanging notes in the back of the room?"

STUDE: "Them ain't notes, them's cards. We're playing bridge."

PROF: "Beg your pardon."

A little man in the office of a psychiatrist.

"I was wondering," the little man said timidly, "if you couldn't split my personality for me."

The doctor looked puzzled. "Split your personality? Why would you want that done?"

Tears tumbled down the little man's face. "Oh, Doctor," he wailed, "I'm so lonesome!"

A lawyer, a doctor, an architect, and an ardent American communist fell to arguing over which profession had been established first in the world.

"A lawyer, of course," said the first. "Man could never have survived without a few simple laws to govern him."

"Nuts," said the doctor. "Without a gynecologist, how could Cain and Abel have been born?"

The architect sneered. "Long before that, my friend, before Adam and Eve, some architect must have been on the job to bring order out of that chaos."

"Ah, ha!" beamed the communist. "And who created that chaos?"

It seems a traveling salesman was journeying along a country road in the midst of a howling storm when he came to a washed-out bridge. He could not remain in the car so he got out and went to the nearest farmhouse. An old, wrinkled man answered the door.

"I'm looking for a place to spend the night," said the salesman.

"Well, you can stay here," said the farmer, "but you'll have to sleep with my three sons."

"With your three sons!"

"That's right."

"Excuse me," said the salesman, "I must be in the wrong joke."

"I thought I saw you taking a gentleman up to your room last night, Miss Smith."

"Yeah, that's what I thought, too."

PROF: "A fool can ask more questions than a wise man can answer."
STUDENT: "No wonder so many of us flunk our exams."

STUDENT (*from the back of the room*): "Are you sure the third test question is in the book?"
PROF: "Certainly."
STUDENT: "Well, I can't find it."

And if I refuse will you commit suicide?
That's been my usual custom.

Did you get home all right after the party last night?
Fine, thanks; except that just before I turned into my street some fool stepped on my fingers.

SHE: "I nearly fainted when the fellow I went out with asked me for a kiss."
HE: "Baby, you're gonna die when you hear what I have to say."

HIM: "Why is it you have so many boy friends?"
SHE: "I give up."

Pedro had recently been married and a friend asked him how things were going.
"O.K. I theenk—but I theenk maybe I married my seester!"
"Why do you theenk that?"
"All the time she geegle and say to me, 'Oh, Brother!'"

The little moron's watch had stopped ticking and he tried to find the trouble. Finally he took the back off it, went into the works, and found a dead bug. "No wonder it doesn't work," he said, "the engineer's dead."

SHE WAS ONLY . . .

the minister's daughter, but you couldn't get anything pastor.
the chauffeur's daughter, but she could shift for herself.
the film-censor's daughter, but she knew when to cut it out.
the quarryman's daughter; she took everything for granite.
the chimney-sweep's daughter, but she soots me fine.
the sergeant's daughter, but she knew when to call a halt.
a carnival queen, but she made a lot of concessions.
the bottlemaker's daughter, but nothing could stopper.
the governor's daughter, but what a state she was in!
the attorney's daughter, but what a will to break. *Cornell Widow*

SHE WAS ONLY . . .

a fireman's daughter, but she sure did go to blazes.
a judge's daughter, but she could dispose of any case.
a plumber's daughter, but she had good connections.
a milkman's daughter, but she was the cream of the crop.
a surgeon's daughter, but, oh, what a cutup.
a real estate man's daughter, but oh, what development.
a hash-slinger's daughter, but how she could dish it out.
a boxer's daughter, but she knew when to faint.
a plumber's daughter, but oh, those fixtures.
a parson's dàughter, but she had her following.
a blacksmith's daughter, but she knew how to forge ahead.
a golfer's daughter, but her form was perfect.
a stableman's daughter, but all the horsemen knew her.

Marquis (Lafayette College)

DO YOU KNOW WHAT . . .

One ocean said to the other ocean?
They didn't say anything, just waved.

The little stream said as the elephant sat down in it?
Well, I'll be damned.

One eye said to the other eye?
Just between us, there's something that smells.

The big rose said to the little rose?
Hiya, bud.

The executioner said as he pulled the switch?
This'll kill you.

The mayonnaise said to the icebox?
Shut the door, I'm dressing.

One stocking said to the other stocking?
So long, I gotta run.

The salmon said as he bit the hook?
I'll probably get canned for this.

The key said to the keyhole?
What do ya hear from the knob?

The cub said to the north wind?
Don't blow so hard, I'm a little bear.

The ceiling said to the wall?
Hold me up, I'm plastered.

The calf said to the silo?
Is my fodder in there?

The scarf said to the hat?
You go ahead—I wanna neck.

The rug said to the floor?
Don't move, I've got you covered.

March 1—"FOR SALE: Slightly used farm wench in good condition. Very handy. Phone Lg. 2222 A. Q. Smith."

March 2—CORRECTION: Due to an unfortunate error Mr. Smith's ad last night was not clear. He has an excellent winch for sale. We trust this will put an end to jokesters who have called Mr. Smith and greatly bothered his housekeeper, Mrs. Jones, who loves with him.

March 3—"NOTICE: My W-I-N-C-H is not for sale. I put a sledge hammer to it. Don't bother calling Lg. 2222. I had the phone taken out. I am NOT carrying on with Mrs. Jones. She merely L-I-V-E-S with me. A. Q. Smith."

THEY SAID IT FIRST:

ADAM: "It's a great life if you don't weaken."
PLUTARCH: "I'm sorry that I have no more lives to give to my country."
SAMSON: "I'm strong for you, kid."
JONAH: "You can't keep a good man down."
CLEOPATRA: "You're an easy Mark, Antony."
DAVID: "The bigger they are the harder they fall."
HELEN OF TROY: "So this is Paris."
COLUMBUS: "I don't know where I'm going but I'm on my way."
NERO: "Keep the home fires burning."
SOLOMON: "I love the ladies."
NOAH: "It floats."
METHUSELAH: "The first hundred years are the hardest."

CLASSROOM BONERS

A yokel is part of an egg.
One of the main causes of dust is janitors.
A lyric is something to be sung by a liar.
A geyser used to rule Germany before the war.
Two occupations of the civilized race are work and looking for work.
Disinfectant is a smell that is greater than the original smell.
A sirloin is the only article of clothing worn by Gandhi.

The Spartan boys were beaten to death sometimes to see if they could stand it.

A trust is a large firm that hopes business will get better in the near future.

The animal which possesses the greatest attachment for man is woman.

Mushrooms always grow in wet places and so they look like umbrellas.

A punch bowl is the place where prize fights are staged.

Justifiable homicide is when a woman kills her husband.

A triangle is a circle with three corners to it.

Revolution is a form of government abroad.

A metaphor is a thing you shout through.

SHE
WAS
THE
KIND
OF
GIRL
YOU
LOOK
AT
LIKE
THIS.

"WAITER, THERE'S A FLY IN MY SOUP."

"That's all right, mister, he won't drink much."

"Shhh, not so loud, the other customers will want one."

"Hmmmm–there were two of them when I left the kitchen."

"I know, watch the cute little rascals dive for parsley."

"Oh, fudge! I mixed my orders again."

"Go ahead and eat him, there's more where that came from."

"Wring him out before you throw him away."

"Half a fly would be worse."

"You want I should dive in and keep him company?"

"Serves the chef right. I told him not to strain the fat through the fly swatter."

"What do you want me to do, beat him to death with my carnation?"

"If you wanted it with your dessert, why didn't you say so."

"What do you want for thirty-five cents–maybe an elephant?"

"That's all right, he's dead."

"When you finish that one you can have another."
"All right, I'll give you separate checks."
"Don't throw a fit, I'll run get a frog."

TWO COOL CATS

TWO COOL CATS were looking out the porthole of the *Queen Elizabeth* into a very rough and foamy sea. "Hey, Homer," volunteered one cool boy, "dig that crazy Bendix."

TWO COOL CATS were just finishing their meal. One cat said to the waitress, "I think I'll have a piece of apple pie."
"Sorry," said the waitress, "but the apple pie is gone."
"Crazy," answered the cat, "I'll take two pieces."

TWO COOL CATS were being shown through the immense lens at Mount Palomar when one cat turned to the other and expostulated, "Man, dig that crazy monocle."

We have a friend who works down at the state capitol, in Jefferson City, Missouri; and he sent us the following, which are excerpts from WPA investigators' reports on applicants for relief:

"Woman and house neat but bare."
"Man supported parents before marriage."
"Couple breaking up home. Friends helping."
"Milk needed for the baby and father unable to supply it."
"Until a year ago this man delivered ice, and was a man of affairs."
"Man aggressive–has nine children."
"Woman is ailing–eyesight poor–does housework when able to find it."
"Saw woman–has seven children–husband a veteran."
"Woman has 1 child, Lillian, who is 8 months old and owes 12 months rent."
"The daughter is active, mentally and otherwise. She has advanced herself, but not at home."
"Family's savings all used up. Relatives have helped."

"Applicant is a lady and hardly knows what it is all about."
"Woman is willing to struggle if given an opportunity."
"Woman badly bruised—furniture man took bedsprings."

Kangaroo (Kansas City University)

TEMPERANCE LECTURE

And in conclusion, my dear fellow citizens, I will give you a practical demonstration of the evils of the Demon Rum. I have two glasses here on the table: one is filled with water and the other with whiskey. I will now place an angle worm in the glass of water; see how it lives, squirms, vibrates with the very spark of life. Now I will place a worm in the glass of whiskey; see how it curls up, writhes in agony, and then dies. Now young man, what moral do you get from this story?"

"If you drink whiskey, you'll never get worms."

LEXICON OF AN M.D.

CORPUSCLE—An officer in the R.O.T.C.
HORMONE—Blending of notes in music.
NASAL—Pertaining to the Navy.
TONSIL—Decoration used on Christmas trees.
KNUCKLE—Five pennies.
DISEASED—Dead
CYST—Abbreviation for sister.
SURGEON—Rushing forward.
BILE—Provincial for boil.
LUNG—Jump forward.
SCALPEL—Top of the head.
ULCER—Raincoat.
MEDICINE—An Italian family of bankers.
LIVER—A long rod for lifting heavy weights. *Kangaroo*

L FOR BET

A	for ism
B	for lamb
C	for yourself
D	for dumb
E	for Le Gallienne
F	for vescence
G	for creepers
H	for beauty
I	for got
J	for see a dream walking?
K	for ancis
L	for ed. E. Smith
M	for ever blowing bubbles
N	for mation Please
O	for God's sake
P	for relief
Q	for a lovely evening
R	for Godfrey
S	for you
T	for two
U	for me
V	for la France
W	for bidding too much
X	for breakfast
Y	for husband
Z	forst time I saw Paris *Princeton Tiger*

Ah! he thought, at last he had met the lady of his dreams. They had danced together all evening. He had exercised every bit of polish of which he thought himself capable, talking to her about many diversified subjects, and proving himself master of them all. And in spite of his polished sophistication, she had proved herself his equal in it all, even at times appearing to read his mind. At last he turned to her, and said, in soft tones, "Do you know, although I've just met you, you appeal to me greatly. You seem to have a subtle understanding of what I'm thinking. Are you a literary woman?"

"No," she replied, "I'm a kindergarten teacher."

A very dear friend of ours, who also doubles as an instructor in primary grades in the Bloomington school system, told us of an exasperating experience she had the other day in the first grade. That which embarrassed her occurred during a spelling lesson she was conducting during the absence of the regular teacher. The following conversation between pedant and pupil:

"F-E-E-T," our teacher explained. "What does that spell, Agatha?"

"I dunno," came the bright retort.

"Well," the instructor mused, "what is it that a cow has four of and I only have two?"

So Agatha told her. *The Crimson Bull*

A psychology professor went to visit a psychiatrist friend of his. "You're fine, how am I?" he said.

"All right," he said, "but some of my clients are making me worry—they're nuts!"

"How pitifully common," replied the prof, "but what exactly is the trouble?"

"Well, I have a set of stock questions which I ask each patient I interview, as a sort of test. First, I ask, what is it that a cow has four of that a woman has two of?"

"Feet, naturally," responded the other.

"Then I ask what is it that a man does standing up that a woman does sitting down and a dog does on three legs?"

"Why, shake hands, of course."

"Then I ask what it is that a dog does that a man steps into?"

"Pants, obviously enough. But what is wrong with these questions?"

"Nothing! You know the right answers, and I know that they're right, but you should hear some of the ones I get from those crazy clients of mine!" *Jackolantern*

There was once a very famous statesman who was invited to give an address to the graduating class. Being accustomed to public speaking, he didn't bother to prepare a speech beforehand, confident that a suitable inspiration would dawn upon him from some local situation. He got all the way to the door of the auditorium before he found what he wanted, something on which to base his message of hope and inspiration. On the door was a brass plate bearing the word "Push." Confidently he entered the hall, took his place on the podium, and awaited his turn to speak.

He began: "Members of the graduating class; you are going out into the cold, hard world of reality where perseverance is necessary in order to get what you want from life. And to get ahead, you will also need a certain quality which even now is engraved on the doors of this very hall . . ."

At this, everyone turned around and looked at the doors. There, engraved clearly on the brass plate, was the single word "Pull."

Jackolantern

At one of the better New England colleges for young ladies, there is an English professor who is noted for his fine sense of humor which is occasionally a little on the low side. Most of the girls think he's great, but last year one particular section got the notion in their pretty little domes that said professor often embarrassed them with his off-color jokes. So they sent him an ultimatum to the effect that if he ever said even one word that could be construed as being smutty, they would immediately get up and leave his class.

When the girls came to class the next day, they found the professor sitting with his feet propped up on his desk and his head buried in the morning newspaper. After all the girls had settled down and were ready for the lecture, the professor finally looked up and said, "I see here on page twenty that the Army is going to send a few dozen prostitutes to Guam to see what can be done about raising our soldiers' morale." Immediately most of the young ladies stood up and headed for the door. Then the professor said, "Oh, there's no hurry girls; the boat doesn't leave for a month yet." *Jackolantern*

A student on his way back to school recently bought a basket of grapes, and after everyone had retired for the night, he climbed into his upper berth and lay there reading and eating the grapes. Every so often he would come to a bad one and casually flick it over the curtain and across the aisle. He was almost asleep when he heard an exclamation from the opposite berth. Looking out, he saw a man's hand holding one of the grapes which was squeezed to a pulp, and the man shouting for the porter. "Look at this," the man said indignantly to the porter, "look what I killed."

"Lawd," said the porter, "I never saw one as big as that before."

The student kept very quiet and threw the grapes out of the window just before Albany. *Jackolantern*

Two owls were sitting on a branch one night, hooting and discussing dialectic materialism.

Neither knew too much Hegel, but their conversation had a modern flavor.

"Death," said one, "is merely a change in the status of matter."

"Rubbish. After enough time all dead are the same. We lose more than that state of matter.

We lose the self ingredient." At this point a nocturnal naturalist shot both owls. They are now mounted in a famous museum in New York.

MORAL: ALL THAT'S CERTAIN IS DEATH AND TAXIDERMISTS. *The Purple Cow*

Everyone is familiar with the open-book test, and most of us have at one time or another brought a sizable reference library into a quiz room. The day before a big test given in the mechanical-engineering department the professor in charge announced that the students would be permitted to bring anything they could carry on their backs. One ingenious fellow, obviously destined for success, staggered in carrying a grad student on his back. The ME department is now contemplating only closed-book exams. *Voo Doo*

HISTORY OF A JOKE

Birth: A freshman thinks it up and chuckles with glee, waking up two fraternity men in the back row.

Age five minutes: Freshman tells it to senior who answers, "Yeah, it's funny, but I've heard it before."

Age 1 day: Senior turns it into the college humor rag.

Age 10 days: Editor has to fill magazine, prints joke.

Age 1 month: Thirteen college comics reprint joke.

Age three years: *Froth* reprints joke as original.

Age three years, one month: *College Humor* reprints joke crediting it to *Froth*.

Age ten years: Seventy-six radio comedians discover joke simultaneously, tell it accompanied by howls of mirth from boys in the orchestra.

Age twenty years: Joke is reprinted in *Reader's Digest*.

Age about one hundred years: Professors start telling it in class. *Froth*

THREE WAYS TO END A DINNER CONVERSATION:

1. Ask the lady on your right if she's married. Should she say "Yes," ask her if she has any children. If she says "No," ask her how she does it.

2. Ask the lady on your left if she is married. If she says "No," ask her if she has any children.

3. Ask the lady across from you if she has any children. If she says "Yes," ask her if she is married. *Yale Record*

An old gentleman riding the top of a Fifth Avenue bus noticed that every few minutes the conductor would come from the back and dangle a piece of string down before the driver underneath. Whereupon the driver would utter profanity terrible to hear. Finally the old gentleman could stand it no longer so he asked the conductor why he dangled the string and why the driver swore.

"Oh," the conductor answered naively, "his father is being hung tomorrow and I'm just kidding him a little."

Those young men of ours eligible for the armed forces should not attempt to evade service by the device used during a recent examination by a chap who had visions of beating the draft board. At least he could have shown more originality than he did. Standing outside the door to the medical examination room he saw a friend on the way out.

"Did they accept you?" asked the anxious one.

"No. Rejected. Because I've worn a truss for twelve years."

"Let me borrow it, will ya?" The exchange was quickly made. When the slick guy appeared before the sharp-eyed medical man, he was asked, "How long have you worn that truss?"

"Twelve years," said the liar.

The examiner looked him over, then marked his sheet, N.E.

"What's the N.E. mean, Doc?"

The doctor answered him, "Near East. Anyone who can wear a double truss upside down for twelve years can easily ride a camel."

FRESHMAN: Her Motto: "Mother knows best."
SOPHOMORE: Her Motto: "Death Before Dishonor."
JUNIOR: Her Motto: "Nothing ventured, nothing gained."
SENIOR: Her Motto: "Boys will be boys."

"See that fellow over there?"

"Yes, what about him?"

"Oh, he's a terrible guy, awful low life; let's ostracize him."

"O.K.; you hold him and I'll do it."

If you love me
Like I love you–
Then shame on us!

YALE MAN: "Say, my boy, I'm a stranger here in Cambridge. Could you tell me where I might stop at?"

HARVARD MAN: "I would suggest you stop before the at."

A lobbyist, who was opposing any large appropriation for a state college, approached a legislator who boasted of his self-education.

"Do you realize," asked the portly lobbyist gravely, "that up at the state college, men and women students have to use the same curriculum?"

The legislator looked startled.

"And that boys and girls often matriculate together?"

"No," exclaimed the lawmaker.

The lobbyist came closer and whispered, "And a young lady student can be forced at any time to show a male professor her thesis?"

The legislator shrank back in horror. "I won't vote them a damn cent!" *Rammer Jammer*

A hard-working husband, back from the office early one afternoon, surprised his wife in bed with another man.

His wife cried, "Don't shoot him, Christy; when you were out of work, who do you think paid the bills? And that wrist watch I gave you for Christmas; who do you think paid for that? And the time I needed all that money for the operation; how do you think I got that?"

The husband looked puzzled for a moment and then, with a grand gesture, told his wife: "Cover him up, darling, do you want him to catch cold?"

He knocked at the door of my room.

"May I come in? It's the room I had when I went to college in '09," he said.

I invited him in.

"Yes, sir," he said, lost in reverie. "Same old room. Same old windows. Same old furniture. Same old view of the campus. Same old closet."

He opened the door. There stood a girl, terrified.

"This is my sister," I said.

"Yes, sir. Same old story."

Two fleas fell in love and one lovely June day they got married. Young, industrious, and ambitious, the fleas worked hard and saved their money. They sacrificed fun to assure the future. One day they counted their money and were overjoyed to find they'd saved five dollars.

"If we can save five we can save ten," they agreed, so they continued their thrift. They toiled, economized, and planned, spurning the frivolous pleasures of other fleas. Finally came the day when their savings totaled ten dollars.

That day they went out and bought a dog.

"It is my considered opinion that a man of your age shouldn't marry a girl of eighteen," said the doctor to his ancient friend. "I can find nothing physically wrong, but I have the gravest reservations about your marital happiness and hers."

"We've already set the date," replied the old gent, oblivious as hell.

"Do one thing for me: Be sure and take in a boarder." The venerable one promised he would and left the office. Some months later the doctor met him on the street. "You're looking awfully well. How's your wife?"

"She's pregnant."

"Splendid! I see you followed my advice about taking in a boarder."

"Yep, she's pregnant too."

SWEET YOUNG THING TO HUSKY FULLBACK: "Are you the 'bull of the campus'?"

H.FB.: "That's me, Toots."

S.Y.T.: "Moo!"

Two little amoebae who were swimming around in the veins of a horse decided that they were hungry. So they wandered into the horse's arteries, a most fatal step, as both of them soon died. The moral of this story is that you shouldn't change streams in the middle of a horse.

A young man and his fiancée had wed and were spending their honeymoon at a large hotel. When bedtime came the bride went to bed and the groom sat by the window gazing at the moon and the stars.

The bride called to him, "Why don't you come to bed?"

He answered, "Mother told me that tonight would be the most beautiful night of my life, and I'm not going to miss a minute of it."

An unconfirmed report has it that a mare was recently graduated from Bennington. At the commencement exercise a guest speaker (from Dartmouth, no doubt) remarked, "This is the first time that Bennington has graduated an entire horse."

A psychologist is a man who, when a beautiful girl enters the room, watches everybody else.

Once upon a time there was a little girl who had many boy friends. They each asked her: "Do you love me?" She answered "Yes," to each of them. This went on for many years, but she died an old maid.

MORAL: Don't love everybody. Leave that to God. *Specialize!*

One day a little baby stork was very perturbed because his mother was gone all night and he asked his father about it. "Why, your mother has been making people very happy," the father stork replied. The next night the father stork was gone and the baby stork asked his mother where he was. "Your father is out making people very happy," the mother stork replied. The next night the baby stork was gone till the wee hours. When he came in, mother stork and father stork asked where he had been. "Oh, out scaring the hell out of college kids," baby stork replied.

From the Economics Department comes the neatest "last word" story that we have found yet. It concerns another of those professors who, always anxious to improve their courses, add to the last question of their final examination: "What have you thought of this course?" The professor in question, upon reaching the end of what had been the worst of his papers, found the following notation: "I think that this was a very well-rounded course. Everything not given during the semester has been included in the final examination."

A college student is one who enters his alma mater dressed in green and emerges as a senior dressed in black. The intermediate process of decay is known as college education.

NEWS ITEM: A roaring twister last Wednesday carried off Jim Benson's house and all three of his children are missing. Neighbors donated a bed to give Jim and his wife a new start.

A sensible girl isn't so sensible as she looks because a sensible girl has more sense than to go around looking sensible.

It happened the other day in one of the psych classes. The lecture for the day was on job aptitudes. The prof finished up the morning's lecture by saying, "The point is, that a good poker player can hold down any sort of an executive position. Now, then, are there any questions?" Came then the proverbial voice from the back of the room: "Just one, sir—what would a good poker player want with a job, anyway?"

A drunk, sitting at a local bar, had been eying a voluptuous blonde for some time and finally summoned enough courage to approach her. "Shay," he mumbled, "how about spending the night with me, baby?"

"Fine," she replied, "shall we go to your place or mine?"

"Hell," responded the drunk, "if you're going to quibble, we'll jusht forget about it."

PROF: How many revolutions took place in France during this period?

SOPH: Four.

PROF: Enumerate them.

SOPH: One, two, three, four.

The neighbors were complaining about the noises Mrs. Jones's husband was making. "All the time he goes around cackling like a chicken," they griped.

"I know," Mrs. Jones said. "We get tired of it, too. Sometimes we think he's not in his right mind."

"But can't you do something for him? Can't you cure him?"

"Oh yes, I suppose we could, but we need the eggs." *Pelican*

Two old maids were driving along through the country. As they passed a farmhouse, a hen came tearing out of the yard, hotly pursued by a rooster. Not watching where she was going, the hen ran right under the wheels of the old maids' car.

After they had driven on for a while, one of the old maids clucked: "The sweet thing. She preferred death."

PHI KAPPA: "Wonder where that old sot ever got the idea that he was a professor. Everybody hates him. He doesn't have any idea of how to teach. He starts off on one subject and then veers to another and you can't keep notes. About the only thing he's good for is to give cows a hand. He ought to be back on the farm."

DELTA CHI: "Yeah. I flunked, too."

Jimmy was assigned by his teacher to write a composition about his origin. He questioned his mother.

"Mom, where did Grandma come from?"

"The stork brought her."

"Well, where did you come from?"

"The stork brought me, and you, too."

So the small modern wrote as the introduction to his composition: "There have been no natural births in our family for three generations."

A judge was examining a prisoner who was accused of stealing a bundle of silverware. "Where did you get it?" he asked the thief.

"From the fraternity house, Your Honor."

"Call up the hotels, Sergeant, and distribute the stuff."

SHE: "*Adieu.*"
HE: "You do?"

PROFESSOR: Every time I breathe someone passes into eternity.
STUDENT: Why don't you try Sen-Sen?

A gullible man is one who thinks that his daughter has got religion when she comes home with a Gideon Bible in her suitcase.

If you write illegibly when you sign out, it won't be so obvious when you sign in.

SHE: Would you like to see where I was operated on for appendicitis?
HE: No. I hate hospitals.

Then there's the gal who was so thin that when she swallowed an olive ten men left town.

Home is where you can scratch any place that itches.

"How many students are enrolled in the university?" asked the old grad, with deceptive politeness.

"Eight thousand," replied the coach.

"Is it too much to ask to have two of them in front of the ball carrier?" snapped the alum.

They had been sitting in the swing in the moonlight alone. No word broke the stillness for half an hour until—

"Suppose you had money," she said, "what would you do?"

He threw out his chest, in all the glory of young manhood. "I'd travel."

He felt her warm, young hand slide into his. When he looked she was gone.

In his hand was a nickel.

"Doctor, my trouble is that I dream the same dream over and over, every night. I'm in a girls' dormitory and the girls run from room to room, dressed in nothing at all."

"I see. You want me to make you stop dreaming about the girls?"

"No. I want you to make them stop slamming the doors and waking me up just when I am about to catch one of them."

A professor is a man whose job is to tell students how to solve the problems of life which he himself has tried to avoid by becoming a professor.

Don't ever try to fool your mother, boys. It can't be done. Remember the young man who pawned his nice suit of clothes and didn't want his mother to know anything about it? He finally redeemed them and brought them home in a suitcase. While he was busy in his room, his mother, in the parlor, started to unpack the suitcase. She found the pawn ticket on the coat and called:

"John, what is this tag on your coat?"

John lost very little time in calling back: "I was at a dance last night, Mother, and checked my coat."

A moment later mother came across the trousers, tagged in the same way. With a puzzled tone she asked: "John, what kind of a dance was that?"

PSYCHIATRIST: A man who tries to find out if infants have more fun in infancy than adults do in adultery.

An American soldier goes into a London restaurant and sits down at a table. After a few moments a good looking filly jaunts over to his table and lays down the menu.

"What's good today?" he asks of the waitress.

"Rhubarb, rutabagas, ravioli, rice, and roast," is her answer.

"Baby, you sure roll yours r's."

"Yeah, maybe it's because of the high heels I'm wearing."

We know a girl who said she'd do anything for a mink coat and now she can't button it.

The main trouble with the straight and narrow is that there's no place to park.

PART EIGHT

THE OLD GRADS

What old grads write about undergrads

Up to this point the book has been, in the main, undergrads writing about undergrads.

Now we take up the fraught and pregnant question: Can an old grad, far removed from green fields and ivory towers, continue to write about undergrads with force, clarity, and truth?

The answers follow.

UNIVERSITY DAYS*

BY JAMES THURBER

I passed all the other courses [illegible] ... never pass botany. [illegible] several hours a [illegible] plant cells [illegible] ... cells through a [illegible] would wander around [illegible] students were making [illegible] interesting structure of [illegible] ... beginning them. I [illegible] patiently enough, expla[illegible] ... scope but he would [illegible] ... not see through a [illegible] ... takes away from the [illegible] "We are not concerned [illegible] "We are concerned with [illegible] "Well, I'd say, it [illegible] ... say, and I would put [illegible] except now and again [illegible] of maladjustments. [illegible] of sharply defined plant [illegible] ... would tell him. This, [illegible] ... adjusted the microscope [illegible] rages for himself. And I [illegible]

I finally took a deferred [illegible]

* From *My Life and Hard Times*, copyright 1933, by James Thurber. Originally published in "The [illegible]"

UNIVERSITY DAYS*

BY JAMES THURBER

I passed all the other courses I took at my university, but I could never pass botany. This was because all botany students had to spend several hours a week in a laboratory looking through a microscope at plant cells, and I could never see through a microscope. I never once saw a cell through a microscope. This used to enrage my instructor. He would wander around the laboratory pleased with the progress all the students were making in drawing the involved and, so I am told, interesting structure of flower cells, until he came to me. I would just be standing there. "I can't see anything," I would say. He would begin patiently enough, explaining how anybody can see through a microscope, but he would always end up in a fury, claiming that I could *too* see through a microscope but just pretended that I couldn't. "It takes away from the beauty of flowers anyway," I used to tell him. "We are not concerned with beauty in this course," he would say. "We are concerned solely with what I may call the *mechanics* of flars." "Well," I'd say, "I can't see anything." "Try it just once again," he'd say, and I would put my eye to the microscope and see nothing at all, except now and again a nebulous milky substance—a phenomenon of maladjustment. You were supposed to see a vivid, restless clockwork of sharply defined plant cells. "I see what looks like a lot of milk," I would tell him. This, he claimed, was the result of my not having adjusted the microscope properly, so he would readjust it for me, or rather, for himself. And I would look again and see milk.

I finally took a deferred pass, as they called it, and waited a year

* From *My Life and Hard Times,* copyright, 1933, by James Thurber. Originally published in *The New Yorker.*

and tried again. (You had to pass one of the biological sciences or you couldn't graduate.) The professor had come back from vacation brown as a berry, bright-eyed, and eager to explain cell structure again to his classes. "Well," he said to me, cheerily, when we met in the first laboratory hour of the semester, "we're going to see the cells this time, aren't we?" "Yes, sir," I said. Students to right of me and to left of me and in front of me were seeing cells; what's more, they were quietly drawing pictures of them in their notebooks. Of course, I didn't see anything.

"We'll try it," the professor said to me, grimly, "with every adjustment of the microscope known to man. As God is my witness, I'll arrange this glass so that you see cells through it or I'll give up teaching. In twenty-two years of botany, I—" He cut off abruptly for he was beginning to quiver all over, like Lionel Barrymore, and he genuinely wished to hold onto his temper; his scenes with me had taken a great deal out of him.

So we tried it with every adjustment of the microscope known to man. With only one of them did I see anything but blackness or the familiar lacteal opacity, and that time I saw, to my pleasure and amazement, a variegated constellation of flecks, specks, and dots. These I hastily drew. The instructor, noting my activity, came back from an adjoining desk, a smile on his lips and his eyebrows high in hope. He looked at my cell drawing. "What's that?" he demanded, with a hint of a squeal in his voice. "That's what I saw," I said. "You didn't, you didn't, you *did*n't!" he screamed, losing control of his temper instantly, and he bent over and squinted into the microscope. His head snapped up. "That's your eye!" he shouted. "You've fixed the lens so that it reflects! You've drawn your eye!"

Another course I didn't like, but somehow managed to pass, was economics. I went to that class straight from the botany class, which didn't help me any in understanding either subject. I used to get them mixed up. But not as mixed up as another student in my economics class who came there directly from a physics laboratory. He was a tackle on the football team, named Bolenciecwcz. At that time Ohio State University had one of the best football teams in the country, and Bolenciecwcz was one of its outstanding stars. In order to be eligible to play it was necessary for him to keep up in his studies, a very difficult matter, for while he was not dumber than an ox he was not any smarter. Most of his professors were lenient and helped him along. None gave him more hints, in answering questions, or asked him simpler ones than the economics professor, a thin, timid man named Bassum. One day when we were on the subject of transportation and distribution, it came Bolenciecwcz's turn to answer a question. "Name one means of transportation," the professor said to him. No light came into the big tackle's eyes. "Just any means of transportation," said the professor. Bolenciecwcz sat staring at him. "That is," pursued the professor, "any medium, agency, or method of going from one place to another." Bolenciecwcz had the look of a man who is being led into a trap. "You may choose among steam, horse-drawn, or electrically propelled vehicles," said the instructor. "I might suggest the one which we commonly take in making long journeys across land." There was a profound silence in which everybody stirred uneasily, including Bolenciecwcz and Mr. Bassum. Mr. Bassum abruptly broke this silence in an amazing manner. "Choo-choo-choo," he said, in a low voice, and turned instantly scarlet. He glanced appealingly around the room. All of us, of course, shared Mr. Bassum's desire that Bolenciecwcz should stay abreast of the class in economics, for the Illinois game, one of the hardest and most important of the season, was only a week off. "Toot, toot, too-tooooooot!" some student with a deep voice moaned, and we all looked encouragingly at Bolenciecwcz. Somebody else gave a fine imitation of a locomotive letting off steam. Mr. Bassum himself rounded off the little show. "Ding, dong, ding, dong," he said, hopefully. Bolenciecwcz was staring at the floor now, trying to think, his great brow furrowed, his huge hands rubbing together, his face red.

"How did you come to college this year, Mr. Bolenciecwcz? asked the professor. "*Chuffa,* chuffa, *chuffa,* chuffa."

"M' father sent me," said the football player.

"What on?" asked Bassum.

"I git an 'lowance," said the tackle, in a low, husky voice, obviously embarrassed.

"No, no," said Bassum. "Name a means of transportation. What did you *ride* here on?"

"Train," said Bolenciecwcz.

"Quite right," said the professor. "Now, Mr. Nugent, will you tell us——"

If I went through anguish in botany and economics—for different reasons—gymnasium work was even worse. I don't even like to think about it. They wouldn't let you play games or join in the exercises with your glasses on and I couldn't see with mine off. I bumped into professors, horizontal bars, agricultural students, and swinging iron rings. Not being able to see, I could take it but I couldn't dish it out. Also, in order to pass gymnasium (and you had to pass it to graduate) you had to learn to swim if you didn't know how. I didn't like the swimming pool, I didn't like swimming, and I didn't like the swimming instructor, and after all these years I still don't. I never swam but I passed my gym work anyway, by having another student give my gymnasium number (978) and swim across the pool in my place. He was a quiet, amiable blonde youth, number 473, and he would have seen through a microscope for me if we could have got away with it, but we couldn't get away with it. Another thing I didn't like about gymnasium work was that they made you strip the day you registered. It is impossible for me to be happy when I am stripped and being asked a lot of questions. Still, I did better than a lanky agricultural student who was cross-examined just before I was. They asked each student what college he was in—that is, whether Arts, Engineering, Commerce, or Agriculture. "What college are you in?" the instructor snapped at the youth in front of me. "Ohio State University," he said promptly.

It wasn't that agricultural student but it was another a whole lot like him who decided to take up journalism, possibly on the ground that when farming went to hell he could fall back on newspaper work. He didn't realize, of course, that that would be very much like falling back full-length on a kit of carpenter's tools. Haskins didn't seem cut out for journalism, being too embarrassed to talk to anybody and unable to use a typewriter, but the editor of the college paper assigned him to the cow barns, the sheep house, the horse pavilion, and the animal-husbandry department generally. This was a genuinely big "beat," for it took up five times as much ground as the College of Liberal Arts. The agricultural student knew animals, but nevertheless his stories were dull and colorlessly written. He took all afternoon on each of them, on account of having to hunt for each letter on the typewriter. Once in a while he had to ask somebody to help him hunt. "C" and "L," in particular, were hard letters for him to find. His editor finally got pretty much annoyed at the farmer-journalist because his pieces were so uninteresting. "See here, Haskins," he snapped at him one day, "why is it we never have anything hot from you on the horse pavilion? Here we have two hundred head of horses on this campus—more than any other university in the Western Conference except Purdue—and yet you never get any real low-down on them. Now shoot over to the horse barns and dig up something lively." Haskins shambled out and came back in about an hour; he said he had something. "Well, start it off snappily," said the editor. "Something people will read." Haskins set to work and in a couple of hours brought a sheet of typewritten paper to the desk; it was a two-hundred-word story about some disease that had broken out among the horses. Its opening sentence was simple but arresting. It read: "Who has noticed the sores on the tops of the horses in the animal-husbandry building?"

Ohio State was a land-grant university and therefore two years of military drill was compulsory. We drilled with old Springfield rifles and studied the tactics of the Civil War even though the World War was going on at the time. At eleven o'clock each morning thousands of freshmen and sophomores used to deploy over the campus, moodily creeping up on the old chemistry building. It was good training for the kind of warfare that was waged at Shiloh but it had no connection with what was going on in Europe. Some people used to think that there was German money behind it, but they didn't dare say so or they would have been thrown in jail as German spies. It was a period of muddy thought and marked, I believe, the decline of higher education in the Middle West.

As a soldier I was never any good at all. Most of the cadets were glumly indifferent soldiers, but I was no good at all. Once General Littlefield, who was commandant of the cadet corps, popped up in front of me during regimental drill and snapped, "You are the main trouble with this university!" I think he meant that my type was the main trouble with the university but he may have meant me individually. I was mediocre at drill, certainly—that is, until my senior year. By that time I had drilled longer than anybody else in the Western Conference, having failed at military at the end of each preceding year so that I had to do it all over again. I was the only senior still in uniform. The uniform which, when new, had made me look like an interurban railway conductor, now that it had become faded and too tight made me look like Bert Williams in his bellboy act. This had a definitely bad effect on my morale. Even so, I had become by sheer practice little short of wonderful at squad maneuvers.

One day General Littlefield picked our company out of the whole regiment and tried to get it mixed up by putting it through one movement after another as fast as we could execute them: squads right, squads left, squads on right into line, squads right about, squads left front into line, etc. In about three minutes one hundred and nine men were marching in one direction and I was marching away from them at an angle of forty degrees, all alone. "Company, halt!" shouted General Littlefield. "That man is the only man who has it right!" I was made a corporal for my achievement.

The next day General Littlefield summoned me to his office. He was swatting flies when I went in. I was silent and he was silent, too, for a long time. I don't think he remembered me or why he had sent for me, but he didn't want to admit it. He swatted some more flies, keeping his eyes on them narrowly before he let go with the swatter. "Button up your coat!" he snapped. Looking back on it now, I can see that he meant me although he was looking at a fly, but I just stood there. Another fly came to rest on a paper in front of the general and began rubbing its hind legs together. The general lifted the swatter cautiously. I moved restlessly and the fly flew away. "You startled him!" barked General Littlefield, looking at me severely. I said I was sorry. "That won't help the situation!" snapped the general, with cold military logic. I didn't see what I could do except offer to chase some more flies toward his desk, but I didn't say anything. He stared out the window at the faraway figures of co-eds crossing the campus toward the library. Finally, he told me I could go. So I went. He either didn't know which cadet I was or else he forgot what he wanted to see me about. It may have been that he wished to apologize for having called me the main trouble with the university; or maybe he had decided to compliment me on my brilliant drilling of the day before and then at the last minute decided not to. I don't know. I don't think about it much any more.

FROM *DECLINE AND FALL**

BY EVELYN WAUGH

Mr. Sniggs, the Junior Dean, and Mr. Postlethwaite, the Domestic Bursar, sat alone in Mr. Sniggs's room overlooking the garden quad at Scone College. From the rooms of Sir Alastair Digby-Vaine-Trumpington, two staircases away, came a confused roar and breaking of glass. They alone of the senior members of Scone were at home that evening, for it was the night of the annual dinner of the Bollinger Club. The others were all scattered over Boar's Hill and North Oxford at gay, contentious little parties, or at other senior common rooms, or at the meetings of learned societies, for the annual Bollinger dinner is a difficult time for those in authority.

It is not quite accurate to call this an annual event, because quite often the Club is suspended for some years after each meeting. There is tradition behind the Bollinger; it numbers reigning kings among its past members. At the last dinner, three years ago, a fox had been brought in in a cage and stoned to death with champagne bottles. What an evening that had been! This was the first meeting since then, and from all over Europe old members had rallied for the occasion. For two days they had been pouring into Oxford: epileptic royalty from their villas of exile; uncouth peers from crumbling country seats; smooth young men of uncertain tastes from embassies and legations; illiterate lairds from wet granite hovels in the Highlands; ambitious young barristers and Conservative candidates torn from the London season and the indelicate advances of debutantes; all that was most sonorous of name and title was there for the beano.

"The fines!" said Mr. Sniggs, gently rubbing his pipe along the side of his nose. "Oh, my! the fines there'll be this evening!"

There is some highly prized port in the senior common-room cellars that is only brought up when the College fines have reached £50.

"We shall have a week of it at least," said Mr. Postlethwaite, "a week of Founder's port."

A shriller note could now be heard rising from Sir Alastair's rooms; any who have heard that sound will shrink at the recollection of it; it is the sound of the English country families baying for broken glass. Soon they would all be tumbling out into the quad, crimson and roaring in their bottle-green evening coats, for the real romp of the evening.

"Don't you think it might be wiser if we turned out the light?" said Mr. Sniggs.

In darkness the two dons crept to the window. The quad below was a kaleidoscope of dimly discernible faces.

"There must be fifty of them at least," said Mr. Postlethwaite. "If only they were all members of the College! Fifty of them at ten pounds each. Oh, my!"

"It'll be more if they attack the Chapel," said Mr. Sniggs. "Oh, please God, make them attack the Chapel."

"I wonder who the unpopular undergraduates are this term. They always attack their rooms. I hope they have been wise enough to go out for the evening."

"I think Partridge will be one; he possesses a painting by Matisse or some such name."

"And I'm told he has black sheets in his bed."

"And Sanders went to dinner with Ramsay MacDonald once."

"And Rending can afford to hunt, but collects china instead."

"And smokes cigars in the garden after breakfast."

"Austen has a grand piano."

"They'll enjoy smashing that."

"There'll be a heavy bill for to-night; just you see! But I confess I should feel easier if the Dean or the Master were in. They can't see us from here, can they?"

It was a lovely evening. They broke up Mr. Austen's grand piano, and stamped Lord Rending's cigars into his carpet, and smashed his china, and tore up Mr. Partridge's sheets, and threw the Matisse into his water jug; Mr. Sanders had nothing to break except his windows, but they found the manuscript at which he had been working for the Newdigate Prize Poem, and had great fun with that. Sir Alastair Digby-Vaine-Trumpington felt quite ill with excitement, and was supported to bed by Lumsden of Strathdrummond. It was half-past eleven. Soon the evening would come to an end. But there was still a treat to come.

Paul Pennyfeather was reading for the Church. It was his third year of uneventful residence at Scone. He had come there after a creditable career at a small public school of ecclesiastical temper on the South Downs, where he had edited the magazine, been President of the Debating Society, and had, as his report said, "exercised a wholesome influence for good" in the House of which he was head boy. At home he lived in Onslow Square with his guardian, a prosperous solicitor who was proud of his progress and abysmally bored by his company. Both his parents had died in India at the time when he won the essay prize at his preparatory school. For two years he had lived within his allowance, aided by two valuable scholarships. He smoked three ounces of tobacco a week—John Cotton, Medium—and drank a pint and a half of beer a day, the half at luncheon and the pint at dinner, a meal he invariably ate in the Hall. He had four friends, three of whom had been at school with him. None of the Bollinger Club had ever heard of Paul Pennyfeather, and he, oddly enough, had not heard of them.

Little suspecting the incalculable consequences that the evening was to have for him, he bicycled happily back from a meeting of the League of Nations Union. There had been a most interesting paper about plebiscites in Poland. He thought of smoking a pipe and reading another chapter of the *Forsyte Saga* before going to bed. He knocked at the gate, was admitted, put away his bicycle, and diffidently, as always, made his way across the quad towards his rooms. What a lot of people there seemed to be about! Paul had no particular objection to drunkenness—he had read rather a daring paper to the Thomas More Society on the subject—but he was consumedly shy of drunkards.

Out of the night Lumsden of Strathdrummond swayed across his path like a druidical rocking stone. Paul tried to pass.

Now it so happened that the tie of Paul's old school bore a marked resemblance to the pale blue and white of the Bollinger Club. The difference of a quarter of an inch in the width of the stripes was not one that Lumsden of Strathdrummond was likely to appreciate.

"Here's an awful man wearing the Boller tie," said the Laird. It is not for nothing that since pre-Christian times his family has exercised chieftainship over uncharted miles of barren moorland.

Mr. Sniggs was looking rather apprehensively at Mr. Postlethwaite. "They appear to have caught somebody," he said. "I hope they don't do him any serious harm."

"Dear me, can it be Lord Rending? I think I ought to intervene."

"No, Sniggs," said Mr. Postlethwaite, laying a hand on his impetuous colleague's arm. "No, no, no. It would be unwise. We have the prestige of the senior common room to consider. In their present state they might not prove amenable to discipline. We must at all costs avoid an *outrage.*"

At length the crowd parted, and Mr. Sniggs gave a sigh of relief. "But it's quite all right. It isn't Rending. It's Pennyfeather—someone of no importance."

"Well, that saves a great deal of trouble. I am glad, Sniggs; I am, really. What a lot of clothes the young man appears to have lost!"

Next morning there was a lovely College meeting.

"Two hundred and thirty pounds," murmured the Domestic Bursar ecstatically, "*not* counting the damage! That means five evenings, with what we have already collected. Five evenings of Founder's port!"

"The case of Pennyfeather," the Master was saying, "seems to be quite a different matter altogether. He ran the whole length of the quadrangle, you say, *without his trousers*. It is unseemly. It is more: it is indecent. In fact, I am almost prepared to say that it is flagrantly indecent. It is *not* the conduct we expect of a scholar."

"Perhaps if we fined him really heavily?" suggested the Junior Dean.

"I very much doubt whether he could pay. I understand he is not well off. *Without trousers,* indeed! And at that time of night! I think we should do far better to get rid of him altogether. That sort of young man does the College no good."

Two hours later, while Paul was packing his three suits in his little leather trunk, the Domestic Bursar sent a message that he wished to see him.

"Ah, Mr. Pennyfeather," he said, "I have examined your rooms and notice two slight burns, one on the window sill and the other on the chimney piece, no doubt from cigarette ends. I am charging you five-and-six-pence for each of them on your battels. That is all, thank you."

As he crossed the quad Paul met Mr. Sniggs.

"Just off?" said the Junior Dean brightly.

"Yes, sir," said Paul.

And a little farther on he met the Chaplain.

"Oh, Pennyfeather, before you go, surely you have my copy of Dean Stanley's *Eastern Church?"*

"Yes. I left it on your table."

"Thank you. Well, good-bye, my dear boy. I suppose that after that reprehensible affair last night you will have to think of some other profession. Well, you may congratulate yourself that you discovered your unfitness for the priesthood before it was too late. If a parson does a thing of that sort, you know, all the world knows. And so many do, alas! What do you propose doing?"

"I don't really know yet."

"There is always commerce, of course. Perhaps you may be able to bring to the great world of business some of the ideals you have learned at Scone. But it won't be easy, you know. It is a thing to be lived down with courage. What did Dr. Johnson say about fortitude? . . . Dear, dear! *no trousers!"*

At the gates Paul tipped the porter.

"Well, good-bye, Blackall," he said. "I don't suppose I shall see you again for some time."

"No, sir, and very sorry I am to hear about it. I expect you'll be becoming a schoolmaster, sir. That's what most of the gentlemen does, sir, that gets sent down for indecent behaviour."

"God damn and blast them all to hell," said Paul meekly to himself as he drove to the station, and then he felt rather ashamed, because he rarely swore.

FROM *THE COMPLEAT PRACTICAL JOKER**

BY H. ALLEN SMITH

A boy's talent for practical jokes doesn't reach its full burgeoning until he gets in college. It was at Cornell that Hugh Troy, our country's most accomplished man in the business, began his adventures. And it was at Cornell, just a couple of years ago, that a group of students seized the campus radio station.

Around eleven o'clock one night ten students, wearing masks, walked into the radio station, tied up two announcers, and took over the microphone. For eight minutes they broadcast bulletins that Russian planes had bombed London and Marseilles, that other planes were now over Newfoundland—that the world was once again at war. The bulletins caused panic in some quarters of the campus and girls in the sorority houses were reported to have suffered fainting and hysteria. Some twenty-five students were involved in the plot, and were suspended after they confessed. This stunt was not original, having been pulled on a lesser scale in other schools.

Another group of Cornell students developed a grudge not long ago against the girls in a certain sorority house. They figured out a way to embarrass the girls. They dressed themselves as workmen, with red signs and lanterns and tools. They blocked off a thoroughfare leading from the campus proper to a bridge. The girls, in order to get from the campus to their house, had to cross this bridge; otherwise, it was necessary for them to take a long, arduous roundabout way to get home. The boys timed their roadblock so the girls would be late getting to their house, and find themselves in trouble. Ah, youth.

Collegiate jokers often concern themselves with bells. The early American humorist Henry W. Shaw, who wrote under the name of Josh Billings, was expelled from Hamilton College for removing the clapper from the college bell. There have been other cases in which cords were attached to bells, and strung off across rooftops so that the pranksters could set the bells to ringing during the night. The best of these jokes occurred at Harvard. The clock in one of the university towers began performing in a most unusual manner. It would strike thirteen times at noon. At midnight it was content to strike the customary twelve times, but at noon there would be that extra stroke. The deviation was quickly noticed and an investigation was started. Clockmakers were called in to examine the mechanism. They couldn't make out what caused the thirteen strokes at noon. The bell itself was examined, but there were no cords, or other contrivances, connected to it. The thing went along for quite a while, a great mystery to be sure. It was solved by the villain's being caught in the act. He was a student, living on one of the upper floors of a house near by. Each noontime he sat at the window of his room with a rifle. The clock struck twelve and then, with perfect timing, the student pulled the trigger to create the thirteenth stroke.

Among the legends at New Haven is that of the time Lucius Beebe brought in the famous clergyman from the West. Mr. Beebe conceived the joke after having met a man who was an expert ventriloquist. He had the man dress in somber clothes and arrive on the Yale campus for a visit. Mr. Beebe quickly introduced him to the Yale chaplain as one of the most celebrated preachers of the Far West. The chaplain immediately invited the visitor to preach a sermon in the Yale Chapel. A goodly crowd was there and the impostor acquitted himself well, working himself up to a pitch of excitement. Suddenly he paused, threw back his head, cupped his hands to his mouth and shouted toward the ceiling: "Am I right, Lord?" Back from the rafters came the faint but audible response: "You are right, my son!"

Stanley Halle has told me of a torment he had to put up with regularly during his undergraduate days at Yale. Quite a few of the students would leave New Haven to spend weekends in New York City. On Sunday night there was a certain train which most of them took out of Grand Central—a train that would just get them under the wire at university curfew time. The boys, as a rule, would be dog-tired and perhaps a little woozy when they boarded the train and most of them would collapse in the seats and go to sleep. The train would move out of Grand Central and pull up at 125th Street station. Almost invariably, says Mr. Halle, just as it was coming in to the 125th Street stop, someone would yell out, "New Haven!" The cry would rouse the sleepers and they'd stumble out of the cars to the platform, their train would depart, and they'd have to wait another couple of hours before resuming their journey. . . .

An acquaintance of mine in the book publishing business attended Syracuse University twenty-odd years ago. He remembers, with some pleasure, a dance that was given at his fraternity house. Since the house would be co-ed for that one evening, it was necessary to reapportion the toilet facilities. One large bathroom on the second floor was, accordingly, turned over to the girls and a "Ladies" sign placed on the door. Before the hour for the dance to begin, my friend had an idea. He went out to a pet store and bought three goldfish. There were three toilets in the "ladies' room" and he put one of the goldfish in each of them. He says that all during the evening the girls kept going to the room, but not a single one of them used the toilets for fear of harming the fish, and he says further that the girls seemed to get livelier and livelier as the evening wore on, and in the end they were fair leaping around. Demonstrates the essential kindliness of women.

The business of dismantling and then reassembling large pieces of machinery in a person's bedroom is said to have originated at the Massachusetts Institute of Technology. The pioneer practitioners of this form of foolishness took an automobile apart and put it back together in a student's room. The stunt has been repeated, in variation, many times since, especially in Hollywood, where a visiting Englishman once arrived at his hotel room to find it occupied by a gang plow.

Biographers of the late William Randolph Hearst usually tell of his adventures at Harvard, where he once encompassed the entire faculty in one of his jokes. On a certain day each member of the faculty received a package—a chamber pot with the recipient's photograph pasted in the bottom.

Alexander Woollcott was to be the butt of fantastic jokes in his later life, but when he was a student at Hamilton College he was not averse to trying a few himself. He was a member of Theta Delta Chi. During one rushing season, his fraternity was in sharp rivalry with another house in the quest for pledges. Mr. Woollcott attired himself in a fantastic costume and went over and sat on the steps of the rival fraternity house, assuming the air of a drooling idiot, as an advertisement of the type of boy belonging to *that* society.

Two eastern college boys once spent their summer vacation as temporary employees at Yellowstone Park. After a while they became impatient with a certain ranger, a pompous individual whose job was to guide tourists to the famous geysers and lecture to them on the wonders of this unique manifestation of natural force. They came, in fact, to dislike the man heartily and so they put their heads together and came up with a scheme.

There was one geyser which spouted with clocklike regularity and the college boys stationed themselves near it. The ranger would arrive with his party of tourists. The boys had placed themselves beyond a slope where the tourists could see them while they were out of sight of the lecturing ranger. They had a steering wheel and post from an old automobile, and they had stuck the post into the ground. While the pompous ranger lectured, they'd pretend to busy themselves with hidden valves and gauges and so on. They were able to judge the precise moment when the geyser would let go with all its force—it always signaled its intentions with a couple of preliminary puffs of steam. So, at the exact moment, one boy would yell, "Let 'er go, Charlie!" The other would swing the steering wheel vigorously. And the geyser would shoot a hundred and fifty feet into the air. There may still be tourists who believe the Yellowstone geysers are a colossal fraud, operated by an underground steam system.

Some years ago the alumni association of a leading Eastern college held its annual meeting in a New York hotel. The time came for nomination of officers. A man at the side of the room got up and made a short speech, nominating good old Charlie Andrews for president of the association. He said that there wasn't a finer fellow in the whole organization, nay, in the whole wide world, than old Charlie Andrews, and certainly Charlie Andrews worked harder than anybody else for the organization, and even contributed large sums of money out of his own pocket toward the betterment of conditions, and so on. When he sat down a man at the other side of the room got up and loudly seconded the nomination of Charlie Andrews, paying even greater compliments to the man. Within a very few minutes Charlie Andrews had been elected president by acclamation, and the enthusiasm was high for him. There were shouts of "Speech! Speech! We want Charlie Andrews!"

There wasn't any Charlie Andrews. . . .

W. H. De Vere Cole's career as a master prankster began during his student days at Cambridge. He was an excellent actor even in those days.

The dark-skinned Sultan of Zanzibar was visiting in London amid pomp and circumstance. The newspapers were filled with accounts of the endless processions and receptions in the Sultan's honor, and the officials of Cambridge were enchanted when they received a telegram announcing that the distinguished visitor would come to Cambridge for a day.

As the hour for his arrival neared, the Cambridge dignitaries, wearing their finest robes and decorations, gathered at the railway station. Off the train came the Sultan—a prepossssing figure in garments of purple velvet and a turban of the snowiest white. After him came the members of his entourage, also splendidly caparisoned.

The Mayor of Cambridge tendered a scroll of welcome and the party retired in dignity to the Town Hall, where champagne flowed as freely as the purple prose of the speechmakers. There followed a drive around the University and then the royal party took a train back to London.

That evening a touching memento arrived in the hands of the Cambridge officials, a gift from the Sultan himself. On the card he had written in his own hand: "The dorsal fin from the Sacred Shark of Zanzibar—a token of everlasting remembrance."

The Sultan got off the train at the next station and, after a thorough washing, became W. H. De Vere Cole. His attendants were other Cambridge students. The costumes were shipped back to the theatrical shop where they had been hired, and the boys returned to the routine of student life. The hoax was discovered at once, for the real Sultan had never left London, but Cole and his cronies escaped detection. Their part in the affair was not revealed until after they had finished college. . . .

At Cornell University, Hugh Troy was in the School of Architecture. There was one professor who was continually complaining about the weakness of the ceiling in the room where he taught. He demanded that the school authorities repair and reinforce that ceiling before it fell in on himself and his students. One night Hugh and a few of his cronies crept into the place, carrying ladders and other equipment. Hugh mounted a ladder and painted a large black, jagged hole on the ceiling. Then the boys piled plaster and splinters and other debris around the floor, and departed. The following morning the professor arrived, took one horrified look at the ceiling and the general wreckage, and went scampering off to the Building and Grounds Office, full of indignant I-told-you-sos. The instant he left, in came Hugh Troy and his friends. The black paint on the ceiling was quickly removed, and the debris cleaned up. And back came the professor with the head of the Building and Grounds Office. It is said that the professor used language somewhat alien to the science of architecture.

There was an enormous pipe organ in Bailey Hall, the auditorium where many of the University's principal functions were held. Hugh considered this massive instrument for a long while before devising a proper handling of it. He had to enlist the organist in the conspiracy. Then he built an extra pipe for the organ, bigger than the biggest of all the other pipes, and covered it with gilt paint and set it up so that it wouldn't look conspicuous. All this work was performed during the night preceding a day when there was to be a large and dignified ceremony in the Hall.

In the midst of the big meeting the organist was to render a number. He got well into it when, apparently, he discovered a certain mechanical difficulty. He'd press down on one key and an awful sound, a sort of bray, would come from the pipes. He pretended to be embarrassed, and started over again, but at the same point he'd run into the horribly faulty note. Finally, without consulting the chairman, he stepped to a rear entrance and returned with half a dozen workmen–actually Hugh Troy and his friends. He pointed excitedly to the pipes, finally singling out the biggest of them all. The workmen flung up a couple of ladders and attacked the big pipe, wrenching it loose. It fell to the floor with a crash, breaking open, and out of it came live chickens, ducks, pigeons, and assorted other fowl, both wild and domestic.

Troy and his gang went to great length and considerable expenditure of money sometimes to have their fun. During the period when Lindbergh and the others were making a big thing out of transatlantic flights, Hugh and his friends created a lot of excitement for one day in Ithaca. The wreckage of an airplane was found in a field near the town. Assorted cheeses were scattered over the field, and also a number of letters and other documents. The papers showed that the plane had flown non-stop from Amsterdam, Holland, bound for Amsterdam, New York, bearing good will and cheese. The boys had done a first-rate job of creating airplane wreckage without an airplane.

The best of all Troy jokes at Cornell, in my estimation, was the rhinoceros joke. Visiting one day in the home of the artist Fuertes, Hugh noticed a wastepaper basket fashioned from the foot of a rhinoceros. He borrowed the thing from Fuertes and then waited for the proper weather conditions. On a night when a couple of inches of snow had fallen, Hugh and one of his friends went out on the campus with the rhinoceros foot. They had filled it with scrap metal to give it weight, and they had attached a length of clothesline to either side of it. Now they moved across the campus, each holding an end of the clothesline at a distance of perhaps thirty feet from the rhinoceros foot. Carefully they raised it and lowered it to make rhinoceros tracks at the proper intervals in the snow.

When the campus awoke the next morning the strange tracks were found. Professors who knew about animals were summoned, and they inspected the tracks, and exclaimed over them. "Gad, Whitley!" they cried. "It's a *rhinoceros!*"

The trail of the rhinoceros was followed. It led across the campus and down to the shore of Beebee Lake, from which the University gets its water supply. The lake was frozen over, and the rhinoceros tracks led out across the ice to a point about fifty feet from shore and ended at a large gaping hole. Clearly the vagrant rhinoceros had wandered onto the ice too far, and crashed through and drowned.

There wasn't much to be done about it. The local newspapers trumpeted the story, and almost at once half the population of Cornell quit drinking tap water. Those who continued to drink it swore they could taste rhinoceros in it. And then, after a few days, Troy let the word get out that the whole thing was a joke—without, of course, any clue to the identity of the jokers.

FOOTBALL GIRL*

BY KATHARINE BRUSH

"It's cold in this stadium," said the girl behind me.

She had a slow little voice, clear and sweet, with a trace of Southern accent. Just a trace. You thought perhaps she visited in Macon or in Memphis—it was that much of an accent and no more. She had just arrived at her seat, escorted by a long-legged undergraduate in a ponderous black bearskin coat. They were late. The game had begun some moments before.

I knew what she looked like though I did not turn around. I had watched her coming up the steps. Everybody in thirty rows had watched her. She was that sort of girl. Little she was, and slim in a coat of soft tan fur, belted tight at the waist with broad brown leather. The collar of the coat was high and puffy and immense: it held her face as velvet holds a jewel. She was very young. She could not have been more than sixteen or seventeen. An exquisite child, with black hair curling under a tight hat, with a spoiled red mouth, with extravagant dark blue eyes. The eyes were older than the girl. They were adult with self-assurance. They had a lazy stare for the staring world.

The boy was mad about her. He had looked it, coming up the steps —though he had tried hard not to, he had looked almost fatuously proud.

Now, when she remarked that it was cold in this stadium, he repeated, "Cold?" in instantaneous alarm.

"Wait!" he said. "Wait'll I get this ole robe unfolded. You won't be cold with this ole robe around you."

"My face will be," she said.

On the field a halfback made a gain of thirteen yards.

"Lift your feet a minute," said the boy, "while I tuck it under. "There! How's that? Okay?"

"I guess so."

"Warm enough now?"

"Maybe I will be in a minute," she said doubtfully.

In a minute she said: "It's cold underneath, that's the trouble. It's sitting on this icy cold stone."

"Well here," said the boy. "Sit on one of these programs. Get up a minute—now try that."

"That's slick," said the girl. "And let's put another one under where my feet are, hmmm'm, Jake? Because my feet always practically freeze."

"They're so little," the boy said, in the voice of one bent double. "There now!" he added more clearly. "Now you're all set."

"Um-hmmm. Now I am. What's the score?"

"Nothing to nothing."

"Oh," said the girl, "then we're not really late. You kept saying we were going to be late."

"Well, we were, a little."

"I'm never late," the girl said dreamily.

The boy did not answer. *"Watch that pass!"* he shouted hoarsely instead. *"Watch it!"*

"Look," said the girl. "Before you get all excited, may I please have one of your cigarettes?"

"Ye-e-eah!" the boy was yelling. "Get 'im! Nail 'im! *Ye-e-eah!* What's trouble, baby?" he added softly.

"I want a cigarette."

"Oh, gosh," said the boy, "now where did I— Wait a minute."

"Ye-e-eah!" he cried again, but faintly now.

He began a subdued muttering. "Wallet," he said. "Keys. Lighter. Handkerchief. 'Nother handkerchief. Powder—here's your powder gadget, Judy. And here's your purse, and here's your comb. And your rouge or whatnot. But where in hell're the cigarettes?"

"Isn't my lipstick there?" the girl asked anxiously.

"I'll look."

"I never saw so many pockets."

The cigarettes were finally found, but the rejoicing was halfhearted. The lipstick, it appeared, was missing still.

"It was one I bought in Paris," the girl said sadly. "And now it's gone goodness knows where through a hole in your pocket."

"But I tell you it couldn't've, honey! This is a new suit!"

"It was a new lipstick. It was a bra——"

"Here it is!" he crowed triumphantly. "I've got it!"

"Oh, good. I'm so glad."

"Here, take it," said the boy. "Don't you want it?"

"Uh-uh," said the girl. "Not now. I just wanted to be sure it wasn't lost. . . . Look, Jake. This lighter won't light in this wind."

"Sure it will. Give it here."

"I told you," the girl said presently. "Haven't you got some matches?"

Matches were borrowed, and many were scratched in succession. This took some time, and a touchdown was meanwhile made by the visiting team. In the accompanying tumult the girl's small voice was lost to me. I thought she was saying, "Try putting your head inside your coat and lighting it, why don't you?" But I could not be sure.

The first quarter ended shortly. The boy, withdrawing his gaze from the sky, where he had been urged to direct it with a view to determine whether it wasn't really terribly, terribly dangerous for that airplane to be swooping down so low over all these people—the boy remarked the end of the first quarter with surprise.

"Say," he said, "it's the quarter already."

"Oh, is it?" said the girl. "Well, now's our chance to fix this robe. I didn't tell you, but I've been getting chillier by the minute."

"Say! You haven't!"

"Oh, it'll be all right when we fix it," she assured him soothingly. "The trouble is that it's *over* me and then tucked under, instead of *under* me and then wrapped *over*. Do you see what I mean?"

He did. He was able to fix it in a little less than four minutes.

"There!" said the girl. "That's marvelous! I won't be cold now. . . . Oh, look, they're all playing down our end of the field."

"You bet they are!" said the boy. "And we're going to score—we're gonna *sco-o-ore—— There you* GO!" he howled. "THERE YOU—— Oh, tough. Tough. *Hard luck, Red, old boy. Next time!*" He beat his hollowed gloved palms together once, making a loud report. "*Come on,* TEAM!"

"Jake," said the girl. "I smell something burning."

"What?"

"I smell something burning. I think the robe must be on fire. I think," said the girl, "we must have wrapped my cigarette up in it."

It turned out after a wild interval that she was partly right, though only partly. It was her cigarette, but it was the robe of the gentleman next to her.

"What a time!" she sighed exhaustedly, when it was all over and the boy was carefully wrapping her up again. "After that, I'll have to have my make-up, please, Jake. Not the rouge, just the powder and lipstick."

"You look all right," he demurred. "You look great."

"Oh no, I don't. I'm all hot and bothered. Such a horrible, mean old man I never did see in all my days," she added clearly.

"Hush!" said the boy. "Here! Here's your things!"

"And may I have your hanky? Because mine must have blown away."

Her next remark was about a cheerleader. It was her most enthusiastic remark so far, though it was brief. It was, "Oh, looky! Who's *he?*"

"Who?"

"That cheerleader!"

"Oh, him," said the boy. "I believe his name's Adams or something. Or maybe it's Andrews. Something like that."

"But I want to *know,* Jake!"

"What for?" Jake asked suspiciously.

"I just do. Listen, wouldn't it be in the program somewhere?"

The boy didn't think so.

"Well, look and see, silly!" the girl suggested sweetly, adding: "You can take the one that's under my feet. It isn't keeping them a bit warm."

The search for the cheerleader occupied the boy for quite a while. He said nothing, but he was to be heard turning pages rapidly. "Don't go so fast," the girl said once, and once she accused him of skipping. She had previously explained that she herself would look through the program—"only my hands would freeze if I didn't keep them in my sleeves."

There were several interruptions. Once the girl sneezed, a tiny sneeze like a little cat's, and the boy was obliged to produce his handkerchief again in a hurry. "And the powder again, too," said the girl. "Oh, and the lipstick! Because look, it all rubbed off on your handkerchief."

Somewhat later she said suddenly and pitifully, "I'm hungry."

The boy stopped turning pages. "Hungry?" he said. "But you just had lunch!"

"I didn't have anything but that old salad."

"Well," said the boy, "can you wait until between the halves? I can get you a hot dog or something then."

"I suppose I can if I have to," the girl said. "But I'm awfully hungry."

"Well, shall I go out now and try to find something? I will if you say so, only you'll be all alone——"

"No," sighed the girl. "I'll wait."

"But I'm awfully hungry," she added low, a moment later.

"Smoke another cigarette," said the boy. "Maybe that'll help."

"All right," said the girl. "You light me one."

The intermittent hissing of matches began again.

"Look at that child," the girl observed, in the midst of it.

"Where?"

"Two rows down. Climbing all over his father's lap. Can't you see him?"

It was a little bundled red-faced boy about five years old, with the feather of his father's alma mater in the cap.

"Imagine bringing a child that age to a football game!" the girl said. "Imagine *bothering!*"

The youth agreed with her. It was plain from his tone that he wagged his head.

"Can you beat it?" he demanded solemnly.

HOMER AND HUMBUG, AN ACADEMIC DISCUSSION*

BY STEPHEN LEACOCK

I do not mind confessing that for a long time past I have been very sceptical about the classics. I myself was trained as a classical scholar. It seemed the only thing to do with me. I acquired such a singular facility in handling Latin and Greek that I could take a page of either of them, distinguish which it was by merely glancing at it, and, with the help of a dictionary and a pair of compasses, whip off a translation of it in less than three hours.

But I never got any pleasure from it. I lied about it. At first, perhaps, I lied through vanity. Later on I lied through habit; later still because, after all, the classics were all that I had and so I valued them. I have seen thus a deceived dog value a pup with a broken leg, and a pauper

* From *Laugh with Leacock*, copyright, 1930, by Dodd, Mead & Company, Inc. Reprinted by permission.

child nurse a dead doll with the sawdust out of it. So I nursed my dead Homer and my broken Demosthenes though I knew in my heart that there was more sawdust in the stomach of one modern author than in the whole lot of them. Observe, I am not saying which it is that has it full of it.

So, as I say, I began to lie about the classics. I said to people who knew no Greek that there was a sublimity, a majesty about Homer which they could never hope to grasp. I said it was like the sound of the sea beating against the granite cliffs of the Ionian Esophagus; or words to that effect. As for the truth of it, I might as well have said it was like the sound of a rum distillery running a night shift on half time. At any rate this is what I said about Homer, and when I spoke of Pindar—the dainty grace of his strophes—and Aristophanes, the delicious sallies of his wit, sally after sally, each sally explained in a note calling it a sally—I managed to suffuse my face with an animation which made it almost beautiful.

I admitted of course that Virgil in spite of his genius had a hardness and a cold glitter which resembled rather the brilliance of a cut diamond than the soft grace of a flower. Certainly I admitted this: the mere admission of it would knock the breath out of anyone who was arguing.

From such talks my friends went away sad. The conclusion was too cruel. It had all the cold logic of a syllogism (like that almost brutal form of argument so much admired in the Paraphernalia of Socrates). For if:

Virgil and Homer and Pindar had all this grace, and pith, and these sallies,
And I read Virgil and Homer and Pindar,
And if they only read Mrs. Wharton and Mrs. Humphry Ward,
Then where were they?

So continued lying brought its own reward in the sense of superiority and I lied more.

When I reflect that I have openly expressed regret, as a personal matter, even in the presence of women, for the missing books of Tacitus, and the entire loss of the Abracadabra of Polyphemus of Syracuse, I can find no words in which to beg for pardon. In reality I was just as much worried over the loss of the ichthyosaurus. More, indeed. I'd like to have seen it: but if the books Tacitus lost were like those he didn't, I wouldn't.

I believe all scholars lie like this. An ancient friend of mine, a clergyman, tells me that in Hesiod he finds a peculiar grace that he doesn't find elsewhere. He's a liar. That's all. Another man, in politics and in the legislature, tells me that every night before going to bed he reads over a page or two of Thucydides to keep his mind fresh. Either he never goes to bed or he's a liar. Doubly so; no one could read Greek at that frantic rate; and anyway his mind isn't fresh. How could it be, he's in the legislature. I don't object to this man talking freely of the classics, but he ought to keep it for the voters. My opinion is that before he goes to bed he takes whiskey: why call it Thucydides?

I know there are solid arguments advanced in favor of the classics. I often hear them from my colleagues. My friend the professor of Greek tells me that he truly believes the classics have made him what he is. This is a very grave statement, if well founded. Indeed I have heard the same argument from a great many Latin and Greek scholars. They all claim, with some heat, that Latin and Greek have practically made them what they are. This damaging charge against the classics should not be too readily accepted. In my opinion some of these men would have been what they are no matter what they were. . . .

This is what I should like to do. I'd like to take a large stone and write on it in very plain writing:

"The classics are only primitive literature. They belong in the same class as primitive machinery and primitive music and primitive medicine." And then throw it through the windows of a University and hide behind a fence to see the professors buzz!!

FROM *THE HERMAN HICKMAN READER**

BY HERMAN HICKMAN

Heywood Broun, the famous columnist of years ago, told me this story: The incident happened at a combined Harvard-Yale dinner and, of course, this oldest of all rivalries is a very warm one. A Yale man told a story about a brave Yale football captain saving a crippled newsboy's life when he had fallen in front of a streetcar in New Haven on a frozen, slippery day. The brave Yale football captain rushed out and picked up the newsboy just in the nick of time and saved his life. Heywood Broun, a Harvard man, said this was nothing. Practically the same event had taken place at Harvard, except that instead of it being a cold day, there was a blizzard blowing, and instead of it being a street-car, it was a fast interurban moving at sixty miles an hour, and instead of it being a crippled newsboy, a mother had been crossing the street and she slipped and she and her little baby had fallen on the track before the onrushing interurban car, and instead of it being the captain of the Harvard team, a substitute end of the Harvard junior varsity rushed out, and instead of picking up the baby and the mother who had fallen on the tracks—he tackled the interurban car and threw it for a 100-yard loss!

I had a close friend by the name of Petie Jackson, who is dead now, but used to be one of the finest small-college coaches in the country. He had a great record at little Emory and Henry College in Virginia, in both football and basketball, and also at King College in Bristol, Tennessee. Petie didn't weigh but about one hundred and thirty pounds soaking wet, but he was quite a disciplinarian and really drove the big mountain boys on his football squad to the limit. During one of his games things had been going pretty badly in the first half, particularly for his big two hundred and thirty pound tackle who was having a very poor day, so Petie hopped on him in the dressing room. He said, "Why you big so-and-so. If I were as big and strong as you are, I would tear that other team apart," and continuing said, "If I were as big and strong as you are and weighed two hundred and thirty pounds, I would be the heavyweight champion of the world." Without batting an eye the big tackle looked down at little Petie and said slowly but respectfully, "Well, Coach, what is wrong with you being the lightweight champion?"

I am afraid that pep talks don't have too much effect any more, but I was giving one several years ago during the half of the Harvard-Yale football game, and it went something like this: Y is for youth and and that is something all of you have; A is for alma mater, and that is what we are fighting for today; L is for loyalty, loyalty to your team; loyalty to your school; E is for effort, the extra effort that it takes to win that ball game. Put them all together and you have YALE. Now, let's go out there and tear them apart in the second half!

I opened the door and we started down the runway to the Bowl. I was very well satisfied with the fact that I had gotten my team into a fighting mood when I overheard a couple of the linemen talking behind me. One of them said, "I'm sure glad that old Herman isn't coaching at MASSACHUSETTS INSTITUTE OF TECHNOLOGY, or we never would get this second half started."

In 1949 I had a mighty fine guard at Yale named Bud Philipp, and I never will forget that September, when we were having our preseason workouts, I was giving the team the customary lecture after lunch. The boys had gotten up early, already had a morning workout, and after a rather heavy lunch they were usually sleepy. This particular day I was talking to the squad on the importance of the line in football, and as I remember it, I said: "It is up in the line, where the guards and tackles are, where the men are, that the games are won or lost." I noticed that Bud Philipp had fallen asleep and I hollered out, "Philipp, where are most games lost?"—and Bud woke up suddenly and said, "Here at Yale, Coach."

During the 1950 season we were playing Cornell up at Ithaca, and although we were doing well on defense, we just couldn't seem to get our offensive plays clicking. Finally we got a break, and our halfback ran 55 yards for a touchdown, but just as I was getting excited the referee gave the signal for backfield in motion, nullifying the touchdown run. He also started pacing off the 5-yard penalty. I ran out on the field protesting as loudly as I could, and said, "What team are you on? It is hard enough to beat Cornell without having the referee playing for them." I kept standing there while he walked off the 5-yard penalty. Finally I shouted at him: "You stink!" and instead of stopping at 5 yards he paced off an additional 15 yards, and turned around and looked back at me and said, "How do I smell from here, Hickman?"

The moral of the story is: "The men in white are always right."

The next year things were going badly, as usual, against Princeton. Yale would fumble the ball, and Princeton would recover. Princeton would fumble, and Princeton would recover. We would make 10 yards on an off-tackle play and then be penalized 15 yards for illegal use of the hands. Nothing that we could do was right. Finally I became so disgusted that I shouted to Jim Ryan, our quarterback, and said, "Go ahead and kick the ball, Jim. They aren't going to give us anything anyway." The referee heard me and walked over to where I was sitting and he said: "That is going to cost you, Hickman. Coaching from the sidelines." He took the ball and walked off ten yards. I jumped off the bench and ran out on the field and said, "Why you dumb so-and-so, you don't even know that coaching from the sidelines is a 15-yard penalty!" He turned around to me and said, "Listen, Hickman, for the kind of coaching you are doing, it is just 10 yards."

THINGS USED TO BE DIFFERENT*

BY ALONZO CLARK ROBINSON

I was engaged in a desperate struggle to get into Yale before all my friends graduated.

The entrance exams were held in the Y.M.C.A. building at the corner of Fourth Avenue and Twenty-third Street and I had taken them so many times that when I appeared the fellow at the door said, "Just take your same old seat, please."

Finally they did let me in—class of '98—with the limit of conditions. I suppose they got tired of seeing me around. The outlook wasn't too bright and everybody expected to see me back in New York by Christmas, but when I got to New Haven I learned a lot of things I didn't know before. I saw at once that if you expected to stay in Yale in 1894 you had to do one of two things—either be a brilliant scholar or attend all the recitations. This left me no choice. The brilliant-scholar role was quite impossible.

I had entered Yale for the sole purpose of having a good time, and not, as my father put it, to prepare myself for life's battle. As a matter of fact I didn't expect to have any battle with life, so why prepare for it? That meant I had to discover some method which would allow me to stay in college without doing any work.

I determined to play the part of the dumb and earnest student. I attended all the recitations and when called upon to recite I never said "Unprepared." I always got up and always got sat down. Then when the class was over I would go up to the professor and ask the stupidest questions I could think of. Tell him how much I wanted to understand but just couldn't do it. I'd keep him there talking for fifteen minutes or so. After a while most of them got so bored with this performance and being late for lunch, or wherever they were going, that they only called on me about once a month. This method together with a very high stand in French and English got me by. Not that I did any studying in these subjects either but I spoke French from childhood and had been brought up on Shakespeare which appealed highly to our English professor, Billy Phelps.

The now celebrated Dr. William Lyon Phelps was the youngest and most popular professor at Yale. His classes were so entertaining that students went to them who didn't have to. That was unheard of and got him in bad with some of the other professors. . . .

However, neither Billy Phelps nor anybody else could have pulled me through if I hadn't had a break on the Greek exam. I knew as much Greek as my dog. "From thence they marched forward five parasangs," was all I could recognize. I was saved by a miracle.

Here's what happened. About half an hour before we were due to show up for the exam, I was having my shoes shined in the shoe-shining emporium on Chapel Street, and right next to me sat the Greek professor. Just by chance I looked in his direction and there was a paper sticking out of his side pocket. Only the top was showing, but that was enough. I distinctly saw the number of the chapter and verse. I shoved away the boy who was working on my shoes and started for Vanderbilt Hall, across the street, on the dead run. I didn't have time to go to my place but I knew that Jimmy Wadsworth and Freddie Kernochan were in their room on the top floor.

When I burst in on them they were sitting on the window seat disconsolate. They had about decided not even to go to the exam.

I said, "Come on, boys, get out the trot. I know what the exam's going to be." We only had about twenty minutes and we didn't know how far the text went—as a matter of fact I translated much more than was on the paper; and did that take some explaining!

Dear old Yale today is just about as much like what it used to be as nothing at all. We none of us had any money, and those who did have wouldn't dare spend it. . . . Of course there weren't any automobiles. That meant that all the fun went on right in town. This isn't strictly true. Some of us liked to spend a weekend in New York if we could scrape up the necessary—ten dollars was considered ample. There was a boat called the *Richard Peck* which left New Haven at twelve o'clock Friday night. By taking one or two cuts Saturday you could get aboard and have two days in the big city.

A lot of funny things happened on the *Peck*. Sometimes you found yourself aboard when you didn't mean to. I remember one Sunday morning when to my astonishment I woke up sitting on a bench in Madison Square. According to all I could remember I should have been in Boston, but there I was right in front of Dr. Parkhurst's church, and the people were just going in. It came to me that my family had a pew, so I thought I'd go in and say hello. They were surprised and I hope delighted to see me and they said, "Sit down and keep quiet if you can." Anyway there was nothing boring about listening to Dr. Parkhurst. He was heading a vice crusade and he liked to tell his congregation all about it.

It's not quite clear in my mind why we were always trying to get to New York. The beer wasn't any better than in New Haven and the trip cost money. Probably it was Jack's. That was a restaurant on Sixth Avenue between Forty-third and Forty-fourth Streets kept by an Irishman by the name of Jack Dunston. There was an oyster bar in the front and about a dozen tables in the back. He called it a chop-house. It was open as long as anybody wanted to stay. In the course of time it expanded and became the most celebrated after-dinner place in the city. . . .

There was one grave danger connected with our trips to New York and that was missing the milk train back. It left the Grand Central at 3 A.M. and landed you in New Haven just in time to make chapel at 8:10. If you didn't get it that meant three cuts Monday morning and the finish.

The regular procedure at the Grand Central was for those who arrived in good shape to institute a search through the whole place, to see if there wasn't a comrade asleep somewhere who would miss the train without succor. The conductor was used to us and he made a point of seeing that all hands got off safely. I'll never forget how you felt after sleeping four or five hours in one of those regular passenger-coach seats.

It's a funny thing but I haven't the faintest recollection of what the Grand Central Station looked like, either outside or in. I remember just before you got there you came through a thing called the tunnel where everybody nearly choked, and I have a hazy idea that the platforms were made of wood, but I can't resurrect a picture of the place. I know it was about the size of a way station today.

I haven't thought of it before but that train was never late. Some divine dispensation, I suppose.

Those who didn't have the price of a hack had to walk and that meant missing chapel but they could still make recitation.

Those Monday morning recitations were something fierce. I remember once when Billy Phelps called on Gib Hinsdale in the Shakespeare class. Gib struggled to his feet and remained perfectly dumb looking at his book.

"Well," said Phelps, "Mr. Hinsdale, can't you read?"

"No, sir," said Gib, and sat down. . . .

I remember one year when we played football at Cambridge. Payne Whitney got himself a private car and invited about twenty of his classmates to go and see the game. We left New Haven the afternoon before and the idea was to sleep in the car and start from there the next morning. It didn't entirely work out to schedule but the idea was sound.

In Boston the night before the game the rival collegians met at the Adams House. And it was packed. I don't know what happened to the guests. This year I'm talking about we had a fellow with us by the name of Willie Thompson. He'd saved up a lot of money to bet on the game, say a hundred dollars. After dinner we all went up to the Adams House. The odds were 8 to 5 that Harvard would win. I don't exactly know what happened, whether it was liquor or some fundamental defect but later in the evening there was a commotion and when things got sorted out we found that Willie had gone in and bet his hundred at 2 to 1 that Harvard wouldn't score. Well, that was just one of those things. Too bad, but nothing to be done about it. So we returned to the bar.

Next morning when we got Willie awake—he was one of the ones who came back to the car—and convinced him what he had done he was most disturbed. But he got the old bean working and decided the only thing to do was to hedge. He borrowed another hundred from Payne and went back to the Adams House. He said he was going up there to hedge his bet. Nobody could figure out how he was going to do it and he didn't say. What he actually did was to bet 2 to 1 that Yale wouldn't score. I can see him now sitting in the grandstand eating grapes—that was all he could get down—with only the haziest idea where he was and none at all of the position into which he had maneuvered himself.

Well, the score was nothing, nothing! . . .

The stretch from the Christmas holidays till the beginning of spring was pretty dull, especially if you were broke, which was very apt to be the case. We tried everything we could think of to break monotony. Once we had a cockfight.

The Sage brothers, Heff, Andy, and Witt, had a big farm especially for the breeding of real gamecocks. Each bird had his little house—there were rows and rows of them—and a name just like a race horse. There were trained men to take care of them and they were worth a lot of money. We didn't know all this at the time and Hinsdale thought Witt was just showing off. He talked so much about his gamecocks that Gib got fed up. He said he'd get a bird from his own old ancestral farm in Hinsdale, Massachusetts, and fight him for money. He didn't believe Witt's birds were as good as he said they were.

I forget where Gib actually did get his rooster but the next thing I knew there he was in the clothes closet. I didn't know a thing about gamecocks but this one didn't look so hot to me. All he wanted to do was sleep. He wasn't any trouble so long as the door was closed but the moment you opened it to get something he'd start in to crow. You could hear him clear out in Chapel Street. I suppose he thought it was sunrise. We were scared to death somebody would hear him and investigate and we had no idea what we'd say if they did. He didn't do the clothes any good either.

We kept the whole thing as dark as we could for we had an idea that it wouldn't be received with enthusiasm by the dean. Still a rumor did get around. I think the colored boy who looked after our room was responsible. Naturally he had discovered the fowl and we had to tell him all about it.

We made arrangements with a farmer about a mile out of town to use his barn, and one night about twenty chosen companions set out in the snow to walk there. Witt had his bird in a swell basket made on purpose but Gib carried his in a sack. I didn't like the look of things and told Gib so but he said he knew a stouthearted bird when he saw one and that I was a quitter, so just to satisfy him I had to put a small bet down against my better judgment.

The temperature was about zero and I was afraid our champion would come out of the sack frozen stiff. When we shook him out and

I saw he could almost stand up it was a great relief. Witt's bird seemed to be feeling the weather too, so the farmer said we could take them to his kitchen and thaw them out.

On arriving at the barn we had found a number of the farmer's friends plus a whole crowd of darkies our boy had collected. We didn't like the idea of having so many witnesses if things got hot, but what could we do? They wouldn't leave.

It was so cold in that barn that the breath from the crowd looked like a fog. But even with the low visibility—there were only a couple of lanterns—we decided to go ahead. There was great excitement, especially among the blacks. They all bet on us, out of a sentiment of loyalty, I suppose. Though I will say that side by side our bird showed up just as good as Witt's, better, if anything, to the untrained eye.

I wouldn't be surprised if Gib was right about that rooster. I believe he was stouthearted if he had been given a chance to show it. Anyway he certainly was out of luck.

I don't know if you have ever seen a cockfight. I hadn't at that time. They fasten some sort of a gadget like a knife to the bird's ankles so when he hops on the other fellow he gives him a slash. I have since learned that this is called heeling. Gib said he knew all about heeling a bird and as it was a sure thing nobody else did we had to let him do it. That was a fatal error. He put the spurs, or whatever they're called, on wrong—turned in or something—and at the very first pass our boy made at the other he cut his own head off clean as a whistle.

We hoisted the protest flag right away but it was no go. We had to pay up.

Sometime during the winter term of freshman year Gib and I held a contest which created no little interest even among the upper classmen. We each bet the other he couldn't drink a keg of beer in six hours. There were exactly fifty-three glasses in the kind of keg we had in mind so the contest became known as the fight of the fifty-three beers.

According to the rules we made up we had to do all the drinking at the same place and start at the same time. If either one of us was unable to finish the fifty-three glasses in six hours he lost.

We each had two seconds. They were there to see that we got home dead or alive. Outside of that they couldn't interfere. Ruffy King was appointed umpire. His job was to keep track of the glasses and the time, and see that each glass was the same, had the regulation amount of foam, etc., also that every one was emptied to the last drop. The bartender had to sign the record too.

We elected to hold the bout at the Lyons Park Hotel, a roadhouse a little way out of town toward the field and to begin at 3 P.M. so there would be no more recitations that day.

The local interest ran high and there was a good deal of money bet, mostly that neither one of us would finish. They were all wet. It was a cinch. I made my expenses for the rest of the term out of that stunt.

We chose entirely different methods. Gib figured that he had to drink fifty-three beers in three hundred and sixty minutes; that was approximately one beer every six and three fourths minutes. He called it six minutes to be on the safe side. It only takes about five seconds to put down a glass of beer and it sounded easy. So it would have been with twenty beers but when you come to drag it out for six hours that is different again.

My system was to drink as fast as I could for the first hour and then take a rest.

I got through twenty-one, which was a shade better than one every three minutes and put me ten ahead of Gib. I've got the official record somewhere, signed by Ruffy and the bartender, and on it is marked the number of times I was sick in that first hour. I can't find the paper but my recollection is it was about three times. Then I went and took a walk and when I came back it was just as if I hadn't had a drink.

The rest of the time I just coasted and finished with a lot to spare.

I believe if Gib had stuck to his schedule he wouldn't have made it. That six minute interval which was pie at first began to get awful short. He went to sleep a couple of times and according to the rules his seconds couldn't wake him up. But when he saw how things were going he pulled himself together and sped it up. That made him sick and he was all right. He got under the wire handily so there was no victory, one side or the other. We went down to Polis Wonderland Theater and were at chapel next morning feeling as usual. . . .

In the middle of junior year an event occurred which very nearly put an end to our college careers. Some fifteen of us formed an eating club at old Mrs. Swift's boardinghouse. As I remember, the price was eight dollars per week, three meals a day, and the food wasn't bad. Maybe we could have done better somewhere else but we liked the old girl and she liked us, so we stuck. For breakfast and lunch we were in a hurry but after dinner we used to sit around and talk. There was a premium on repartee. We had a gold brick—the gold being gold foil—which was presented to whoever laid himself open to a smart remark; and he had to keep it by his plate till he could get the laugh on somebody else. We called this "passing the brick." Everybody was lying in wait for everybody else and there were some pretty sharp tongues in that crowd. I think Mr. Gouverneur Morris and Mr. James Wadsworth were the best at it. They never got the brick that I can remember.

Another exciting pastime we invented was the toothpick game. Everybody took a wooden toothpick, dipped it in butter, and then threw it up against the ceiling. If it didn't stick you were out of luck right away, but most of them stuck. The heat of the room would gradually melt the butter and finally they'd fall down. The fellow whose toothpick stayed up the longest got the pot. Mrs. Swift objected to this form of amusement on account of the dripping butter and we had to give it up. . . .

But the most important and the most celebrated thought we ever had was the Corbett Club. As a matter of fact we didn't know at the time we had formed it.

James J. Corbett was about to fight Robert Fitzsimmons for the heavyweight championship of the world, somewhere out West—Carson City, I think. Of course the topic was of major importance. We favored Corbett to a man and somebody said he thought it would be a good idea to write him a letter and tell him so. This met with instant approval and after due consideration we wrote, "The heart of every Yale man is with you in your grand battle of the seventeenth." Then just to clinch matters we sent along a Yale flag and all hands signed the letter.

The first thing that broke was that all the papers came out with our letter on the front page. Then Corbett made a speech and said how proud he was and that he was going to have that Yale flag in his corner on the day of the fight. Wow! Did things get hot! Anson Phelps Stokes, who headed the Y.M.C.A. minority, got right up on his hind legs. What he said about us was nobody's business. But the faculty didn't need anyone to push 'em. Without a moment's hesitation they suspended every man who had signed that letter—all the names were there in the newspaper so there was no getting away from it—and they began considering if they wouldn't fire us for good and all. Some of the boys were panic-stricken and nobody was pleased. We had to admit we'd overdone it. Right away the fathers began taking a hand. It all seems too ridiculous today, but, believe it or not, then a prize fighter and a horse thief were just about on the same level. He's not exactly a Bourbon today but he's not an outcast.

It's an actual fact that the faculty maintained that Yale had been disgraced and unless something was done about it no respectable family would ever send their boy there again. Fortunately, there was one member of the faculty, Billy Phelps, who didn't entirely share this view.

The fathers got together and brought pressure. There was a lot of weight behind 'em. Their contention was that it was only a joke and why make a mountain out of a molehill. We were only boys and if we apologized that was all there was to it. But the stout fellows like Payne Whitney, Jimmy Wadsworth, and Jim Rogers flatly refused to apologize. We held a meeting up in Jimmy's room in Vanderbilt Hall while the fathers sat across the street in the New Haven House. They had wanted to be present at our meeting but Payne said "No." Some of the boys were pretty scared and some of the fathers pretty mad. There was a lot of discussion but Jimmy got the massive brain to work and put the thing in a nutshell. We had no right to act for the college. We had no right to send a flag and we would write a letter retracting all that part of it. But we had a right to our personal opinion. If we believed in prize fighting and liked a prize fighter we proposed to say so as individuals and we'd stand on that. If they wanted to fire us on those grounds they could go ahead. "And," said Jimmy, "they won't dare do it." He was right.

I can't think of anything that indicates more clearly the difference between yesterday and today than the Corbett Club affair. Nobody objects to going to a fight now, except for the price—lots of ladies do it —but then it was just one step above going to a fast house.

When the faculty got down to cases they found out they were going to make an awful hole in the class of '98—the prospective captains of the football and baseball teams and the crew, plus a lot of social prominence. They didn't dare do it. Our letter went through and the incident was closed. The fathers went back home and we went back to recitations. But we considered that we had had a lot of fun and won a moral victory. So we formed the Corbett Club.

FRATERNITY ROW*

BY CHARLES W. MORTON

Every year as the freshman class moves in and unpacks, the Greeks begin winnowing the barbarians along Fraternity Row. Some thousands of "charges" enter the annual ecstasy of self-renewal. The undergraduate of sufficiently bland racial, religious, and financial status awaits the call of brotherhood. The insufficiently bland join the Commons Club or whatever euphemism the college has devised for barb-solidarity. The college president turns resolutely away from the whole subject; these are matters of taste and congeniality for the boys to settle among themselves—and besides, the college could never afford to take over all that real estate at today's prices.

Fraternity Row is a neighborhood of teen-age Little Scorpions Clubs, each with its secret grips, passwords, and recognition signals. It may well be that all fraternities are using the same grip without knowing it; but no matter, since secrets of this caliber, like the mysterious meanings of the Greek letters themselves, can never be divulged, let alone compared. Each group or chapter occupies, or hopes to occupy, a rather more expensive house than it can afford. (Fraternity-house mortgages usually run for a fixed term of, say, two hundred years and represent about 150 per cent of the property's estimated market value as of the spring of 1929.) The local chapter keeps decently to itself, avoiding traffic with neighbor fraternities and above all with the barbs, but it maintains, or would if the occasion arose, a vehemently brotherly relationship with its "affiliated" chapters elsewhere. Thus, whether the college is large or small, the fraternity man can go through it as one entitled not to meet more than forty or fifty other undergraduates. Moreover, he can wear a pin which identifies him as the holder of this privilege. Fraternity meals, like the fraternity mortgage—and probably in consequence of it—are distinctive, and few Americans not confined in a state prison eat anything comparable to them as a steady diet. Consumption of ketchup along Fraternity Row is estimated at 1.27 gallons per week per brother.

By the simple method of Greek letter groupings, the undergraduate

* From *How to Protect Yourself Against Women,* by Charles W. Morton, copyright, 1945, 1946, 1947, 1948, 1949, 1950, 1951, by Charles W. Morton. Published by J. B. Lippincott Company.

can tick off the qualities of the student body in a jiffy, and the social definitions which he learns at this stage will stay with him forever; the Alpha Alphas are grinds; the Beta Betas are a bunch of hicks; all Gamma Gammas are bonehead athletes; Delta Deltas drink too much; Theta Thetas are rich, very well-off; the Phi Phis, a new crowd that used to be a local club, are quite impossible. All non-fraternity men, the culls, would prove to have some extraordinary defect of character if the truth were known.

Beyond what it offers the undergraduate, the college fraternity is highly regarded by manufacturing and retail jewelers, dealers in seed pearls and chip diamonds, and, naturally, by the ketchup industry.

The principal beneficiary of the whole setup, however, is none of these, but an individual known as the executive secretary, perhaps the alumni secretary, of the national fraternity itself. It's a life job, and because no one really knows quite how the executive secretary got it, there is no ready way of getting rid of him and no reason for doing so anyhow. All executive secretaries die in harness, leaving a home in Scardale or Kenilworth, with a three-car garage and a comfortable estate in high-grade securities.

Death must seem a welcome release to the executive secretary, whose entire life is spent in confecting doleful yet enthusiastic appeals for funds. Never was the crisis so dark or the prospect so brilliant for dear old Zeta Zeta—such is the schizoid theme which he is forever restating, in far-flung goat rooms which he visits annually, and in countless mimeographed communications to the graduate brotherhood.

The crisis is just as peculiar to the fraternity system as the food and the mortgage. It never changes and each year it looms again, as predictable as the ocean tides. Word of it comes in the executive secretary's report to the graduates about affairs at their old chapter house. Everything at the house is wonderful, but the graduates themselves are amazingly indifferent to the money needs of the national organization. Without the strong national patterns—lacking which, the secretary declares, no local chapter can keep afloat—the whole fellowship is going to smash.

Here again is one of the mysteries of the fraternity, for it must seem to the graduate that his local chapter is floating very buoyantly indeed, in spite of the woes of the national outfit.

Of all the mysteries of the fraternity system, none is more inexplicable than the complete disappearance of the fraternity man, as such, shortly after his graduation from college. No managing editor was ever heard to say, even in a Hollywood film, "Lead the paper with Himmelfarber's story—he's a Sigma Sigma from the Wingding School of Mines! I understand the Tau Taus were after him, too."

And the hostess still sizes up the extra man in terms of his availability for marriage rather than his Greek letter pedigree. Who ever heard of a fraternity man, even with distress signals flying, beating out a son-in-law for a fat job in the family business?

SWEETNESS AND LIGHT

It always irks me to go to the trouble of making an extremely disagreeable statement only to learn that I should have made a far more disagreeable statement. It's a case of denouncing something on incomplete data and finding out, once the battle has been joined, that the real story is much worse than it had seemed. It makes me feel like a perennial Pollyanna, happens all the time.

I wrote a somewhat negative piece about college fraternities, in the fall of '48. It landed me in heated correspondence, and further inquiry. I found that I had woefully understated fraternity goings on. What I had alleged on information and belief was only about a tenth as rugged as it should have been.

Subsequently, it occurred to me that the virtual disappearance of national fraternities from Harvard was a fine thing, worth looking into. It's still a fine thing in effect but the reasons for it are not quite what I had expected.

National fraternities withered away at Harvard not because they were childish or undemocratic but for other reasons. It seems that "brothers" from newer chapters in newer universities—some of them in the unknown areas west of Albany—began turning up in Cambridge at football games and holiday occasions. The outlanders in their innocence claimed fraternal hospitality in the Harvard chapters in the notion that they were one with the Harvard men, joined in the indissoluble bond of brotherhood. The Harvard brothers lost no time in diabusing their unwelcome relatives of these ideas and in shifting undergraduate club life to a drastically local basis.

How many alumni secretaries broke their picks on the delinquent dues payers of Harvard in the final fade-out will never be known.

WHAT THE COLLEGE INCUBATOR DID FOR ONE MODEST LAMBKIN*

BY GEORGE ADE

One Autumn Afternoon a gray-haired Agriculturist took his youngest Olive Branch by the Hand and led him away to a Varsity. Wilbur was 18 and an Onion. He had outgrown his last year's tunic, and his Smalls were hardly on speaking terms with his Uppers. He had large warty Hands, which floated idly at his sides and his Wrists resembled extra Sets of Knuckles. When he walked, his Legs gave way at the Hinge and he Interfered. On his Head was a little Wideawake with a Buckle at the Side. Mother had bobbed his Hair and rubbed in a little goose grease to make it shine. The Collar that he wore was a size 13, and called the Rollo Shape. It rose to a Height of a half inch above his Neck-Band. For a Cravat he had a piece of watered Silk Ribbon with butterflies on it.

Wilbur had his Money tied up in a Handkerchief and he carried a Paper Telescope, loaded down with one complete Change and a Catalogue of the Institution showing that the Necessary Expenses were not more than $3.40 per week.

As the train pulled away from Pewee Junction, Wilbur began to Leak. Salt Tears trickled down through the Archipelago of Freckles. He wanted to Crawfish, but Paw bought him a box of Crackerjack and told him that if he got an education and improved his Opportunities some day he might be County Superintendent of Schools and his $900 a year just like finding it. So Wilbur sparked up and said he would try and stick it out. He got out the Catalogue and read all of the copper-riveted Rules for the Moral Guidance of Students.

The Curriculum had him scared. He saw that in the next four years he would have to soak up practically all the Knowledge on the Market. But he was cheered to think that if he persevered and got through he would be entitled to wear an Alpaca Coat and a Lawn Tie and teach in the High School, so he took courage and began to notice the Scenery.

Wilbur was planted in a Boarding House guaranteed to provide Wholesome Food and Home Influence. Father went back after making

* From George Ade's *Breaking into Society*, copyright, 1902, 1903, by Robert Howard Russell, and copyright, 1904, by Harper & Brothers.

a final Discourse on the importance of learning most everything in all of the Books.

Nine Months later they were down at the Depot to meet Wilbur. He had written several times, saying he could not find time to come Home, as he was in pursuit of Knowledge every Minute of the Day, and if he left the Track, Knowledge might gain several Laps on him. It looked reasonable, too, for the future Superintendent of Schools had spent $400 for Books, $200 for Scientific Apparatus, and something like $60 for Chemicals to be used in the Laboratory.

When the Train suddenly checked itself, to avoid running past the Town, there came out of the Parlor Car something that looked like Fitz, on account of the Padding in the Shoulders. Just above one ear he wore a dinky Cap about the size of a Postage Stamp. The Coat reached almost to the Hips and was buttoned below. The Trousers had enough material for a Suit. They were reefed to show feverish Socks of a zigzag design. The Shoes were very Bull-Dog and each had a wide Terrace running around it. Father held on to a Truck for Support. Never before had he seen a genuine case of the Inflammatory Rah-Rah.

Wilbur was smoking a dizzy little Pipe from which the Smoke curled upward, losing itself in a copious Forelock that moved gently in the Breeze. Instead of a Collar, Wilbur was wearing a Turkish Towel. He had the Harvard Walk down pat. With both Hands in his Pockets, the one who had been pursuing Knowledge Teetered toward the Author of his Being and said, "How are you, Governor?"

Father was always a Lightning Calculator, and as he stood there trying to grasp and comprehend and mentally close in, as it were, on the Burlap Suit and the Coon Shirt, and the sassy Pipe, something told him that Wilbur would have to Switch if he expected to be County Superintendent of Schools.

"Here are my Checks," said Wilbur, handing over the Brasses. "Have my Trunks, my Golf Clubs, my portable Punching Bag, the Suit-Case, and Hat Boxes sent up to the House right away. Then drive me Home by the Outside Road, because I don't want to meet all those Yaps. They annoy me."

"You'd better git out of that Rig mighty quick if you don't want to be joshed," said his Parent. "Folks around here won't stand for any such fool Regalia, and if you walk like a frozen-toed Hen you'll get some Hot Shots or I miss my Calkilcations."

"Say, Papa, I've been eating Raw Meat and drinking Blood at the Training Table, and I'm on Edge," said Wilbur, expanding his Chest until it bulged out like a Thornton Squash. "If any of these local Georgie Glues try to shoot their Pink Conversation at me I'll toss them up into the trees and let them hang there. I'm the Gazabo that Puts the Shot. Anyone who can trim a Policeman and chuck a Hackman right back into his own Hack and drive off with him doesn't ask for any sweeter Tapioca than one of these Gaffer Greens. The Plowboy who is muscle-bound and full of Pastry will have a Proud Chance any time that he struts across my Pathway. In my Trunks I have 8 suits a little warmer than this one and 47 pairs of passionate Hose. I'm out here to give the Cornfields a Touch of High Life. It's about time that your Chaws had a Glimpse of the Great Outside World. Anyone who gets Fussy about the Color Combinations that I spring from Day to Day will be chopped up and served for Lunch. To begin with, I'm going to teach you and Mother to play Golf. If these Mutts come and lean over the Fence and start to get off their Colored Weekly Jokes we'll fan the Hillside with them."

"What do they teach you up at your School—besides Murder?" inquired the Father. "I thought you wanted to be County Superintendent of Schools?"

"I've outgrown all those two-by-four Ambitions," was the Reply. "I'm going to be on the Eleven next Fall. What more could you ask?"

That very week Wilbur organized a Ball Team that walloped Hickory Creek, Sand Ridge, and Sozzinsville. He had the whole Township with him. Every Cub at Pewee Junction began to wear a Turkish Towel for a Collar and practice the Harvard Walk.

MORAL: A Boy never blossoms into his Full Possibilities until he strikes an Atmosphere of Culture.

APES AND ELMS*

BY HEYWOOD BROUN

New Haven should be gay and all agog after its striking football victory over Harvard. But Yale is gloomy, suspicious and furtive, and all because of a little rumor.

Several years ago a fund was left for the care and rearing of apes by the psychologists of Yale. At first there was a feeling that it might be necessary to lower the entrance requirements, but this scare soon blew over.

Every prospect was pleasing except the climate. The anthropoids could "Boola Boola" with the best of them, but they couldn't stand the chilling breezes from the Sound. Some three years ago the suggestion was made that the colony should be moved to Florida. In fact, an official announcement was made to this effect. There was some comment in the newspaper at the time, in which, as I remember, I joined, offering appropriate condolences to the football coaches.

According to the present rumor, the transfer never took place. The coaches and the psychologists sat down in secret conference, and one of the football men offered a way out of the difficulty. It was a practical suggestion, and the psychologists had never thought of it.

"Africa is a moist, warm country," began the coach.

"Yes," replied one of the professors testily, "and the American Great Lakes are the largest bodies of fresh water in the world. What about it?"

"Just this," said the coach. "When the wind blows free and cold what does a Yale man do?"

"He goes out for hockey," suggested an assistant professor, trying to get into the spirit of the proceedings.

"No, no," said the football mentor; "I mean what does he wear?"

Since the psychologists were all trained observers, it didn't take the head of the department long to answer, "A gray suit of clothes with a thin green stripe, a sweater with a large 'Y', a purple necktie, pink and magenta woolen socks, occasionally underwear—except in Sheff, of course—and a raccoon coat."

"Now you've got it," said the coach.

"You mean that we should give 'Y's to all the anthropoid apes in the Yale ape farm so that they can wear sweaters?" the assistant professor asked. He was a little duller than the rest, which was the reason they made him an assistant professor.

"Not at all," exclaimed the athletic intructor; "that would cheapen the 'Y'. Let them earn it like everyone else. Under proper direction an undergraduate is just as good as the best anthropoid on the campus any day in the week. I mean to give the apes raccoon coats and then who on earth will know the difference?"

"Done and done," cried the professors and clapped their hands in glee. They swore a mighty oath of secrecy, and the janitor of the building where they met was let in on the compact so that there should be no leak.

Yale athletic prowess boomed mightily, and it was not until last spring that any inkling of suspicion crept out. It was an unfortunate occurrence.

I am not referring to the slight unpleasantness which was created when it was discovered that a gorilla had been selected for Phi Beta Kappa. After all, that was known only to the few who watched the poor fellow cling to the chandelier and chatter when they approached him with a key. No, I mean the little scandal which marred the last tap day.

"Go to your room!" said a senior to a stalwart athlete, slapping him on the shoulder. He went, but to the horror of all beholders he reached it by swinging through the branches of an elm, and in transit he paused long enough to heave down a few coconuts.

The story never got out, and all the newspaper correspondents agreed to suppress it. But I think that sound journalism should not only permit but require some mention of the extraordinary episode which occurred in the Bowl immediately after the Harvard game. After all, some 50,000 people were present. And I for one will not keep silent.

As the final whistle blew, a substitute Yale tackle bounded from the bench and ran to the goal posts. Some thought that under the excitement of the victory he was intent on tearing down his own posts. But he did nothing of the sort. Leaping high in the air, he swung from the crossbeam. Even that could have been pardoned as a bit of youthful exuberance but for one little fact. He swung by his tail.

And so today there are gloom, suspicion, and furtiveness down at Yale. Indeed, it has grown to such an extent that whenever one undergraduate makes an offensive remark to another—be it in classroom, study, or parlor—it is customary to answer, "Take off that raccoon coat!"

LOVE IS A FALLACY*

BY MAX SHULMAN

Cool was I and logical. Keen, calculating, perspicacious, acute and astute—I was all of these. My brain was as powerful as a dynamo, as precise as a chemist's scales, as penetrating as a scalpel. And—think of it!—I was only eighteen.

It is not often that one so young has such a giant intellect. Take, for example, Petey Burch, my roommate at the University of Minnesota. Same age, same background, but dumb as an ox. A nice enough fellow, you understand, but nothing upstairs. Emotional type. Unstable. Impressionable. Worst of all, a faddist. Fads, I submit, are the very negation of reason. To be swept up in every new craze that comes along, to surrender yourself to idiocy just because everybody else is doing it—this, to me, is the acme of mindlessness. Not, however, to Petey.

One afternoon I found Petey lying on his bed with an expression of such distress on his face that I immediately diagnosed appendicitis. "Don't move," I said. "Don't take a laxative. I'll get a doctor."

"Raccoon," he mumbled thickly.

"Raccoon?" I said, pausing in my flight.

"I want a raccoon coat," he wailed.

I perceived that his trouble was not physical, but mental. "Why do you want a raccoon coat?"

"I should have known it," he cried, pounding his temples. "I should have known they'd come back when the Charleston came back. Like a fool I spent all my money for textbooks, and now I can't get a raccoon coat."

"Can you mean," I said incredulously, "that people are actually wearing raccoon coats again?"

"All the Big Men on Campus are wearing them. Where've you been?"

"In the library," I said, naming a place not frequented by Big Men on Campus.

He leaped from the bed and paced the room. "I've got to have a raccoon coat," he said passionately. "I've got to!"

"Petey, why? Look at it rationally. Raccoon coats are unsanitary.

They shed. They smell bad. They weigh too much. They're unsightly. They——"

"You don't understand," he interrupted impatiently. "It's the thing to do. Don't you want to be in the swim?"

"No," I said truthfully.

"Well, I do," he declared. "I'd give anything for a raccoon coat. Anything!"

My brain, that precision instrument, slipped into high gear. "Anything?" I asked, looking at him narrowly.

"Anything," he affirmed in ringing tones.

I stroked my chin thoughtfully. It so happened that I knew where to get my hands on a raccoon coat. My father had had one in his undergraduate days; it lay now in a trunk in the attic back home. It also happened that Petey had something I wanted. He didn't *have* it exactly, but at least he had first rights on it. I refer to his girl, Polly Espy.

I had long coveted Polly Espy. Let me emphasize that my desire for this young woman was not emotional in nature. She was, to be sure, a girl who excited the emotions, but I was not one to let my heart rule my head. I wanted Polly for a shrewdly calculated, entirely cerebral reason.

I was a freshman in law school. In a few years I would be out in practice. I was well aware of the importance of the right kind of wife in furthering a lawyer's career. The successful lawyers I had observed were, almost without exception, married to beautiful, gracious, intelligent women. With one omission, Polly fitted these specifications perfectly.

Beautiful she was. She was not yet of pin-up proportions, but I felt sure that time would supply the lack. She already had the makings.

Gracious she was. By gracious I mean full of graces. She had an erectness of carriage, an ease of bearing, a poise that clearly indicated the best of breeding. At table her manners were exquisite. I had seen her at the Kozy Kampus Korner eating the specialty of the house—a sandwich that contained scraps of pot roast, gravy, chopped nuts, and a dipper of sauerkraut—without even getting her fingers moist.

Intelligent she was not. In fact, she veered in the opposite direction. But I believed that under my guidance she would smarten up. At any rate, it was worth a try. It is, after all, easier to make a beautiful dumb girl smart than to make an ugly smart girl beautiful.

"Petey," I said, "are you in love with Polly Espy?"

"I think she's a keen kid," he replied, "but I don't know if you'd call it love. Why?"

"Do you," I asked, "have any kind of formal arrangement with her? I mean are you going steady or anything like that?"

"No. We see each other quite a bit, but we both have other dates. Why?"

"Is there," I asked, "any other man for whom she has a particular fondness?"

"Not that I know of. Why?"

I nodded with satisfaction. "In other words, if you were out of the picture, the field would be open. Is that right?"

"I guess so. What are you getting at?"

"Nothing, nothing," I said innocently, and took my suitcase out of the closet.

"Where are you going?" asked Petey.

"Home for the weekend." I threw a few things into the bag.

"Listen," he said, clutching my arm eagerly, "while you're home, you couldn't get some money from your old man, could you, and lend it to me so I can buy a raccoon coat?"

"I may do better than that," I said with a mysterious wink and closed my bag and left.

"Look," I said to Petey when I got back Monday morning. I threw open the suitcase and revealed the huge, hairy, gamy object that my father had worn in his Stutz Bearcat in 1925.

"Holy Toledo!" said Petey reverently. He plunged his hands into the raccoon coat and then his face. "Holy Toledo!" he repeated fifteen or twenty times.

"Would you like it?" I asked.

"Oh yes!" he cried, clutching the greasy pelt to him. Then a canny look came into his eyes. "What do you want for it?"

"Your girl," I said, mincing no words.

"Polly?" he said in a horrified whisper. "You want Polly?"

"That's right."

He flung the coat from him. "Never," he said stoutly.

I shrugged. "Okay. If you don't want to be in the swim, I guess it's your business."

I sat down in a chair and pretended to read a book, but out of the corner of my eye I kept watching Petey. He was a torn man. First he looked at the coat with the expression of a waif at a bakery window.

Then he turned away and set his jaw resolutely. Then he looked back at the coat, with even more longing in his face. Then he turned away, but with not so much resolution this time. Back and forth his head swiveled, desire waxing, resolution waning. Finally he didn't turn away at all; he just stood and stared with mad lust at the coat.

"It isn't as though I was in love with Polly," he said thickly. "Or going steady or anything like that."

"That's right," I murmured.

"What's Polly to me, or me to Polly?"

"Not a thing," said I.

"It's just been a casual kick—just a few laughs, that's all."

"Try on the coat," said I.

He complied. The coat bunched high over his ears and dropped all the way down to his shoe tops. He looked like a mound of dead raccoons. "Fits fine," he said happily.

I rose from my chair. "Is it a deal?" I asked, extending my hand.

He swallowed. "It's a deal," he said and shook my hand.

I had my first date with Polly the following evening. This was in the nature of a survey; I wanted to find out just how much work I had to do to get her mind up to the standard I required. I took her first to dinner. "Gee, that was a delish dinner," she said as we left the restaurant. Then I took her to a movie. "Gee, that was a marvy movie," she said as we left the theater. And then I took her home. "Gee, I had a sensaysh time," she said as she bade me good night.

I went back to my room with a heavy heart. I had gravely underestimated the size of my task. This girl's lack of information was terrifying. Nor would it be enough merely to supply her with information. First she had to be taught to *think*. This loomed as a project of no small dimensions, and at first I was tempted to give her back to Petey. But then I got to thinking about her abundant physical charms and about the way she entered a room and the way she handled a knife and fork, and I decided to make an effort.

I went about it, as in all things, systematically. I gave her a course in logic. It happened that I, as a law student, was taking a course in logic myself, so I had all the facts at my finger tips. "Polly," I said to her when I picked her up on our next date, "tonight we are going over to the Knoll and talk."

"Oo, terrif," she replied. One thing I will say for this girl: you would go far to find another so agreeable.

We went to the Knoll, the campus trysting place, and we sat down under an old oak, and she looked at me expectantly. "What are we going to talk about?" she asked.

"Logic."

She thought this over for a minute and decided she liked it. "Magnif," she said.

"Logic," I said, clearing my throat, "is the science of thinking. Before we can think correctly, we must first learn to recognize the common fallacies of logic. These we will take up tonight."

"Wow-dow!" she cried, clapping her hands delightedly.

I winced, but went bravely on. "First let us examine the fallacy called Dicto Simpliciter."

"By all means," she urged, batting her lashes eagerly.

"Dicto Simpliciter means an argument based on an unqualified generalization. For example: Exercise is good. Therefore everybody should exercise."

"I agree," said Polly earnestly. "I mean exercise is wonderful. I mean it builds the body and everything."

"Polly," I said gently, "the argument is a fallacy. *Exercise is good* is an unqualified generalization. For instance, if you have heart disease, exercise is bad, not good. Many people are ordered by their doctors *not* to exercise. You must *qualify* the generalization. You must say exercise is *usually* good, or exercise is good *for most people*. Otherwise you have committed a Dicto Simpliciter. Do you see?"

"No," she confessed. "But this is marvy. Do more! Do more!"

"It will be better if you stop tugging at my sleeve," I told her, and when she desisted, I continued. "Next we take up a fallacy called Hasty Generalization. Listen carefully: You can't speak French. I can't speak French. Petey Burch can't speak French. I must therefore conclude that nobody at the University of Minnesota can speak French."

"Really?" said Polly, amazed. "*Nobody?*"

I hid my exasperation. "Polly, it's a fallacy. The generalization is reached too hastily. There are too few instances to support such a conclusion."

"Know any more fallacies?" she asked breathlessly. "This is more fun than dancing even."

I fought off a wave of despair. I was getting nowhere with this girl, absolutely nowhere. Still, I am nothing if not persistent. I continued. "Next comes Post Hoc. Listen to this: Let's not take Bill on our picnic. Every time we take him out with us, it rains."

"I know somebody just like that," she exclaimed. "A girl back home

—Eula Becker, her name is. It never fails. Every single time we take her on a picnic——"

"Polly," I said sharply, "it's a fallacy. Eula Becker doesn't *cause* the rain. She has no connection with the rain. You are guilty of Post Hoc if you blame Eula Becker."

"I'll never do it again," she promised contritely. "Are you mad at me?"

I sighed deeply. "No, Polly, I'm not mad."

"Then tell me some more fallacies."

"All right. Let's try Contradictory Premises."

"Yes, let's," she chirped, blinking her eyes happily.

I frowned, but plunged ahead. "Here's an example of Contradictory Premises: If God can do anything, can He make a stone so heavy that He won't be able to lift it?"

"Of course," she replied promptly.

"But if He can do anything, He can lift the stone," I pointed out.

"Yeah," she said thoughtfully. "Well, then I guess He can't make the stone."

"But He can do anything," I reminded her.

She scratched her pretty, empty head. "I'm all confused," she admitted.

"Of course you are. Because when the premises of an argument contradict each other, there can be no argument. If there is an irresistible force, there can be no immovable object. If there is an immovable object, there can be no irresistible force. Get it?"

"Tell me some more of this keen stuff," she said eagerly.

I consulted my watch. "I think we'd better call it a night. I'll take you home now, and you go over all the things you've learned. We'll have another session tomorrow night."

I deposited her at the girls' dormitory, where she assured me that she had had a perfectly terrif evening, and I went glumly home to my room. Petey lay snoring in his bed, the raccoon coat huddled like a great hairy beast at his feet. For a moment I considered waking him and telling him that he could have his girl back. It seemed clear that my project was doomed to failure. The girl simply had a logic-proof head.

But then I reconsidered. I had wasted one evening; I might as well waste another. Who knew? Maybe somewhere in the extinct crater of her mind, a few embers still smoldered. Maybe somehow I could fan them into flame. Admittedly it was not a prospect fraught with hope, but I decided to give it one more try.

Seated under the oak the next evening I said, "Our first fallacy to-night is called Ad Misericordiam."

She quivered with delight.

"Listen closely," I said. "A man applies for a job. When the boss asks him what his qualifications are, he replies that he has a wife and six children at home, the wife is a helpless cripple, the children have nothing to eat, no clothes to wear, no shoes on their feet, there are no beds in the house, no coal in the cellar, and winter is coming."

A tear rolled down each of Polly's pink cheeks. "Oh, this is awful, awful," she sobbed.

"Yes, it's awful," I agreed, "but it's no argument. The man never answered the boss's question about his qualifications. Instead he appealed to the boss's sympathy. He committed the fallacy of Ad Misericordiam. Do you understand?"

"Have you got a handkerchief?" she blubbered.

I handed her a handkerchief and tried to keep from screaming while she wiped her eyes. "Next," I said in a carefully controlled tone, "we will discuss False Analogy. Here is an example: Students should be allowed to look at their textbooks during examinations. After all, surgeons have X rays to guide them during an operation, lawyers have briefs to guide them during a trial, carpenters have blueprints to guide them when they are building a house. Why, then, shouldn't students be allowed to look at their textbooks during an examination?"

"There now," she said enthusiastically, "is the most marvy idea I've heard in years."

"Polly," I said testily, "the argument is all wrong. Doctors, lawyers, and carpenters aren't taking a test to see how much they have learned, but students are. The situations are altogether different, and you can't make an analogy between them."

"I still think it's a good idea," said Polly.

"Nuts," I muttered. Doggedly I pressed on. "Next we'll try Hypothesis Contrary to Fact."

"Sounds yummy," was Polly's reaction.

"Listen: If Madame Curie had not happened to leave a photographic plate in a drawer with a chunk of pitchblende, the world today would not know about radium."

"True, true," said Polly, nodding her head. "Did you see the movie? Oh, it just knocked me out. That Walter Pidgeon is so dreamy. I mean he fractures me."

"If you can forget Mr. Pidgeon for a moment," I said coldly, "I would like to point out that the statement is a fallacy. Maybe Madame Curie would have discovered radium at some later date. Maybe somebody else would have discovered it. Maybe any number of things would have happened. You can't start with a hypothesis that is not true and then draw any supportable conclusions from it."

"They ought to put Walter Pidgeon in more pictures," said Polly. "I hardly ever see him any more."

One more chance, I decided. But just one more. There is a limit to what flesh and blood can bear. "The next fallacy is called Poisoning the Well."

"How cute!" she gurgled.

"Two men are having a debate. The first one gets up and says, 'My opponent is a notorious liar. You can't believe a word that he is going to say.' . . . Now, Polly, think. Think hard. What's wrong?"

I watched her closely as she knit her creamy brow in concentration. Suddenly a glimmer of intelligence—the first I had seen—came into her eyes. "It's not fair," she said with indignation. "It's not a bit fair. What chance has the second man got if the first man calls him a liar before he even begins talking?"

"Right!" I cried exultantly. "One hundred per cent right. It's not fair. The first man has *poisoned the well* before anybody could drink from it. He has hamstrung his opponent before he could even start. . . . Polly, I'm proud of you."

"Pshaw," she murmured, blushing with pleasure.

"You see, my dear, these things aren't so hard. All you have to do is concentrate. Think—examine—evaluate. Come now, let's review everything we have learned."

"Fire away," she said with an airy wave of her hand.

Heartened by the knowledge that Polly was not altogether a cretin, I began a long, patient review of all I had told her. Over and over and over again I cited instances, pointed out flaws, kept hammering away without letup. It was like digging a tunnel. At first everything was work, sweat, and darkness. I had no idea when I would reach the light, or even *if* I would. But I persisted. I pounded and clawed and scraped, and finally I was rewarded. I saw a chink of light. And then the chink got bigger and the sun came pouring in and all was bright.

Five grueling nights this took, but it was worth it. I had made a logician out of Polly; I had taught her to think. My job was done. She was worthy of me at last. She was a fit wife for me, a proper hostess for my many mansions, a suitable mother for my well-heeled children.

It must not be thought that I was without love for this girl. Quite the contrary. Just as Pygmalion loved the perfect woman he had fashioned, so I loved mine. I determined to acquaint her with my feelings at our very next meeting. The time had come to change our relationship from academic to romantic.

"Polly," I said when next we sat beneath our oak, "tonight we will not discuss fallacies."

"Aw, gee," she said, disappointed.

"My dear," I said, favoring her with a smile, "we have now spent five evenings together. We have gotten along splendidly. It is clear that we are well matched."

"Hasty Generalization," said Polly brightly.

"I beg your pardon," said I.

"Hasty Generalization," she repeated. "How can you say that we are well matched on the basis of only five dates?"

I chuckled with amusement. The dear child had learned her lessons well. "My dear," I said, patting her hand in a tolerant manner, "five dates is plenty. After all, you don't have to eat a whole cake to know that it's good."

"False Analogy," said Polly promptly. "I'm not a cake. I'm a girl."

I chuckled with somewhat less amusement. The dear child had learned her lessons perhaps too well. I decided to change tactics. Obviously the best approach was a simple, strong, direct declaration of love. I paused for a moment while my massive brain chose the proper words. Then I began:

"Polly, I love you. You are the whole world to me, and the moon and the stars and the constellations of outer space. Please, my darling, say that you will go steady with me, for if you will not, life will be meaningless. I will languish. I will refuse my meals. I will wander the face of the earth, a shambling, hollow-eyed hulk."

There, I thought, folding my arms, that ought to do it.

"Ad Misericordiam," said Polly.

I ground my teeth. I was not Pygmalion; I was Frankenstein, and my monster had me by the throat. Frantically I fought back the tide of panic surging through me. At all costs I had to keep cool.

"Well, Polly," I said, forcing a smile, "you certainly have learned your fallacies."

"You're darn right," she said with a vigorous nod.

"And who taught them to you, Polly?"

"You did."

"That's right. So you do owe me something, don't you, my dear? If I hadn't come along you never would have learned about fallacies."

"Hypothesis Contrary to Fact," she said instantly.

I dashed perspiration from my brow. "Polly," I croaked, "you mustn't take all these things so literally. I mean this is just classroom stuff. You know that the things you learn in school don't have anything to do with life."

"Dicto Simpliciter," she said, wagging her finger at me playfully.

That did it. I leaped to my feet, bellowing like a bull. "Will you or will you not go steady with me?"

"I will not," she replied.

"Why not?" I demanded.

"Because this afternoon I promised Petey Burch that I would go steady with him."

I reeled back, overcome with the infamy of it. After he promised, after he made a deal, after he shook my hand! "The rat!" I shrieked, kicking up great chunks of turf. "You can't go with him, Polly. He's a liar. He's a cheat. He's a rat."

"Poisoning the Well," said Polly, "and stop shouting. I think shouting must be a fallacy too."

With an immense effort of will, I modulated my voice. "All right," I said. "You're a logician. Let's look at this thing logically. How could you choose Petey Burch over me? Look at me—a brilliant student, a tremendous intellectual, a man with an assured future. Look at Petey—a knothead, a jitterbug, a guy who'll never know where his next meal is coming from. Can you give me one logical reason why you should go steady with Petey Burch?"

"I certainly can," declared Polly. "He's got a raccoon coat."

FROM: *BAREFOOT BOY WITH CHEEK**

BY MAX SHULMAN

CHAPTER III

Où est mon chapeau?—ANATOLE FRANCE

St. Paul and Minneapolis extend from the Mississippi River like the legs on a pair of trousers. Where they join is the University of Minnesota.

I stood that day and gazed at the campus, my childish face looking up, holding wonder like a cup, my little feet beating time, time, time, in a sort of runic rhyme. A fraternity man's convertible ran me down, disturbing my reverie. "Just a flesh wound," I mumbled to disinterested passers-by.

With eager steps I proceeded to explore the campus. All around me was the hum of happy men at work. Here were masons aging a building so they could hang ivy on it. There were chiselers completing the statue of Cyrus Thresher, first regent of the University. It was Thresher, as you know, who said, "It takes a heap o' learnin' to make a school a school." Yonder were landscapers cleverly trimming a twelve-foot hedge to spell "Minnesota, Minnesota, rah, rah, ree. Little brown jug, how we love thee."

The architecture at Minnesota is very distinctive, and thereby hangs a tale. It goes back a good many years, back to the time when the mighty, sprawling University was just an infant. At that time Art Chaff, the son of a wealthy Minneapolis flour miller named Elihu Chaff, was expelled from Harvard for playing buck euchre on the Sabbath. Old Elihu was deeply incensed by the indignity. He was determined that Art should go to college, and, moreover, to a bigger college than Harvard.

So Elihu went to work on the University of Minnesota campus. He erected twenty buildings. They all looked like grain elevators, for that is what Elihu intended to use them for after Art had been graduated. But Elihu never fulfilled his plan.

One week end Elihu went fishing, accompanied only by an Indian guide named Ralph Duckhonking. They went into a deep forest, and after two days Duckhonking came out alone. He was wearing Elihu's suit and carrying all of his valuables. He said he knew nothing about Elihu's disappearance. Duckhonking was indicted for murder, but he was never tried because it was impossible to obtain twelve English-speaking veniremen in that judicial district. Duckhonking walked about free until he died more than twenty years later of nepotism. This case later became famous as the *Crédit Mobilier* scandal.

Elihu's elevators therefore, remained part of the University. In fact, out of respect to Elihu, all the buildings which were subsequently erected on the campus were built to resemble grain elevators.

But this was no time to be gawking about the campus. I had things to do. First I had to see Mr. Ingelbretsvold, my freshman adviser, about making out a program of studies for the year. Obtaining directions from a friendly upperclassman who sold me a freshman button, freshman cap, subscription to *Ski-U-Mah,* the campus humor magazine, a map of the campus, and a souvenir score card of last year's home-coming game, I proceeded to the office of Mr. Ingelbretsvold.

A line of freshmen stood in front of his door. I knew how they must feel, about to embark on this great adventure, and I could not help cheerily hollering "Halloa" to them. They stoned me in an amiable fashion.

At last a voice came from behind the door bidding me come in. How my heart beat as I opened the door and trod across the luxuriant burlap rug to Mr. Ingelbretsvold's desk.

"My name is Asa Hearthrug and I've come for advice," I said.

He stood up and smiled at me kindlily. "Sit down, young man," he said, "and have a glass of kvass." He pointed at the pitcher and glasses.

"Thank you," I said, making a low curtsey.

"Well, it's certainly a nice day."

"Yes," I agreed. "Almost twelve inches of rain since sunup."

"That's what I meant," he said. "It's a nice rain. It will help the potato crop."

"Yes," I agreed, "it should wash out every potato in Minnesota."

"That's what I meant," he said. "It will get rid of those damn potatoes. People are eating altogether too many potatoes. But enough of this meteorological chitchat. Let's get down to business. First of all, I want you to know that I'm your friend."

I licked his hand gratefully.

"You are about to enter a new phase of your life. I wonder whether you realize just how important this is."

"Oh, I do, sir, I do," I exclaimed.

"Shut up when I'm talking," he said. "Now, I have a little story that I like to tell to freshmen to impress them with the importance of college. I have had a great many students who were graduated from Minnesota and went out to take their places in the world come back after many years and say to me, 'Mr. Ingelbretsvold, I can never thank you enough for that little story you told me when I first came to the University.' Yes, young man, this story has helped a great many people, and I hope it will help you."

"So tell it already," I said.

"Well, sir, when I was a boy I had a good friend named Kyrie Eleison. We went through grade school and high school together, and on the night we were graduated from high school I said to him, 'Well, Kyrie, what are you going to do now?'

" 'Oh,' he said, 'I've got a chance to get a job in a nepotism business in North Dakota.'

" 'Kyrie,' I told him, 'don't take it. Come to college with me, or else you'll always regret it.'

"But he didn't choose to take my advice. I went to college, and he took the job. Yes, he did well at his work. By the time he was thirty he had seventy-five million dollars, and he has been getting richer ever since. He built a fine big house in which he holds the most lavish social affairs in the whole Northwest.

"Well, sir, one night I was invited to a party at Kyrie's house. I rented a suit and went. The house was filled with prominent people. A hundred-and-twenty-piece orchestra was playing. When we went in for dinner the table groaned with all sorts of expensive delicacies. And at the head of the table sat Kyrie, the monarch of all he surveyed.

"But during the course of the dinner a well-dressed young woman leaned over and said to Kyrie, 'Who was the eighth avatar of Vishnu?' and Kyrie, for all his wealth and power, did not know the answer."

"How ghastly!" I cried, throwing up my hands.

"Yes," said Mr. Ingelbretsvold. "You will find that sort of thing all through life. People come up to you on the street and say, 'Does a paramecium beat its flagella?' or 'How many wheels has a fiacre?' or 'When does an oryx mate?' and if you have not been to college, you simply cannot answer them."

"But that cannot happen to me. I am going to the University," I said.

"Ah, but it can," Mr. Ingelbretsvold answered. "It happens to many who go to college."

"But how?"

"You see, my boy, a great many people go to college to learn how to *do* something. They study medicine or law or engineering, and when they are through they know how to trepan a skull or where to get a writ of estoppel or how to find the torque of a radial engine. But just come up to them and ask how many caliphs succeeded Mohammed or who wrote *Baby Duncan's Whistling Lung* and they stare at you blankly."

I shuddered. "Oh, please, Mr. Ingelbretsvold," I begged, "what must I do?"

"You must do like I tell you. You must let college make you a well-rounded-out personality. That is the chief function and purpose of this University: to make you a well-rounded-out personality. Now you get out a pencil and paper and write down the names of the courses I am going to give you. If you follow this program you will find yourself a well-rounded-out personality."

I took out a pencil and poised it over my dickey bosom.

"Ready. Here they are: Races and Cultures of Arabia, Egypt, and North Africa; Ethnology of India; History of Architecture; Greek; Latin; Sixteenth-Century Literature; Seventeenth-Century Literature; Eighteenth-Century Literature; Nineteenth-Century Literature; Twentieth-Century Literature; Geography; Ancient History; Medieval History; Modern History; Ancient Philosophy; Modern Philosophy; Contemporary Philosophy; History of Religion; American Government; British Government; Chinese Government; Japanese Government; Lett Government; First Aid; Public Health; General Psychology; Psychology of Learning; Psychology of Advertising; Psychology of Literature; Psychology of Art; Psychology of Behavior; Animal Psychology; Abnormal Psychology; Norwegian; Swedish; Danish; French; German; Russian; Italian; Lett; Urban Sociology; Rural Sociology; Juvenile Sociology; Statistical Sociology; Criminology; Penology; Elocution; Speech Pathology; and Canoe Paddling.

"That will do for a start. As you go into these courses you will find others that will interest you too."

"And these will make me a well-rounded-out personality?" I asked.

He laughed gently. "Oh no, my boy. That is only a small but essential part of rounding out your personality. There is the social life too." He nudged me and winked. "A fellow can have a good time here."

"Sir," I said, and blushed.

"But you'll soon find out all about that. Now, one more thing. In addition to the work you do for these courses I have named you should do a lot of reading that has not been assigned in your classes. Do you read anything now?"

"A mystery story now and then," I confessed.

"Oh, have you read Rex Snout's latest, *The Case of the Gelded Gnu?*"

"No, but I read the one before that, *The Case of the Missing Lynx.*"

"I missed that one. What was it about?"

"Well, a horribly mutilated corpse is found on the railroad tracks near Buffalo. This corpse is in such a state that it is impossible to identify it or even to tell whether it is a man or a woman. The story is concerned almost entirely with trying to establish the identity of the corpse. In the end it is discovered that it is not a corpse at all, but a pan of waffle batter that fell out of the window of a New York Central dining car."

"How interesting. Well, I guess that's all the time I can give you. Others are waiting," he said, taking cognizance of the stones they were throwing through the window.

"Just one more thing, Mr. Ingelbretsvold," I said. "I don't know quite how to say this, but I think I would like to be a writer when I grow up. Will the program you made out for me help me to be a writer?"

"Why, bless you, child," Mr. Ingelbretsvold said, "you follow that program and there's nothing else you can be."

CHAPTER V

Qui est dans le corridor?—SAINT SAËNS

After I left the Health Service I went for a walk. I wanted to think about all the wonderful things that had happened to me. I could scarcely believe that in just a few days I was going to walk into a university class, a belonger, a cog in a great machine where everyone puts his nose to the grindstone and pulls together. I glowed all over as I walked upon the handsome promenade called fraternity row.

Minnesota has one of the finest fraternity rows in the country. Behind luxuriant, well-kept lawns stand the ornate but tasteful fronts of the fraternity houses. Doric columns adorn their façades, and through the leaded panes of their windows I could see gay, well-dressed young men lounging casually in the living rooms. My fellow students, I thought rapturously. I gave a little jump in my unbridled joy. As I landed, two cunningly hinged sidewalk stones gave way, and I hurtled into a pit below.

"We got one," someone yelled. Immediately two youths beset me and tied me with baling wire. Then I was carried through a devious tunnel into the living room of a fraternity house. "We got one, Roger," announced my bearers.

The one called Roger was sitting at a table playing Michigan rummy with three others. "O.K.," he said. The others drew guns, and each one walked over to a door. "Untie him," Roger commanded.

The two who had brought me in produced an acetylene torch and loosed me. Roger pulled out a buffer and dental floss and got his teeth ready. Then he smiled. "I'm Roger Hailfellow, the president. I'm certainly glad that you decided on this fraternity. Yes sir, you can't find a better fraternity than Alpha Cholera. How about that, fellows?" he asked, turning to the three who were guarding the exits.

"Friend, you did right," they said to me.

"I'll tell you, chum," said Roger, putting his arm around me, sticking a cigarette in my mouth, and lighting it, "there's fraternities and there's fraternities. I don't like to knock anybody, but there's some bad fraternities as well as good fraternities. A fellow who joins a bad fraternity is almost as bad off as a fellow who don't join no fraternity at all. And you know how bad off a fellow is who don't join no fraternity at all. Damn barb." Roger spat angrily.

The three at the doors fired shots into the wall to indicate their feelings about a fellow who didn't join any fraternity.

"But you're lucky," Roger continued, sticking another cigarette in my mouth and lighting it. "You picked the best fraternity first crack off the bat. How about that, fellows?"

"Friend, you did right," they said.

"Yes sir, the very best. Alpha Cholera isn't one of those little upstart fraternities. No sir. Do you know when we were founded?"

"No," I said.

"Five hundred B.C. Alpha Cholera was founded in ancient Greece by three fellows named Aeschylus, Sophocles, and Euripides. They did not give their last names. Even in those days people knew a good thing when they saw one, and all the right people in Greece joined Alpha Cholera. The spring formal at the Parthenon was the high spot of the social year in Athens. They had the best orchestra in the country, Oedipus Rex. 'Fling and flex with Oedipus Rex' was his slogan.

"But just like it is today, Alpha Cholera was choosy about who it let in. The mayor of Athens, Nick, tried to get his son into the fraternity, but Alpha Cholera was not going to take nobody with a ram's head. It meant banishment.

"So the members hied themselves off to Rome. They were carried most of the way on the back of their sergeant at arms, a chap named Aeneas. When they finally reached Rome, they were so exhausted that they collapsed on the ground. They would have perished, had it not been for a passing she-wolf who suckled them.

"In Rome Alpha Cholera did not fare well. The members were relentlessly hunted out and murdered by the barbarous Romans. Finally there was only one Alpha Cholera left, a fellow called Androcles. He hid for a time in the basement of a sympathetic Roman candlestick maker named Phelps or Mazinik. Eventually Androcles was apprehended, and it was decided that he was to be thrown to the lions.

"While thousands of spectators sat in the Colosseum and roared for blood, Androcles bravely entered the lion's cage. The beast rushed at him. Stout-hearted Androcles proceeded to grapple. Unwittingly, as he seized the lion's paw, he gave him the secret Alpha Cholera handshake. The lion paused. He licked Androcles' face and refused to do further battle. He, too, was an Alpha Cholera, Swahili chapter.

"Androcles was spared and lived to carry forward the torch of Alpha Cholera. After his death, we know that Alpha Cholera continued to exist, but we are not sure of the details. We believe that there was a chapter in Pompeii. When the noted archaelogist, Dudley Digs, excavated the ruins of Pompeii, he found a corpse wearing a pin that bore the initials A. C. We think that stood for Alpha Cholera. Digs, himself, holds to another theory. The corpse who was wearing the pin also held a dulcimer in his hand, and Digs believes that the A. C. meant "AD Carthage" where the Roman musicians' union was going to hold its convention the year of the Pompeiian disaster.

"Be that as it may, we know that somehow Alpha Cholera went forward unbrokenly. In the writings of Cellini we find this passage: 'I saw this night a comely wench upon the thoroughfare. After pleasant amenities she accompanied me to my quarters where we deported ourselves pleasantly until she, seeing a bauble upon my blouse, expressed a desire for it. I gave her that and other things and having done, hit her in the mouth, took back the bauble, and flung her from my casement.' The bauble was, of course, an Alpha Cholera pin.

"We are certain, too, that Robespierre was an Alpha Cholera. The motto for the French Revolution was originally 'Liberty, Equality. Robespierre inserted the 'Fraternity.'

"And who do you think brought Alpha Cholera to America? The pilgrim fathers, no less. They were an Alpha Cholera chapter in London, but they lost the lease on their house when their landlady, the old lady of Threadneedle Street, found out that they were dancing on Saturday nights. She hated dancing since years before when she had gone out with an adagio dancer named Ike, who had snatched her purse and thrown her into a passing circus wagon where she had been assaulted four times by an orang-utan. So the pilgrim fathers came to America where nobody could interfere with their Saturday-night hops."

"My. You certainly have an illustrious history," I exclaimed, removing the cigarettes from my mouth so I could talk.

"Friend, you said right," said the three at the doors.

"Now, you just sit here and smoke a cigarette while I get you a pledge card to sign," Roger said, inserting another cigarette in my mouth.

"Well, wait a minute," I protested. "I really hadn't intended to join a fraternity today. I was just walking along the sidewalk here when I happened to fall into your pit. I really wasn't thinking about joining a fraternity. I hope you understand I have nothing against your fraternity. It seems to be a totally admirable institution. And I certainly do appreciate all these cigarettes I am smoking. I am grateful, too, for the time you have spent telling me all about Alpha Cholera. But, to be perfectly frank, I wasn't even thinking about joining a fraternity—at least, not today."

The three with guns moved in on me. Roger waved them back. "Of course," he said simply. "How stupid of me. You want a little time to think it over. Well, why don't you have lunch here, and perhaps we can talk about it some more?"

"Oh, I don't think I should. You have done too much for me already."

"Oh, pooh," said Roger. "It's nothing. Harry, go get something to eat for our friend."

One of the doorkeepers left.

"Really, Roger," I cried, "you shouldn't!"

"Tut, tut," Roger said. "I want you to think of the Alpha Cholera house as your home away from home."

I felt a lump rise in my throat. "I think that's the nicest thing anybody has ever said to me," I said simply.

Roger lowered his eyes modestly. Harry came in with my lunch. I looked, and for a moment I thought my senses were deceiving me, for Harry had laid a plate of hominy grits before me, and they were arranged to spell out:

> Alpha Cholera is glad you're here.
> Eat these grits in all good cheer.

Unable to speak, I looked at Roger. He smiled reassuringly and bade me eat. As I started to eat, the three at the doors came over to Roger. They all patted me on the shoulder, and then, putting their arms about one another, proceeded to sing this song:

> "Stand, good men, take off your hat
> To Alpha Cholera, our swell frat.
> In our midst you'll find no rat,
> And don't let anyone tell you that.

"Be you lean or be you fat,
Join Alpha Cholera, our swell frat.
Since long ago, when first we mat,
Our swell bunch is together yat."

As their last soft chords died, I could see through the leaded panes of the window the flaming orb of the sun expire gently into the west. The earth was bathed in the soft pastel of the vanishing day.

"Want some salt on those grits?" Roger asked gently.

I shook my head, for my tears were salt enough. Understanding, Roger perceived my condition and said, "Let's go, fellows. He wants to be alone for a while." They patted my throbbing shoulders and left, still singing the Alpha Cholera song in close harmony.

I finished the grits and licked the plate so they wouldn't have to wash it. Then I wiped my nose on my sleeve and let my thoughts take possession of me. If somebody had told me before I came to the University that my fellow students were going to make such a to-do over me, I would have cried, "Go to, sirrah, and make not light of my innocence." But it was all true. Here was I, a complete stranger, taken without question into the bosom of my fellows. Ah, alma mater, you are indeed my adopted mother, I thought.

Roger and the others returned. "How was it?" Roger asked.

"The lunch? It was divine."

"Well, that gives you a rough idea of the kind of cuisine we have at Alpha Cholera. And hominy grits is only an example of what you'll get. We often have peanut-butter sandwiches, baked beans, turnip greens, and head cheese. And on legal holidays we always have mackerel."

"No!" I exclaimed.

"Yes," said Roger. "And would you believe it, our kitchen shows a profit year after year. But enough. Let's get down to business. Are you ready to join?"

The three at the doors had put their guns in their holsters. Now they drew them again.

"Well," I said, "how much does it cost?"

"Why, bless you," Roger said, "don't you worry about that. Come with me. I'll introduce you to some of the fellows."

He took me by the hand and led me upstairs to the dormitory. "We have one of the biggest B.M.O.C.'s in Alpha Cholera," he said, as we walked up the stairs.

"What's a B.M.O.C.?" I asked.

"A Big Man on Campus," he explained.

We stopped in front of a room near the head of the stairs. "This room belongs to Eino Fflliikkiinnenn," Roger said reverently.

"Not Eino Fflliikkiinnenn, the football player!" I cried.

"Yes," said Roger. "He will be your fraternity brother."

I was all shaky inside as we entered Fflliikkiinnenn's room. He was standing in a corner beating his head methodically against the wall. "He's toughening up for the football season," Roger whispered.

"Eino," Roger called, "here's a man who wants to meet you. He is going to pledge Alpha Cholera."

Eino grabbed my hand in a hearty grip. "Ay tink dot's real nice," he said. "Ay am happy to call you my brudder."

I did not trust myself to speak.

"Did I do good, Roger?" said Eino.

"Yes, Eino," Roger answered. "Now let go of his hand and go back to your exercises."

"Say, Roger," Eino said, "you didn' pay me yat dis mont'."

"Is that so?" said Roger. "Well, it's just an oversight. I'll see that you get your money right away."

"You batter," Eino said. "Ay got a goot offer from Mu Beta Fistula to live over dere. Dey pay on time too."

"I'll see that you get your money. Don't worry," said Roger.

"You batter," Eino said, "and cash. No more beer chips."

We left.

"Just think of being a fraternity brother of Eino Fflliikkiinnenn's," Roger said to me.

"I can't imagine anything more heavenly," I answered.

Roger rubbed his hands. "Well, then, should I get the pledge card?"

"Well, I don't know. I really wasn't thinking of joining a fraternity. I just happened to be walking by when I fell into——"

"Let's go take a look at our record collection," Roger interrupted.

We went downstairs to a large radio phonograph with an enclosed record cabinet. " We got everything," Roger said, "Goodman, Shaw, Basie, Dorsey, Herman, anything you want. All the new stuff too. Just got a new Andrews sisters disc today. 'Death and Transfiguration' on one side, 'Dope Me, Doctor, with a Sulfa Drug' on the other. Or maybe you like the heavier stuff. Symphonic. We got all you want. 'Filigree on Derriere's Variation of a Theme of Merde' recorded by the Rush City Four. And 'Afternoon of a Prawn.' Anything you want."

But again he was taking me somewhere. I followed him into a room piled waist high with pictures of girls. "Pictures here of every girl on the campus. Name, address, age, height, weight, habits, and food and liquor capacity written on the back. Also achievement records of all the fellows who have ever taken her out. Join Alpha Cholera and be sure what you're getting into."

"Lands sakes," I said admiringly.

"Now will you pledge?" Roger asked.

I took his two hands in mine and looked him in the eyes. "Whatever you think best, Roger," I said simply.

He rubbed his hands rapidly, starting a minor conflagration on his cuffs. "Now, I suppose you want to discuss finances. Well, just you don't worry about that at all. I'll call our treasurer, and we'll have every little thing all straightened out as fast as you can say Jack Robinson. You'll like our treasurer."

Roger left and came back in a few minutes with the treasurer. "This is our treasurer, Shylock Fiscal," he said.

"Well, you finally got one," he said to Roger.

Roger smiled modestly.

"I was about to go to work," Shylock said.

"Where there's life there's hope," Roger reminded him.

"I just about gave up," Shylock confessed. "It's getting worse each year, what with the other houses serving meat and keeping a dozen B.M.O.C.'s and——"

"That reminds me," Roger interrupted. "Eino wants to get paid."

"Give him some beer chips," suggested Shylock.

"No, he wants cash."

"Cash, huh? Well, let's see what we can get from this turnip." Shylock turned to me. "I'm Shylock Fiscal," he said cheerily. "Just call me Shy. Everybody does. I guess it's because I'm not. Heh, heh, heh."

"Heh, heh, heh," laughed Roger.

I joined the general merriment. How good it was to share a good joke with good men.

"So you've decided to join Alpha Cholera?" Shylock continued. "Friend, you did right. You'll never regret it. There's nothing like a good fraternity, and Alpha Cholera is the best, isn't it, Roger?"

"Yes," Roger admitted.

"Yes, sir. You can't beat a good fraternity. Good fellows living together in a good house, sharing each other's problems, making contacts that are going to be their most precious possessions in later life. But I don't have to tell you about the advantages. Anyone looking at you can tell that you know what the score is."

I blushed becomingly.

Shylock leaned closer and put his hand on my knee. "The surprising thing," he said, "is how reasonable Alpha Cholera is. I mean, looking at it intelligently. You and I know that in this world you don't get something for nothing; the best thing you can hope for is to get a lot of a little. And that's what you get when you join Alpha Cholera.

"Take dues, for instance. We charge $100 a month. I'll admit that $100 is a tidy sum. But remember, if you were going to take a suite in a hotel downtown while you went to school you'd pay a lot more. And besides, you'd be living alone. You wouldn't have all these swell kids to live with and share your problems. Furthermore, $100 a month dues keeps out the riffraff. You can be sure that you're living with the best people at Alpha Cholera.

"Now then, there's meals. Breakfast–$1.75. Lunch–$2.50. Dinner –$4.00. Now you know as well as I do that you can't pay too much for a good meal, attractively served in pleasant surroundings. How about that, Roger?"

"Yes," said Roger.

"And laundry. You just throw your dirty clothes down the chute, and the next time you see them, they're spick-and-span, all ready to wear. None of that wet-wash stuff here. No sir. And all for $12.50 a week.

"Then there's national dues; Alpha Cholera isn't one of your dinky one-chapter houses. Not on your life. You'll find an Alpha Cholera house on every major campus in the country. And that's important. Whenever you visit another college, you don't have to pay four or five dollars a night for a hotel room. You just go to the Alpha Cholera house and they'll put you up without charging you a cent. National dues are $40 a month.

"And that's it, friend. That's every red cent you'll pay for being an Alpha Cholera, except naturally $5.00 a month for the telephone, a quarter a day for hot water, and $300 for your handsome zircon Alpha Cholera pin. Of course there'll be special events from time to time, but we won't worry about those now, will we?"

"No," said Roger.

"Now that you know all the facts about Alpha Cholera, are you ready to make your decision?" Shylock asked. "We want you to go into this thing with your eyes open. This is the most important step you

you have ever taken in your life, and we don't want you to regret it. We want you to *want* to join Alpha Cholera; otherwise we don't want you. The decision is entirely up to you. We have acquainted you with the facts, and that is all we can do. Now, you take your time and think it over. We'll give you ninety seconds."

I knew it was an important decision, and I took the full allotted time. As they twisted my arms, I mentally weighed the considerations in the case. There was only one answer I could reasonably, honestly, and conscientiously give.

"I'll pledge," I said.

We shook hands silently all around, not trusting ourselves to speak.

"Shy," said Roger, after we had choked back our tears, "you tell him about the pledge period while I get everything ready for the ceremony." He left.

"Now," said Shylock, "you are going to be pledged in just a few minutes. For six months after that you are going to be a pledge. Then you get initiated and become what is called an active. During your pledge period you are sort of a little brother to the actives. You come to us with your problems and we give you advice about whatever you want to know. We choose your clothes and your girls for you. You just let us actives worry about everything."

I nuzzled against his sleeve. "There, there," he said quietly.

"All ready," called a voice from down the hall, and I left with Shylock for the pledging ceremony. (The ritual that followed is very secret, and I must ask the reader to keep the ensuing account in strictest confidence.)

We entered a room lit dimly by candles. A group of young men sat cross-legged in a circle on the floor. In the corner of the room on a dais Roger sat, dressed in a curiously inscribed robe. Frankincense and myrrh burned in an icon on the wall.

Shylock led me to the center of the circle. He chanted:

"I bring a man
Into this clan."

"Hubba, gubba,
Goodrich rubba,"

intoned the circle.

A barefoot maiden in a white gown entered bearing a young ram above her head. She deposited the ram in Roger's lap.

"Ram, bam,
Thank you, ma'am,"

he said.

He drew a curiously inscribed kris from his robe and slit the ram's throat. He dipped his finger in the blood and, beckoning me to the dais, made a curious inscription on my forehead.

"He's been washed in the blood of the ram," Roger announced.

"He's been washed in the blood of the ram," repeated the circle. Then they sang:

"Blood, thud,
Fuddy dud."

They leaped to their feet. Each put his hands on the hips of the one in front of him. They proceeded to move around me in a curious dance consisting of three steps and a kick, regularly repeated. After a while they resumed their positions and chanted:

"Simba, marimba,
Richard himba."

The lights went on, and suddenly their smiling faces were shaking my hand. Tears streamed uncheckable from my little eyes. "My brothers! My brothers!" I cried hoarsely.

Now I was on their shoulders, and they were giving three cheers and a tiger for me.

"By the way," said Shylock, "what's your name?"

"Asa Hearthrug," I answered.

"Oh, Jesus," he said.

CHAPTER VI

Je dormais dans un gros lit—COROT

But all was not play at the University of Minnesota. Now I began classes, and that was work—the good, satisfying work of learning.

I shall always remember the first class I attended. It was a class in sociology. I took a seat in the front row and spread my paper and pencils neatly on my desk. Turning to my brother students, I smiled friendlily. They threw lighted matches at me in a demonstration of good fellowship. Then the venerable white-haired professor entered the room. He advanced to the lectern at the head of the class. Putting on his pince-nez, he surveyed us for a moment. "Jeez," he said, "they get crumbier every year."

We laughed appreciatively.

"My name is Schultz," said the professor. "Now, get out paper and pencil, and I'll give you a list of books you'll need for this course. Ready? *Introduction to the Study of Sociology* by Schultz. *Sociology Made Simple* by Schultz. *Sociology for College Freshmen* by Schultz. *Survey of Freshman Sociology* by Schultz. *Sociology for Freshmen in College* by Schultz. *Introductory Monograph to the Study of Freshman Sociology* by Schultz. *Broader Aspects of Sociology* by Schultz. *Bibliography of Schultz's Treatises on Sociology for College Freshmen* by Schultz.

"I'll let you out of class early today so you can run right over to the bookstore and buy these books. And don't try to get them secondhand because you can't. I just wrote them this summer. Don't try to sell them when you're through, either. I'm writing a new set right now. You don't think I live on my salary here, do you? Why, the third-string fullback made more than I did last year.

"But enough of this pecuniary chitchat. Let's get down to business. This is a class in sociology. Now, what is sociology? I'll tell you what sociology is. Sociology is the study of how people live together."

I felt a prod in my ribs. Turning, I saw a dark-eyed, finely mustached girl in a close-knit burlap dress. "Hey," she whispered, "you know what sociology is?"

"The study of how people live together," I answered.

"Nah," she said. "It's the study of how the working class is oppressed under the capitalistic system."

The professor fixed us with a baleful eye. "If you two don't mind," he said, "I'll go on with my lecture."

"Tool," hissed the girl.

"In this course," continued the professor, "we shall study the various forms of communal life, the habits, customs, and mores, as we like to call them, that prevail among the different peoples of the world. After learning the broad backgrounds of the subject we shall take up the most important part of sociology. We shall study the individual from the standpoint of his environment. Sociology has proved that the key to individual behavior can be found in environment. For instance, last year we went through the records of the Minneapolis police department and compiled case histories of all the persons listed there. We found without exception that each one of them had come from what we called a 'bad' home or neighborhood.

"Let me cite a typical case, that of Mildred W., at present an inmate of the Effie T. Libidinous Home for Erring Girls.

"Mildred W. was one of twenty-seven children. Her father, Chauncey W., earned four dollars a week as a taper snuffer, but he seldom worked more than a week or two out of the year because of the meager demand for his talents. The mother was a laconic slattern named Bunny who spent the bulk of her time fretfully paring her nails. The family lived a peripatetic home life in the tender of a Baltimore & Ohio freight train.

"Aside from Mildred the children were generally a normal lot except for four boys, Primus, Secundus, Tertius, and Quartus, who were all joined together at the forehead, and Al, another son, who was six feet, nine inches tall, weighed thirty-five pounds, and spent his days boring holes in a table leg with his head.

"The rest of the children were as happy as children can be who don't eat. Chauncey W. tried to keep the children's minds off of food by organizing games. These were reasonably successful except when the children's attention lagged and they fell upon the youngest child and devoured it.

"Mildred never participated in these games. She was an adopted child, and although the family always tried to make her feel at home and never mentioned that she was adopted, she knew subconsciously that she was an outsider. While her sisters and brothers romped about, Mildred sat in a corner aimlessly cutting an old tarpaulin into isosceles triangles.

"In addition to her feeling that she did not belong, something else was troubling Mildred. She was ten years old at this time and beginning to pass through puberty. She asked her mother to explain the subtle changes that were coming over her, but her mother merely blushed and said, 'It ain't fitten to talk about.'

"Then one day Mildred picked up a circular advertising for peach pickers in California. In the dead of night she appropriated a shift, which was the family's sole article of clothing, and ran away to seek a job picking peaches.

"She met a girl named Frances Fagin on the highway. After hearing Mildred's plans, Frances said, 'Listen, honey, you're too pretty to pick peaches. You come with me and I'll show you how to get your mitts on some real dough.'

"That night Mildred and Frances met a couple of desperadoes, the notorious Nidrick brothers, Norman and Neville, and the four of them held up a Standard Oil station near Lima, Ohio, making off with $65 and a quart of Iso-Vis.

"'They went to Davenport, Iowa, where they dissipated their swag in three months of riotous living. Finding themselves without funds, they knocked over the Farmers and Merchants Bank in Albert Lea, Minnesota. Their loot totaled $983,000,000. (There was an interesting side light to this robbery. The president of the Farmers and Merchants Bank, one Lawrence [Fats] Demijohn, was unable to satisfactorily explain how come he had so much money in his bank. Upon investigation it was learned that Demijohn, himself, had robbed the First Trust Company of Bismarck, North Dakota, the summer before and stored the loot in his own bank.)

"But I digress. Mildred decided not to share the proceeds with her accomplices. She drew a Luger that she had concealed in her tunic and dispatched the three of them.

"Then she packed the money in a valise and caught a train East. On the train there was a mixup in bags and somebody walked off with Mildred's valise. Although she advertised in several papers, her valise was never returned to her. This had a profound effect on her personality. In her own words, 'I made up my mind right there and then never to trust nobody no more.'

"Mildred was now almost twelve years old and in the first flush of young womanhood. It was a simple matter for her to enter a brothel. She stayed there two years, finally leaving in a fit of pique when she discovered that the others girls were getting paid.

"For several weeks she wandered around hungry, keeping alive by snatching bread crumbs from irate pigeons. At length she found work dealing fan-tan in a Chinese joss house. Here she became acquainted with Norbert Huh, a narcotics peddler who put her to work selling hasheesh.

"Unfortunately, Mildred began sampling her wares. One night, while driving her car under the influence of hasheesh, she drove it right into the reading room of the public library and killed two mannish-looking women who were reading *The Well of Loneliness.*

"She was apprehended and convicted, but instead of being put in some dirty old prison, she was committed to a modern, homelike institution of correction. She is given a great deal of freedom and loving care. To help rehabilitate her, she is being taught handicraft. Mildred is responding very well. As soon as she promises to stop decapitating matrons with her crosscut saw she will be released to take her place in society.

"Well, that's all for today. Run along now and buy the books and tomorrow we'll plunge into the study of sociology."

I walked out of class with the girl who had spoken to me. We stopped in the hall while she rolled a cigarette and struck a match on her rope-soled shoe. The label on the sole said "Made in the Workers' Co-operative at Omsk."

"Well," I said, "it looks like sociology is going to be a lot of fun."

She spat obliquely across the hall and did not answer.

"My name is Asa Hearthrug," I said. "What's yours?"

"Call me Yetta Samovar. That's my Party name. I took the name of our great feminine martyr."

"Who was she?" I asked.

She looked contemptuously at me. "Oh, God—to mention a popular figure from the bourgeois religion-myth—don't you know who Yetta Samovar was? Oh well," she sneered, flicking my Alpha Cholera pin with a dirty-nailed forefinger, "what can you expect from a fraternity counter-revolutionist?"

"Madam," I cried, drawing myself up, "I shall not listen to any attack on my fraternity! They're all swell kids, and they're loads of fun."

"Fun! Fun!" she shrieked. "That's what you came to the University for. You're just like the rest of them. Well, have your fun now. The working class is getting damned good and tired of supporting your temple of hedonism on their scarred backs. You'll see the day when the likes of you have your fun in salt mines."

"Permit me to correct you," I remarked coldly. "I did not come to the University for fun. I came to learn how to write."

"*You* want to write! *You!* Tell me, have you suffered?"

"Well, yes," I confessed. "I get awful chafed in summer."

Yetta looked at me for a long time, then she took my hand in hers and spoke. "Friend," she said tenderly, "I spoke hastily. It is now evident that you are not a fascist. You are merely politically undeveloped. But that is dangerous, doubly dangerous because you are in a fraternity."

I raised my hand. "Say of me what you like, but I will not hear a word against Alpha Cholera."

"Asa, you must listen to me. I promise you you will thank me later for that which I am going to tell you now. Let me ask you a question. What does your fraternity do?"

"Do? Why, they listen to records and play bridge and hold dances and——"

"Exactly," she interrupted. "That's my point. They listen to records and play bridge and hold dances. Do they ever go out and join a picket line? Do they discuss ways and means to better the condition of the working class? Do they collect funds for the families of martyrs of the class war? No! No! No!"

"But that doesn't make them fascists," I protested.

"Ah," she screamed, "but it does! They are either for us or against us." Her tone grew softer. "Asa, you want to be a writer. What kind of writer do you want to be? Do you want to be a feeble, sniveling voice of decadent reaction or do you want to be the brave trumpet of a new era?"

"The brave trumpet of a new era," I said promptly.

"Then you must let me guide you. Tonight the Minnesota chapter of the Subversive Elements League is holding a meeting. Will you come with me?"

"Yes," I said simply.

"Good," she said. "I'll meet you at nine in front of the chemistry building. You won't regret it. And maybe later I can help you with your writing. I know a few people on *Poignancy*, the campus literary magazine."

"Oh, Yetta," I cried, "do you think you could——"

"We'll see," she said. "We'll see. Well, I'll meet you tonight."

"All right. Say, by the way, who was the original Yetta Samovar?"

"She was the first Soviet woman to operate a power crane," said Yetta. "One day while working at the Dnepropetrovsk dam she leaned out of her crane to wave a greeting to a young man whose bed she shared and with whom she had become quite friendly. She leaned too far. Down she plunged into a block of newly laid, quick-drying concrete. Her last words as the concrete hardened about her were, 'Solidarity forever!' "

"I see," I said.

CHAPTER IX

Ouvrez la fenêtre.—ZOLA

I decided to go to the Beta Thigh song-title party as "Tea for Two." It took a great deal of practice to master my costume, which was a tea service for two balanced on my head, but when I finally walked up to the door of the Beta Thigh house on Saturday night I carried myself with all the aplomb of an African laundress.

I rang the bell. A gray-haired, matronly woman opened the door. "How do you do?" I said. "I'm Asa Hearthrug, and I've come to the party. I am the guest of Noblesse Oblige."

"Come right in, Asa. I'm Mother Bloor, the house mother. You sit right down here on the sofa and I'll go call Noblesse."

Mother Bloor was back in a few minutes. "She'll be down right away. She's fixing her costume. Well, Asa, you look like a nice boy," she said, putting her hand on my knee.

I smiled modestly.

"You got any older brothers?"

" No ma'am," I said.

"Your father ain't a widower, is he?"

"Not when I left him, he wasn't."

"'Uh. You thought any about getting married?"

"Some," I admitted.

"Well, let me tell you, boy, you could do a lot worse than marrying some nice mature woman that knows how to cook and take care of a house and what a man likes. Get me?" she nudged me and winked.

"Madam!" I cried.

"I tell you, these young puss ain't got any idea of how to treat a man. Oh, sure, they're pretty to look at, but you mark my words, you'll soon get sick of looking at 'em. A man needs a nice mature woman. Well, here comes Noblesse now. You think over what I said. I'm home all the time."

A slender girl in a two-piece gown with an exposed midriff approached. I could not see her face because it was enveloped in a cloud of black smoke that rose from a smudge pot that was cunningly hinged to her navel.

"This is Asa Hearthrug, Noblesse Oblige," said Mother Bloor.

"How do you do?" I said.

"Oh, Asa," she cried in an enchanting little voice like the tinkle of a silver bell, "I think your costume is simply marvy, I mean actually. I mean it's so clever, after all, it's just grand I mean. 'Tea for Two.' How did you ever think of it, I mean really?"

"Shucks," I said, "it's not half as clever as yours. 'Smoke Gets in Your Eyes,' isn't it?"

"Oh, you guessed!" she cried, making a little moue.

"Why don't you children go in and dance?" Mother Bloor suggested.

Noblesse took my arm and we went into the amusement room of the house where several couples were dancing to the music of an automatic phonograph. "Isn't Mother Bloor keen?" asked Noblesse as we walked. "I mean after all, she's just like a real mother to us girls."

"Yes," I said.

We got on the dance floor just as a Benny Goodman record started to play. "Oh, B.G.!" cried Noblesse. "Next to T.D. I like him best. He carves me. I mean he carves me. Does he carve you?"

"Yes," I said, "he carves me."

"Me too," she breathed. "Man, he's murder, Jack."

The next record was a Glenn Miller. "G.M.!" whooped Noblesse. "Man, what solid jive, I mean he's reet. Have you heard his disc of 'Fell Me, Woodsman, with a Snag-Toothed Saw?'"

"No," I said.

"Awful fine slush pump, I mean awful fine. You ought to dig that."

The next record was a Guy Lombardo waltz. Noblesse stopped dancing. "That G.L.," she said, "strictly a square, I mean after all, he's an Ed. Let's go out on the porch and sit down."

I was quite willing because my groin was a mass of first-degree burns from pressing against her smudge pot.

On the veranda, which had been imaginatively decorated with Japanese lanterns and festoons of crepe paper, young couples sat around and smoked and chatted pleasantly. Noblesse spied some friends over in a corner. "Let's go sit with those kids. They're loads of fun," she said.

When we reached them Noblesse introduced me. "This is Asa Hearthrug—Bob Scream and Peggy Orifice."

"How do you do?" I said.

"Hi, Asa, what do you sasa?" Bob yelled jovially.

We chuckled appreciatively.

"What darling costumes you kids have on," said Peggy.

"Thank you," Noblesse replied. "But I don't see yours."

Peggy opened her mouth. A cuckoo, cunningly attached to a pivot tooth, came out and crowed three times.

"'Three O'clock in the Morning!'" cried Noblesse. "How clever, I mean how utterly."

"Wait'll you see mine," Bob boomed. "Hey, c'mere," he called to a figure that stood in the shadows. An elderly man dressed in a shirt of wide, vertical black-and-white stripes, a pair of white knickers, and athletic shoes, with a whistle on a string hung around his neck, came over to Bob. "'My Reverie,'" Bob screamed. "Get it? Referee–reverie. Get it? Referee–reverie."

After our laughter had subsided Noblesse whispered to me, "That Bob, he's terribly clever. I mean he writes all the varsity shows on the campus. I mean I don't know where he thinks up all those gags year after year, I mean after all. He's thinking of enrolling in the University next year."

"I'm glad you kids came," said Peggy, tucking the cuckoo back in her cheek. "We were just having a serious discussion, and we'd like to ask the opinion of you kids about something. I had a coke date with Harvey Vacillate—he's a Sigma Phlegm—this afternoon, and he asked my advice about something. Harvey and I are platonic like that. We just go out on coke dates and ask each other's advice about our problems, and we have helped each other a good deal in the past. But this afternoon he asked me a question, and I mean, I just didn't know what to answer."

"I went on a coke date with him yesterday," said Noblesse. "I'm platonic with him that way, too, I mean. He's platonic with Sally Gelt and Wilma Urbane in our sorority too. Then he's platonic with some Chi Havoc girls too. But what was it he asked you?"

"Well," Peggy said, "he asked me if I thought that intelligent young women should observe the double standard."

"Did you hear about the girl who thought the double standard was two filling stations?" roared Bob.

"Now, Bob," chided Peggy gently, "the double standard is not a subject to joke about. It's a very burning issue of our times."

"Yes," agreed Noblesse. "I mean it's very important. After all, why shouldn't intelligent young people get together and discuss this problem? I mean this is the twentieth century, and women are supposed to be liberated, why shouldn't they have all the freedom that a man has?

"I don't mean that people should be promiscuous, I mean with just anybody. I mean after all there is a limit. And of course I mean all women shouldn't be allowed all this freedom—not until they've had certain advantages and shown themselves to be capable of freedom, I mean.

"I mean that sort of thing has to be done with a certain amount of *savoir faire,* and I say when a woman has been educated and has had advantages, after all she should be allowed to do what she wants."

"A woman like you, for instance," Bob shrieked slyly.

"Well, yes," said Noblesse. "I mean I think I'm intelligent enough not to have my conduct governed by what people did hundreds of years ago."

"'Oh, you are, Noblesse, you are," I said.

"Everybody down to the dance floor," called a voice from the end of the porch. "The prize for the best costume is going to be awarded."

We went back to the dance floor and marched in a line past the judge's stand. Mother Bloor was the judge. When the last couple had gone by Mother Bloor looked over the notes she had been taking and at length announced the winner.

"Noblesse Oblige and Asa Hearthrug."

Suddenly I was up at the front of the room with Noblesse, and all around us was a sea of smiling faces, blurred through my tears. "I can't believe it, I can't believe it," I kept repeating to Noblesse.

"We've won, Asa," she said, taking my hand. "I mean we've won."

Then Mother Bloor, smiling broadly, was putting a silver cup in my hand. "Don't forget it what I told you before," she whispered in my ear.

Now everyone was about us shouting cheery greetings, extending congratulations. I could only mouth brokenly, but Noblesse, cool and serene, spoke graciously for both of us until, at length, the well-wishers had gone.

"Whew," said Noblesse. "I mean I'm glad that's over. Let's take off our costumes and go get some air."

She disengaged the smudge pot from her navel. I saw her face for the first time. She was incredibly lovely. Her crisp brown hair was worn in a jaunty feather bob. Her blue eyes were pools of innocence. Her little nose was pert and saucy. Her mouth, adorned with fashionably dark lipstick, could only be described as kissable. I took the tea tray off my head and followed her into the garden.

We sat on a bench under a spreading banyan tree and lit cigarettes. "Are you having a good time, Asa?" she asked.

"Good!" I cried. "Say, better, marvelous."

"Isn't Bob funny?"

"Devastating," I said.

"You should see him when he puts a lampshade on his head. I mean you could die."

"I can imagine," I said, chuckling.

We smoked silently for a moment. "Noblesse," I said slowly, "all this, these people, this trophy we won, this social grace, I never believed such things existed outside of storybooks."

She laughed silverly. "Yes, it's all true. And it's all the more enjoyable because"—her voice grew more serious—"because we know how to enjoy it. I mean we are the people who belong. After all, there are belongers and non-belongers. We are the belongers."

"Belongers and non-belongers," I said thoughtfully. "Yes, you've hit it, Noblesse. I want to belong to all of this, and—and most particularly I want to belong to you." I took her cool white hand in mine.

She allowed me to hold it for a moment, and then withdrew it. "Do you like football, Asa? I mean I'm crazy about it, I mean simply mad."

"Yes," I said.

"The season opens next Saturday, and I'm just dying to go, I mean actually. But nobody can get a ticket. I mean you really have to *rate* to get a ticket."

A thought struck me. "Noblesse, will you come to the game with me next Saturday?"

"With you? But where will you get a ticket, Asa?"

"Eino Fflliikkiinnenn is a fraternity brother of mine," I said simply.

"Eino Fflliikkiinnenn!" she exclaimed.

"Yes," I said modestly.

"Oh, Asa, I'd love to."

Her hand stole back into mine. "Noblesse," I said, "I don't know quite how to say this, and I know I shouldn't, but I must speak. Am I then made of stone? Noblesse, I shall not bandy words. I—I love you."

"Asa!" she cried. "I mean after all."

"Stay," I said. "Hear me out. I know we have met only this night, but what does love know of time? My heart is my clock and my calendar, and it ticks inexorably that I love you. If I had known you a million years I should only know what I know now: that you are beautiful and as wise as beautiful and gracious and pure and strong and good. Do not speak to me of time, for time is but a picayune in our world, yours and mine. Noblesse, say that you are mine."

"I mean you mean go steady?"

"Yes," I said simply, and I saw the answer in her eyes. Then she was in my arms, my mouth drinking the ambrosia of her lips.

"But we mustn't tell anybody. I mean we must keep it a secret," she said.

"Our secret," I breathed.

"How Fun!" she cried, and clapped her hands. She extended her palm toward me. "The pin."

"The pin? Oh. Oh yes, the pin. I—I left it at the jeweler's to have some more diamonds put in. I'll have it for you Saturday."

"You sure?" she said, frowning.

"As sure, Noblesse, as my love for you."

She smiled. We kissed.

"I am so happy," I said. "Now I can be one of you and join your fun and your serious discussions too."

"Yes," she said. "They're very important. We had some very nice serious discussions tonight, didn't we, Asa?"

"Oh yes," I said. "That was very interesting about the double standard. Tell me, Noblesse, did you mean all you said about the double standard?"

She drew herself up. "Of course. I mean I meant every word of it. I mean after all, I don't just talk to hear myself talk, I mean."

"That's all I wanted to know," I said. I started to divest myself of encumbering garments.

She screamed and ran into the house.

Mother Bloor emerged from behind the banyan tree. "It's like I told you," she said. "You ought to get yourself a nice mature woman."

CHAPTER XX

Le potage est très chaud.—DALADIER

"Graduating seniors, members of the faculty, guests, ladies and gentlemen," said the speaker at the commencement exercises which I attended before I went home for the summer, "as I look out over your faces I am reminded of a story. It seems that three Hawaiians went into a music store. 'What can I do for you, gentlemen?' asked the proprietor.

"'I want a ukulele,' said the first.

"'And what are you going to do with a ukulele?' asked the proprietor.

"'I'm going to serenade my girl,' answered the first.

"'I see,' said the proprietor. He turned to the second. 'What do you want?' he said.

"'I want a guitar,' said the second.

"'And what are you going to do with a guitar?'

"'I'm going to serenade my girl.'

"'I see,' said the proprietor. He turned to the third. 'What do you want?'

"'I want a bass drum,' said the third.

"'And what are you going to do with a bass drum?' asked the proprietor.

"'Well,' he answered, 'I—I—I—'

"Can you beat that? I've forgotten what he said. That'll teach me to make notes. Oh, well, it wasn't really very appropriate anyway. Let's get on with it.

"This night is a happy occasion, happy but at the same time solemn, know what I mean? It is happy because you who are graduating tonight have completed a long and difficult job. It is solemn because now you got to take your places in the world.

"You have a special obligation to the world because you are, like we say, the cream of society. The world is looking to you for leadership. You are going out in the world and make your marks, some of you in business, some in law, some in medicine, some in engineering, some in the arts, and some in business. But all of you are facing the future with the confidence of youth and the comforting knowledge that you are prepared.

"For the University has tried to prepare you. Here the people of the state of Minnesota have provided you with the facilities to partake of the wisdom of the ages. Here, under the good old American horse-sense guidance of the Board of Regents, you have been able to take advantage of one of the finest courses of studies in the country. Here, in addition to your formal education, you have learned something of life—how to make friends, how to deport yourselves, and what democracy really means.

"The University has been for the last few years your alma mater, your adopted mother. But I wonder how much you really know about the University. You have been so busy with your studies and your activities that you probably have not found time to familiarize yourselves with the glorious history and traditions of the University. I think it fitting then that I should use your last hours here to tell you something of the background of the University.

"The University was founded in 1855. That much is certain. Who founded it is a matter for conjecture. One version has it that the University was founded by an Atlanta textbook salesman named Rhett Fink. It seems that Fink had exhausted the market of Southern colleges, and he was in financial straits. A friend is supposed to have asked him where he intended to sell books now. According to the story, Fink replied, 'I guess I'll have to start a college up North.'

"A brief examination shows that this explanation is apocryphal. In

1855 Fink could not have said, 'I guess I'll have to start a college up North,' because there was no North at that time. North did not come into being until 1908.

"In the spring of 1908 a crazed ptarmigan swooped down on a Long Island estate and carried off in its bill an infant named John Ringling North. The child's father, Cedric (Freckles) North, was frantic with grief. He offered a reward of one million dollars for the return of the boy.

"Everybody on the Atlantic seaboard went out to hunt for the baby. It became a quip of the day to say when someone asked where you were going, 'After North.'

"Later this was shortened to simply 'North,' and that is how the direction got its name.

"Another theory about the founding of the University is concerned with Dred Scott. In 1855 Dred Scott came to Minnesota. He took a house in the bend of the Mississippi River where the University now stands and proceeded to write his immortal *Ivanhoe.* One night Scott became involved in a fracas in a Minneapolis rib joint. A quadroon named Joe Riposte was stabbed to death, and Scott was accused of the murder. He was given a summary trial, during the course of which he made his famous 'J'accuse' speech. The jury was unmoved, however, and sentenced him to be hanged.

"Legend has it that after his execution the ghost of Dred Scott returned to haunt the house on the riverbank. On moonless nights it is supposed to have lurked outside the house dismally howling, 'J'accuse.'

"Now, it seems that a St. Paul launderer named Jack Hughes had moved into Scott's house after his (Scott's) execution. One night when Jack Hughes heard the ghost howling 'J'accuse' he thought someone was calling him. He went out to see who it was. In the dark he slipped and fell into the river where he got caught in a strong undertow and drowned.

"Shortly thereafter an itinerant Boston educator named Cotton Mouth drifted by. He saw that the house was vacant and started a little school. That little school, my friends, later became the University of Minnesota, according to the story.

"However it may have begun, Minnesota found itself with a University. But the legislature, except for one member, was singularly unimpressed. That member was William Jennings Bryan. He introduced a bill for funds for the University into the legislature. The solons were apathetic. Then Bryan made his famous 'Cross of Gold' speech.

'What will it be, gentlemen,' he concluded, 'rum, romanism, or rebellion?'

"The legislature was stirred to action. They not only passed the appropriation, but they also lifted Bryan on their shoulders and carried him around the Statehouse. This, however, was not too difficult because Bryan was only six years old at the time and puny for his age.

"Now began a period of expansion. As the campus grew, enrollment figures advanced steadily. More and more farmers, in town for the State Fair, mistook the campus for the fairgrounds, and were seized and pledged into fraternities as they wandered about.

"But physically the campus was still small. Then in 1908 a curious chain of circumstances increased the size of the campus to its present spacious dimensions. Before 1908 the land adjoining the campus belonged to a family called the Chalmers. Perhaps I should not say 'family'; they were more a nation than a family. They were all related. They had an unbreakable custom which allowed only first cousins to marry. Moreover, a woman who was neither pregnant nor nursing was considered something of a pariah.

"You can imagine what their settlement looked like. It was probably the most densely populated place on the whole earth. Every inch of space was occupied by Chalmers—drooling, examining their fingers, snarling over bones, or just staring dully at the ground.

"Curiously enough they had a sort of democracy. One day a year was set aside for elections. On election day they held a monster demonstration. After the monsters were demonstrated the candidates for office made their speeches. Then the elections were conducted.

"But the man who got the *least* number of votes was awarded the office. The theory was that the man who polled the smallest number of votes had the fewest friends, was obligated to the least number of people, and would conduct the least corrupt administration. The funny thing is that the system functioned excellently. The Chalmers enjoyed good government, replete with tax reductions and river and harbor improvement.

"The Chalmers' religion was of the most primitive. From somewhere they had acquired a huge hollow brass statue of Franklin Pierce, an obscure political figure of the last century, I believe. This statue they called Mechel-Dundik and worshiped assiduously. Each evening at nightfall they gathered in front of the statue and stared at it reverently for thirty-five minutes.

"One day in 1908—it was about dusk—two children were playing in front of the statue.—They were a brother and sister named Benny and Consuela Chalmers. Benny, who was an adventurous lad for a Chalmers, discovered a crack in the idol and crept inside. His sister was horrified. 'Benny,' she cried, 'you come right out of there.'

"'No,' said Benny.

"'You come right out of there,' she repeated, 'or I'll tell Ma.'

"'Aw, go jump in the lake,' said Benny.

"Meanwhile, the Chalmers had gathered in front of the statue for their evening worship. They heard Benny's command to jump in the lake come out as if from the mouth of Mechel-Dundik. Without a word the whole Chalmers tribe marched off to Lake Calhoun, a short distance away, and jumped in. Unable to swim, they all drowned.

"Benny came out of the idol and found nobody around. He wandered about absently for several days and was finally dispatched by an excitable moccasin snake.

"The land, now ownerless and uninhabited, was given to the University.

"And that, my friends, is a brief background of the glorious institution from which you are graduating tonight. Those are the traditions that lie behind you as you go out into the world to make your marks, some of you in business, some in law, some in medicine, some in engineering, some in the arts, and some in business.

"You must always bear in mind that because you are university graduates you are the leaders of your communities. It is a responsibility, I will not deny. You will soon learn what it is to have people constantly looking up to you. You will say, 'I would like to trade places with Bill Jones, the welder, or with John Smith, the plumber.' But you really would not. No matter how much more money they make than you, you have advantages that they will never realize.

"For a university is more than just a school. It is a molder of men. And it is more than just a molder of men. It is a molder of ideas. And it is more than just a molder of ideas. It teaches its students not only to think, but to think alike. I am proud to say that wherever you go in this country you find college students holding identical opinions. Often, as a matter of fact, they express them in the same words.

"And when you leave here tonight to go out and make your marks I know that you will not forget your adopted mother any more than you would forget your real mothers. I know that the memory of the University will always remain fresh in your hearts. And I feel sure that all of you, each and every one of you, will join the alumni association and pay your dues promptly. I am positive, too, that each and every one of you will find time to return to the campus occasionally and participate in our reasonably priced reunions. I am certain that you will join wholeheartedly in our new alumni project to subsidize high-school football players in United States territorial possessions like the Hawaiian Islands and Cuba—a veritable gold mine of material, my friends, and completely untouched.

"But it is getting late, and I know you would like to get through here so you can spend this solemn evening among your loved ones. I'll conclude now, and you can get your diplomas.

"Just a word about the diplomas. You get small paper diplomas here tonight, but for another ten dollars you can turn these diplomas in for large, genuine sheepskin reproductions. Naturally, you want a real, long-lasting sheepskin. After all these long and difficult years of going to school you want something more permanent than paper to show for it.

"And in addition to being a thing of beauty, a sheepskin diploma can come in mighty handy sometime. Let me tell you about Mary Ellen N., a girl who graduated from the University a few years ago.

"She graduated in winter. After the commencement exercises a party of her classmates invited her to come on a toboggan party. She tucked her sheepskin diploma in her tunic and accompanied them. It was a dark night and a perilous toboggan slide. The toboggan turned over, and Mary Ellen slid down 1,500 feet of rocky crag. She lost a lot of skin.

"Fortunately, there was a doctor in the party. He saw that quick action was imperative. Quickly he grafted Mary Ellen's diploma on to her skinned member. He saved her life.

"Today Mary Ellen is married to an upholsterer of Rye, New York. She has two lovely children and is prominent in Rye society. Her life is full and perfectly normal except that every time she sits down, she bleats.

"Thank you."

NOTE OF THANKS—NOT AN AFTERTHOUGHT

Without the collaboration of Ralph L. Woods, this book could never have been compiled. Heartfelt thanks are herewith extended.

Special thanks are also tendered to my fellow toilers on *Ski-U-Mah,* Bud Nye, Russell Roth, and Harry Reasoner.

Thanks, too, for the generous co-operation of:

Mrs. Christine Hathaway, Administrative Assistant, Brown University Library; Virginia L. Close, Reference Librarian, Dartmouth College; Victor A. Schaefer, Director of the Library, Notre Dame University; Mr. W. B. Bradbury of the W. B. Bradbury Company; Morrison C. Haviland, Librarian, Wabash College; Virgil K. Whitaker, Executive Head, English Department, Stanford University; Donald F. Cameron, Librarian, Rutgers University; Mary L. Thornton, Librarian, University of North Carolina Library; Hilda M. Reitzel, Reference Librarian, University of Pittsburgh; Mrs. H. Alubowicz, Reference Librarian, Michigan State College; Elkan Buckhalter, Reference Librarian, Temple University; Russel B. Nye, Head of Department of English, Michigan State College; Carlton P. West, Librarian, Wake Forest College; William Rabe, Press Department, University of Detroit; Wyliss E. Wright, Librarian, Williams College; Ruth Scibird, Curator, Stanford Collection, Stanford Universities Libraries; Mrs. Irma L. Tomberlin, University of Oklahoma Library; Alice Reynolds, Harvard University Library; Helena C. Koiner, The Alderman Library of University of Virginia; Malcolm Young, Reference Librarian, Princeton University Library; Henry M. Fuller, Reference Librarian, Yale University Library; Mrs. Louise A. Addison, Assistant Reference Librarian, Smith College Library; Mr. Walter Fredericks, Director of Publications, Associated Students, University of California, Berkeley, Calif.; John R. Adams, Chairman, Department of Languages and Literature, San Diego State College; Mrs. Vivian M. Lawson, Reference Librarian, University of Alabama; Theodore E. Norton, Librarian, Lafayette College; Mr. William H. Carlson, Director of Libraries, Oregon State System of Higher Education; Joe Gold, Editor of University of Missouri *Showme;* Mrs. Ann Todd Rubey, Head, Reference Department, University of Missouri Library; A. Moffit, Librarian, University of Texas; John W. Howard, Editor-in-Chief, *Smoke Signals,* Florida State University; Joseph Doggett, Department of English, Florida State University; Nancy Bird, Periodicals Librarian, Florida State University; Thomas F. Dunn and Charles J. Ritchey, College of Liberal Arts, Drake University; Ward Pafford, Chairman, Department of English, Emory University; Alice McClain, Associate Librarian, Idaho State College; Margaret P. Hazen, Reference Librarian, Massachusetts Institute of Technology; Robert Herron, Editor, *Profile,* University of Cincinnati; John Paul Jones, Chairman, Board of Student Publications, University of Florida; Clyde Miller, Humanities Librarian, University of Florida; Hugh Montgomery, Librarian, University of Massachusetts; Martin Schmitt, Special Collections, University of Oregon Library; Margaret Butterfield, Curator of Local History and University Archives, University of Rochester; Irene Morrow, Reference Librarian, Bradley University; Mr. Wayne Arihood, Executive Editor, *Octopus,* University of Wisconsin; Katharine-Louise Henning, Librarian, Reference Department, University of Wisconsin Library; Elsa C. Lisle, Circulation Librarian, Pennsylvania State University Library; Louis H. Bell, Department of Public Information, Pennsylvania State University; Mrs. Beatrice Henderson, Chief of Interlibrary Loan Division, Syracuse University Libraries; Lester G. Wells, Curator of Special Collection, Syracuse University Libraries; Larry Pike, Managing Editor, *Gargoyle,* University of Michigan; Mahala Saville, Reference Librarian, University of Mississippi; Mr. James E. Savage, Acting Chairman, Department of English, University of Mississippi; Mr. E. W. King, Librarian, Miami University; Virginia C. West, Librarian, Fresno State College; Mrs. Catherine J. Pierce, Head of Reference Department, Duke University Library; Mr. Milton C. Moore, Reference Assistant, Watson Library, University of Kansas; Walter J. Meserve, Jr., Department of English Language and Literature, University of Kansas; Mr. Charles W. Sargent, Curator, Kansas Historical Collections, University of Kansas; Libby Rawlins, Reference Department, Louisiana State University; Ruth Walling, Chief Reference Librarian, Louisiana State University; Ezra L. Gillis, Director, Bureau of Source Materials in Higher Education, University of Kentucky; Harold W. Hatten, Jr., Editor, *Hullabaloo,* Franklin and Marshall College; Flora B. Ludington, Librarian, Mt. Holyoke College; Paul Bixler, Librarian, Antioch College; Mr. L. W. Elder, Curator of Memorabilia, Knox College Library; Caroline C. Drake, Assistant Librarian, Rensselaer Polytechnic Institute; Mr. Robert A. Sencer, Assistant Professor, Department of English, Rensselaer Polytechnic Institute; Mr. R. J. Butler, News Editor, *The Kentucky Colonel,* University of Kentucky; Mr. L. H. Kirkpatrick, Librarian, University of Utah; James Brandon, Editor, *Razor Blade,* University of Arkansas; Claude W. Faulkner, Chairman, Department of English, University of Arkansas; Mr. C. G. Sparks, Librarian, Texas Christian University; Warren K. Agee, Chairman, Department of Journalism, Texas Christian University; Donald M. Powell, Head, Reference Department, University of Arizona Library;

Laurence Lee Howe, Associate Professor, Department of History, University of Louisville; Virginia Windstandley, Assistant Librarian, University of Louisville; Norman D. Christensen, Director of Student Publications, University of Miami; Mrs. Dolores Spurgeon, Adviser to *Lykes,* San Jose State College; Harry Bauer, Director of Libraries, University of Washington Library; Clyde A. Robinson, Manager of Publications, Associated Students, University of Washington; Sue Lyons, Business Manager, *The Rivet,* Purdue University; Mr. J. H. McKee, Department of English, Purdue University; Rose E. Korsmo, Reference Unit, Purdue University Library; Ronald M. Kohn, Business Manager, *Sundial,* Ohio State University; Mr. K. R. Marvin, Head of Department of Technical Journalism, Iowa State College; Mrs. Vera S. Copper, Librarian, De Pauw University; Fred L. Bergmann, Head of Journalism, De Pauw University; Anna Mary Urban, Reference Librarian, University of Maryland; Mary Kay Peer, Secretary, Department of English, University of Illinois; R. B. Downs, Director, University of Illinois Library; Mrs. Yvonne Van Der Boom, University of Minnesota Library; James Gray, Department of English, University of Minnesota; Robert S. Taylor, Assistant Librarian, Lehigh University; E. L. Craig, Reference Librarian, Indiana University; Louis T. Ibbotson, Library, University of Maine; Kenneth J. LaBudde, Director of Libraries, University of Kansas City; William Hinckley, Editor, the *Flatiron,* University of Colorado; Mr. L. L. Lewis, Department of English and Speech, University of Colorado; Mary L. Hilton, Head of Circulation Department, Charles Deering Library of Northwestern University; Jens Nyholm, University Librarian, Northwestern University; John D. Chapman, Assistant Director of Libraries, University of Nebraska; Mr. A. C. Baugh, Department of English and Literature, University of Pennsylvania; Flora L. Delbert, Reference Librarian, University of Pennsylvania; Elizabeth H. Davis, Reference Librarian, Kansas State College; Andrew L. Bouwhis, S.J., Librarian, Canisius College Library; Louise E. Robinson, Reference Librarian, Middlebury College; Martha Ann Peters, Tulane University Library; Vito J. Brenni, Chief of Reference, West Virginia University; Alfred M. Kern, Acting Chairman, English Department, Allegheny College; Francis Sweeney, S.J., Boston College; Karl H. Koopman, Librarian, The Citadel; William G. Harkins, Librarian, College of William and Mary; John Sheldon, Assistant Librarian, Gettysburg College; Brother G. Robert, F.S.C., La Salle College; James W. Dyson, Loyola University, New Orleans, La.; Mrs. Genevieve Porter, Reference Librarian, Southern

Methodist University; John J. Coleman, S.J., University of San Francisco; Frank P. Gill, Faculty Adviser, Student Publications, Wayne University; Everett T. Moore, Head, Reference Department, University of California Library; Edward Malloy, Dean of Students, Columbia University; Robert Rosenthal, Curator, Special Collections, University of Chicago Library; Edward E. Norkis, Reference Assistant, University of Chicago Library; Miss Dorothy A. Plum, Vassar College Library; Charles H. Niles, New Coordinator, The University of Connecticut.

ALMA
PRINCETON